THE NEW ELEMENTARY
SCHOOL SCIENCE

WILLARD J. JACOBSON

Chairman, Department of Science Education
Teachers College, Columbia University

THE NEW
ELEMENTARY
SCHOOL SCIENCE

VAN NOSTRAND REINHOLD COMPANY
New York Cincinnati Toronto London Melbourne

Van Nostrand Reinhold Company Regional Offices:
Cincinnati, New York, Chicago, Millbrae, Dallas

Van Nostrand Reinhold Company Foreign Offices:
London, Toronto, Melbourne

Published by Van Nostrand Reinhold Company
450 West 33rd Street, New York, N.Y. 10001

Published simultaneously in Canada by
D. Van Nostrand Company (Canada), Ltd.

10 9 8 7 6 5 4 3 2

To Carol

Preface

Recent years have seen a flurry of exciting activity in elementary school science. Yet teachers and prospective teachers remain, with some justification, unsure as to what the new approaches mean for their own work with children. Rationales for the several competing programs seem persuasive, yet the task of actually carving out an appropriate science curriculum for a group of children seems to become more complex with each new scientific discovery and each new development in science education. Some of the new programs, for example, are more extensive than a year's work in school can accommodate. Others stress particular aspects of science above others long regarded as primary. It is time for a synthesis of the innovative and the tried-and-true out of which to build a *new elementary school science* for today's and tomorrow's children.

The present text is designed to provide the preservice teacher, as well as his in-service colleague, with such a synthesis. Its organizing principle is the simple, but profound, question: What should children gain from a study of science in the elementary school? We answer with four goals, providing us with the skeletal structure of our text:

1. the building of a world view that is in conformance with the view of our world and our universe now being developed in the sciences
2. the fostering of an understanding of the conceptual structure of science
3. the development of skill in using some of the key processes of science
4. the encouragement of an informed appreciation of man, and of how science affects modern man and his society

Within the framework provided by these fundamental goals, our text explores science content, approaches to teaching, and professional activities of the teacher which can be used to implement a truly contemporary science program in the elementary school.

In Part I, we take our lead from the general discussion of elementary science. Here the thesis is advanced that our styles of teaching ought to be consistent with the nature of science itself, since—in this subject perhaps above all others—so much of what we teach children is dependent upon how we teach it. To state the case negatively, science ought not to be taught in an unscientific manner. To find out is satisfying, but at least half the joy is in the finding. And what are teaching and learning if not processes, or modes of inquiry?

Moving from basic questions about the nature of science, the nature of children, and the nature of successful approaches to teaching science, we take up, in Parts II, III, IV, and V, the four goals of scientific inquiry mentioned above.

Part II provides a view of the world starting on the scale of our universe and moving down into the realm of very small living organisms.

Part III explores aspects of the conceptual structure of modern science through a chapter on the study of objects and systems and a chapter on interactions (biological, chemical, magnetic, electrical, temperature, and light).

From structure we proceed, in Part IV, to process, as we explain and illustrate methods involving, for example, variation and measurement, model formation, and experimentation.

The focus of Part V is man—viewed both in his biological context and within his total environment which includes, among other variables, science itself.

In each of these Parts, self-contained treatments of science content, carefully selected for relevance to teaching, form the basis of the discussions. Presented in a narrative style, these discussions elucidate the most important ideas of science and the processes by which they have been developed and applied. They are supplemented by complete descriptions of useful science experiments, investigations, field studies, and other science activities that stimulate the all-important "doing" of science. Eminently usable with children, the activities are also recommended for the student of science teaching (especially in the company of one or more children), as they serve to illuminate the content discussions.

The concluding section, Part VI, is a guide to the building of a comprehensive, articulated science program in the elementary school. Materials and facilities are recommended, and evaluation of the program and the children is built into the discussion.

It is difficult to give credit to the literally thousands of children and teachers, students and colleagues who have contributed in one way or another to the ideas now finding expression in this book. I should like to acknowledge the many enriching experiences stemming from my work in three science course content improvement projects: the American Association for the Advancement of Science (AAAS) project, Science—A Process Approach; the Science Curriculum Improvement Study (SCIS); and the Science Manpower Project (SMP).

I am also indebted to my colleagues in the Department of Science Education at Teachers College, and particularly to my colleague in elementary school science, Mary Budd Rowe, for many mind-stretching discussions. I am grateful, too, to other able educators who have worked with me in elementary school science, among them Tracy Ashley, Jewell Burgner, Albert Carr, Louis Cox, William Croasdale, John Garone, Morsley Giddings, David Hessong, Robert King, Allan Kondo, Richard Konicek, Allan Leitman, Jerome Notkin, Elizabeth Phelan Lawlor, Reuben Pierce, Clarence Trexler, William Van Houten, Neila Werner, and John Youngpeter. All have made valuable suggestions and have helped to refine many of the experiments and investigations presented in this book.

Finally, I shall always be grateful to my wife, Carol, for her encouragement and support, and to my daughters, Susan and Ellen, and my son, Thomas, for their critical comments.

W. J. J.

Contents

I
Science in Childhood Education

Science is the investigation and interpretation of events in the natural, physical environment and within our bodies. Probably man has always wondered about the world. Certainly, children continue to ask questions, to seek answers, and to make sense out of the "blooming, buzzing confusion" of the world into which they are born. Science is perhaps our most important approach to understanding. It is of special importance that our children become aware of how we strive for understanding and the nature of the conceptual structures that have been built through science.

The methods and processes of science are of special importance in science in childhood education. "How can we find out?" The child may observe, classify, measure, and experiment. "What does it mean?" The child tries to interpret the observations he has made and the data that he has gathered. "How do we know?" The child tries to support statements with data. "How does what I have discovered compare with what others have found?" Investigations are not carried out in a vacuum but, instead, are carried out in relationship to the work of others. These questions are very much like those that are often asked in the sciences. As the child deals with such questions he gains a better understanding of the nature of the scientific enterprise.

Through the use of the methods and processes of science we have developed conceptual schemes that help us organize our knowledge of the world in which we live. The weights of various chemical elements were merely a set of numbers until Mendeleev and others arranged them in order and noticed that in their list various physical properties appeared periodically. Mendeleev built a Periodic Table of the elements. This Periodic Table was such a powerful conceptual scheme it was possible to use it to predict the properties of chemical elements that had not yet been discovered. In elementary school science children are introduced to some of the conceptual schemes of science; they explore some of their meanings, and learn how to use them to interpret their observations and findings.

It is becoming clear that significant experiences in science are of special importance to young children in the early grades of the elementary school. Science experiences can make important contributions to intellectual development. Probably our children, who increasingly live in an urban or suburban environment, have less opportunity for firsthand, primary experiences with the plants and animals, rocks and soil of the natural environment than children of an earlier day. Yet, the symbols they use and the words they hear often refer to the material objects of the environment. In science children can have the firsthand experiences that give meaning to words. Through science children can also develop some of the behavior patterns that lead to healthier and safer living. Apparently, it is easier to build and change habits when we are young than it is later on. Children need a chance to develop the habits that can lead to healthy living.

The nature of the experiences that children have in science is critical. If the study of science becomes associated with the absorption and memorization of "facts" and regurgitation upon request from the teachers, then it would be far better to dispense with this perversion of science. But the study of science can be an exciting undertaking. Children raise questions and strive to find answers; explore the environment and try to interpret what they find; use the tools and apparatus of science to investigate and experiment; wonder, speculate, hypothesize, examine, predict, experiment, interpret, infer, and conclude. The teacher who works with youngsters as they engage in these kinds of activities reaps some of the joys of teaching.

1 Science in the Elementary School

Starlight from outer space, the apparent movement of the sun across the daytime sky, the burrowings of the earthworm in the garden soil, the drifting of snow across the open road, the growth of grass in the narrow cracks of the concrete sidewalk, and the suspended chart on the classroom feltboard are events in our natural, physical environment. Children want to know, "What happens? Why? How can we explain it?" We are born; we grow, and we die. Changes take place within our bodies. At times we are ill, but we strive for health. We use food for energy, growth, and repair of tissues. With eyes, ears, nose, mouth, and skin we become aware of events in the natural, physical environment. The investigation and study of our natural, physical environment and our bodies is the subject matter of science.

Science grew out of man's desire to understand and, to a certain extent, control the environment in which he lives. Early man wondered about the nature of matter. An atomic theory of matter was proposed by the Greek philosopher Leucippus and developed further by Democritus in the fifth century B.C. In the twentieth century, scientists still use an atomic theory and are now probing the incredibly small and strange particles within the atom. Early man gazed up into the starry skies and wondered about the nature of the universe and man's place in it. Today, scientists continue to explore the vastness of space with radio telescopes, space probes, and powerful theoretical models. "What is the nature of life?" This question has long perplexed man. Although much has been learned, scientists are still probing molecules of living protoplasm for the keys to the nature of life.

Lives there a child who has not wondered about the nature of things? Science is the voyage of discovery to find out. It is an exciting undertaking. In the study of science children are invited to climb on board ship and take part in this voyage of discovery.

5

THE NATURE OF SCIENCE

Science is the investigation and interpretation of events in the natural, physical environment and within our bodies. The nature and structure of science can be compared to the framework of a building under construction. A framework characteristically has vertical pillars interlaced with horizontal beams. The upper beams serve as platforms on which the builders use the tools of their trade to extend the framework upward. Below, the framework rests on a solid foundation firmly rooted in the underlying earth.

It should be recognized that an analogy is only an approach to explanation; it is never exactly like that which it is used to explain. For example, science is obviously not a building under construction, but is used merely as an analogy to help explain the nature of science.

The Basic Assumptions

In this analogy the foundations of the framework are the basic assumptions on which science is founded. Perhaps the basic assumption is that the events and phenomena that man encounters can be explained in a rational, consistent manner. The phenomena can be related to the events and experiences that others have witnessed. Neither magic nor strange, unfathomable forces are needed to explain the world; events can be explained using the many scientific laws and principles that have been developed over a long period of time. For example, when lightning strikes it is not considered to be magic or the work of devils. Lightning can be explained by the same laws and principles of electricity that are used to explain other electrical phenomena. As these laws and principles are refined and extended, explanations become more cogent and precise.

The Methods and Processes

The horizontal beams of the framework are the methods and processes of science—subjecting ideas to empirical tests, selecting the particular system to be investigated, the use of hypotheses for investigation, the controlled experiment, the cumulative and public dimensions of science, the use of models to examine ideas, and the development of theory to weld ideas together. These methods or approaches are employed to build the structure and to test it for soundness. Through experience, the methods and processes are refined and become more sophisticated.

The Broad Generalizations

The pillars in our framework are the broad generalizations of science—the conservation of matter and energy, the second law of thermodynamics, and the biological principle of mass production. The pillars in some sections of the framework are higher than in others, for such sciences as physics and physical chemistry are probably more advanced than the sciences of biology and psychology.

Active research may be thought of as going on at the tops of the pillars, which are sometimes extended as a result of investigation. This is the cumulative aspect of the sciences. The extensions are almost always built on top of firm, well-established pillars. Sometimes, however, the upper sections of the framework may not have firm support. For example, if some part of the structure in a field of science has weak support, it may not stand the tests of time. To revamp these generalizations, as is sometimes done, is to shake the structure of at least a part of science. Seldom, however, is an entire framework torn down in order to construct a new framework of generalizations. The broad generalizations are distillations of human experience; as such, they have achieved their status only after thorough testing and retesting.

An Ongoing Enterprise

Science is one form of human activity. It is distinguished by its conceptual structures and the methods and processes employed. It is a dynamic undertaking. As operational answers to questions and problems are found, new questions and problems are formulated. In the world of science there are satisfactions in raising new questions and refining old answers. It is not a settled world, but it is an exciting one. And today's children are living in a period that will probably be influenced more by science than by any other human activity.

SCIENCE IN THE ELEMENTARY SCHOOL

Science is an essential part of elementary school education; it is often recognized as the "4th R." Even in states where the teaching of science in the elementary school is not required, it is usually included in the general elementary program.

Often, the elementary school provides children with their only opportunities to consider the common, everyday phenomena of their environment with the help and guidance of a teacher. The new science courses in the secondary schools and colleges are becoming more abstract and often do not deal with the phenomena of the natural and technological environment. If children are to study and understand these phenomena, they will have to have an opportunity to investigate them in the elementary school.

Experiences in Science

The following are some of the reasons experiences in science are important for children in the elementary school:

Science is one of man's most important endeavors

Undoubtedly, science is one of the most important factors influencing our lives. Such scientific ideas as relativity, evolution, and the expanding universe have profoundly affected the way we look at the world in which we live. The technological products made possible by science, be they hybrid corn, automobiles, or nuclear bombs, have greatly affected our ways of living. The impact and influence of science is growing rapidly. For example, it has been estimated that nine out of ten scientists who ever lived are at work today. The last half century has undoubtedly been the most productive scientific period of time in man's history, and the pace of investigation and discovery quickens. Certainly, our children have a right to share in this great adventure.

Children are keenly interested in science

Often, children who have had little interest or success in other aspects of the elementary school program begin to succeed in school when they have a chance to work in science. In a sense, their interest in science is the door to achievement. Children's interests are only one factor to be considered in planning an educational program, but, if it is present, it is a valuable asset.

The experiences in science contribute to the intellectual growth and development of children

It is becoming abundantly clear that many and varied experiences with physical objects and materials are essential for optimum intellectual development. To learn to read and understand the meaning of such words as "air," the child needs firsthand, primary experiences with it. In our increasingly urban and suburban society one of the major sources of such experiences can be the science program in the school.

The study of science can contribute to the general growth and health of the child

As a child gains a better understanding of his body he learns how to take care of it and to provide the nourishment that is needed for optimum growth and development.

Experiences in science are important for future citizenship

In a democracy, the citizen or his representatives have to decide major issues on the local, state, national, and international levels. Increasingly, these issues are intimately connected with science and technology. In order to deal intelligently with these issues, the citizen must be literate in science and have some understanding of its underlying principles. Since this scientific literacy must be achieved in the education that is common to all, the elementary school should provide a firm foundation of experiences in science.

The Development of Elementary School Science

The roots of elementary school science are evident throughout the history of education. Such founding fathers as Franklin and Jefferson were aware of the need of the study of science for children. The nature of elementary school science has changed, of course, as the society, schools, and science have changed, but some form of science has always been an important part of the education of children.

Over the years, elementary school science has been influenced by the nature of the society it served, the schools in which it was taught, developments in psychology and education, and the growth of basic and applied science. Undoubtedly these same factors will be influential as elementary school science continues to evolve.

Early proponents of science in the elementary school thought of science education as one way to meet practical needs. Franklin and Jefferson saw a need for children to learn how to become more effective farmers, mechanics, and tradesmen. Children needed to learn how to grow plants and care for animals. Success or even survival in the early days depended upon ingenuity and adaptability. Could these things be learned in schools? Franklin, Jefferson, and others had confidence that they could be taught and learned, and urged that practical science become a part of the curriculm of the common school.

Of course, the nature of what is of practical value changes. The farm boy of today needs to know how a tractor and an electric motor operate as well as how to grow plants and care for animals. The city child grows up in an environment of concrete and macadam, trains and planes, and may actually go for weeks without setting foot on soil or grass. The practical needs in such an environment are somewhat different from those of the colonial village or frontier farm. As the practical needs have changed, so has practical science in the elementary school.

Educational Developments and Elementary School Science

Developments in educational theory and practice have influenced the teaching of science in the elementary school. For example, after the Civil War, American education was greatly influenced by the work of such European educators as Pestalozzi, who advocated "object teaching" in training the mind. In object teaching, great emphasis was placed upon methods, particularly methods of observation and investigation. The serial development of mental faculties such as observation and memory was assumed, and an attempt was made to develop these faculties through the study of discrete objects. Elementary school science took the form of rather intensive study of plants, animals, and the human body.

As educators gained more experience with object teaching, it became apparent that they would have to give more attention to the content of elementary school science, along with the continual emphasis on method. It is perhaps more than a coincidence that this development followed the development of the theory of evolution, which emphasized the relationships between objects in the environment rather than their discreteness, and coincided with a period of rapid industrial expansion and revolutionary developments in the physical sciences. The psychological studies of the American educator Edward Thorndike and others also supported the position that children should be helped to see relationships between objects and events. In more recent times, elementary school science has been profoundly influenced by the child-study movement, which expanded views of what children can learn, and by the social-frontiers group, which insisted that children should be prepared through education to deal with problems that face the society in which they live.

Social Needs and Elementary School Science

With the decline of the object-teaching approach, there was increasing emphasis on the study of nature; nature became somewhat romanticized and glorified. However, the nature-study movement attempted to meet a social need. This was a time of economic depression (1891–1893), and the nature-study movement tried to make rural life more attractive in order to induce young people to stay on the farm, rather than to migrate to the city to join the crowded ranks of those already on relief. In the process, it also tried to help young people to become better farmers. This is one of the many examples in the history of elementary school science where the instruction has been planned to help deal with the problems of society.

As our society has become urbanized and our technology highly intricate and complex, our problems have changed and, to a certain extent, elementary school science has evolved to help children meet these problems. A better understanding of human beings and their behavior, for example, gained through modern elementary school science, will help the children to solve the problems of living together in a highly complex society. Although the study of the natural environment continues to be an important dimension of elementary school science, some of the science that serves as a formulation for our modern technology has now been incorporated into the curriculum and future changes in the nature of our society will certainly bring concomitant changes in the nature of elementary school science.

Developments in Science and Technology

Developments in science and technology have also influenced elementary school science. The early years of the twentieth century, a halcyon era for the physical sciences, saw the notable contributions of Einstein, Planck, Becquerel, Rutherford, and the Curies. The harnessing of the internal combustion engine for transportation, the improvement of the electric motor as a source of mechanical power, and the use of electromagnetic radiation as a means of communication were technological developments that profoundly affected our society. And, of course, science in the elementary school had to be broadened to take into account these profound developments.

The Study of Child Development

Since 1920 a number of important studies of child development have influenced elementary school science. These studies have shown that children have a wide-ranging interest in scientific phenomena and are able to deal with some of the most important generalizations of science and to begin the process of developing increasingly more profound concepts of these generalizations.

There is considerable evidence that children pass through successive stages of intellectual development and that these stages are of particular importance in developing their concepts of themselves and the world in which they live.[1] The study of child development has led to the hypothesis that a fruitful approach of some kind or other can be made to almost any area of science in the elementary school. The question is no longer, "Can an area of science be taught in the elementary school?" but instead, "What is it that is most important to study?" and "What is the most effective approach to teaching and learning science?"

Studies of child development continue to have great influence on the planning of elementary school science programs. These studies tend to support a spiral approach, particularly a broad spiral approach, to science programs in which it is planned that children have a chance to explore the same area of science at different times, in different ways, and when they are at different stages of intellectual development. For example, children may study static electricity at a very early level in the elementary grades. But, in a spiral approach, they study electricity in a more sophisticated way later in the elementary school. Also, these studies indicate that children can, with the knowledgeable help and insight of a competent teacher, explore areas of science to considerable depth. This has led to what may be called the "depth approach," with emphasis on a search for deeper meanings and a better understanding of the conceptual structure of science and its methods and processes.

THE CHANGING SCENE IN ELEMENTARY SCHOOL SCIENCE

The years of childhood are precious, and a child's experiences in school are of critical importance. Too often there are missed opportunities, and too seldom can we say that our children have had the best education that we know how to give. In our attempt to ensure that children receive the best possible education, it is essential that we periodically reappraise our elementary school programs. Since science is an area of the curriculum where changes are great and profound, it is especially important to become cognizant of them.

Elementary school science is being influenced by five major developments in our schools and in science.

K–12 Science Programs

The development of Kindergarten-12th grade (K–12) science programs makes it especially important that elementary school science become an integral part of the total school program. An integrated K–12, or K–14,

---

[1] A more extended discussion of these stages of intellectual development and their implications for science in childhood education may be found in Chapter 3.

science program is essential if children are to have some contact with the wide range of the sciences, including some of the newer sciences, and with the growing number of important scientific generalizations. One of the pitfalls to be avoided in the development of K–12 science programs is unneeded, deadening repetition. This makes it essential that the unique contributions of elementary school science in the K–12 science program be delineated.

Since science in the elementary school deals with the broad range of the sciences, elementary school children can have experience with such sciences as nutrition, oceanography, hydrology, and conservation, which may not be encountered in the remaining years of the K–12 science program. Contact with a wide range of sciences also makes it possible to show some of the relationships between the various sciences.

Another important contribution of elementary science is the opportunity of the children to have firsthand experiences with phenomena of the environment. In the elementary school, children should have a chance to germinate seeds to see how they grow, study the mechanism of the electric bell, see some of the effects of the expansion of water on freezing, and to watch the behavior of animals in an aquarium or vivarium.

These firsthand science experiences are important and are best developed during the elementary school years. Many of our sciences are becoming more abstract. Science study in the secondary schools and colleges will deal with abstractions that may seem almost completely unrelated to the phenomena of environment unless children have had previous firsthand experiences with them. An important facet of understanding our natural, physical world is to recognize the relationships between the environment and the abstractions, and children will be in a better position to comprehend these relationships if they have had a variety of experiences in studying phenomena at firsthand and in handling and manipulating science equipment and materials in the elementary school.

Materials and Resources

A wide variety of materials and resources has been developed for the teaching of science, and a wide variety of science textbooks and trade books is now available for use in elementary school science programs. This makes it possible for children to go to many sources for science information and to verify the reliability of information as presented by various authorities. Films and filmstrips can be used to provide children with visual experiences. For example, animation is used to explain processes that cannot be seen by the human eye; time-lapse photography can be used to portray events that take place over a long span of time; and phenomena and features to be found in distant places, such as glaciers and volcanoes, can be shown to children by films, filmstrips, and transparencies. Various forms of programmed instruction can be used to help individual children acquire special skills and understandings and to help the teacher meet the needs of children with a wide range of individual interests and abilities. Radio and television can be used to bring children to the scene of important events as well as to bring noted personalities into the classroom.

Although new materials and resources are available for use in elementary science, experimentation is needed to find out how best to use them. What are some of the ways that a teacher can prepare for and later capitalize on a science program on television? How can closed circuit television be utilized to take advantage of the special skills and knowledge of science consultants and other specialists? Under what conditions can programmed instruction be used most effectively? How can the wide range of science books now available be used to improve both the science and reading programs in the elementary school? We do not have definitive answers to these questions, but throughout this book ways are suggested that these new materials and resources can be tried and tested with considerable hope of success.

The "Information" Explosion in Science

The rapid expansion of scientific knowledge has great implications for elementary school science and the K–12 science program. More scientists are at work today, by far, than at any time in history. At one time, most scientific investigation was carried out by amateurs during their leisure time. Relatively few people were able to devote their full time to scientific investigations. True, some of these talented amateurs forged some of the most important pillars in our structure of science, but their numbers were relatively small. Now, schools, government, and industry are giving unprecedented support to science, and hundreds of thousands of scientists are giving their full-time efforts in the investigation of scientific problems. As a result, old problems are being solved, and new ones discovered. This changing scientific scene has great implications for the future in elementary school science.

Whole new sciences have been developed that should have some recognition in our school science programs. Certainly, all of our youngsters should have an opportunity to have some contact with such relatively new sciences as oceanography, astronautics, hydrology, nutrition, ecology, and the polar sciences. If children are to have contact in school with such sciences, it will probably have to be in the elementary or junior high schools.

The nature of the sciences is also changing. In almost all sciences, more refined mathematics and precise methods of measurement are being used. Does this mean that mathematics and measurement should be accorded larger roles in the elementary school? More sophisticated devices are being used to extend the range of our senses in observation. Does this mean that such tools for observation as the microscope and the telescope should be used to a greater extent in elementary school science? In many of our sciences, new mental models which help us to picture the very small and the very large are being used to make sense out of new discoveries. Certainly, whenever possible, children should have access to these new ways of looking at the world.

Inquiry in Science Education

There is a growing emphasis on inquiry in science education. Inquiry is the attempt to find some answer or resolution to a problem. Inquiry in the laboratory, field, and classroom is central to science. It is also of critical importance in our schools.

Too often our teaching of science is unscientific. Children are asked to "learn" unrelated, relatively insignificant facts without consideration for the methods of inquiry used to develop these facts. The facts may be consistent with our "best" scientific information at any particular time, but will they be consistent in five or ten years? Since we shall then probably have new information and "better" facts, will the young adult be forced to conclude that the science he learned in elementary school was basically unsound?

Actually, our scientific "facts" are reliable only to the extent that our methods of inquiry are reliable. Our "facts," for example, about the wave-length of the radiations making up white light are quite reliable because we have highly sophisticated methods of investigating the wavelength of different kinds of light. Our "facts" about the nature of the interior of the earth, however, are less reliable and are likely to be changed in the near future, because the methods of inquiry used in this area of science are relatively unreliable, and many of our "facts" are really extrapolations from limited information that may eventually be found to be irrelevant. Thus, "to know the facts," we must know something about the nature of the methods of inquiry on which those facts are based. The so-called "facts" may actually be ephemeral in nature, but a knowledge of the methods of inquiry will undoubtedly be of greater value to a child.

In the future we may have the means to be more successful in giving youngsters an opportunity to become acquainted with methods of inquiry used in the sciences. Our children will have available more of the tools of science, such as microscopes, telescopes, binoculars, meters of various kinds, and scales, which can be used to conduct investigations in ways that are more consistent with the nature of scientific inquiry. Also, more books, pamphlets, and other resource materials will be available through which children can check the experiences of others. All of these factors may make it possible for children to have more effective experiences with scientific inquiry.

Research Studies and Projects

Research and development in the elementary school is opening up new possibilities for work with children in science. For example, many of the ideas developed in this book are drawn from research and development in elementary school science.

Research is the systematic study of problems. Recently, for example, we have had studies dealing with how children develop scientific concepts, the nature of children's interests, and the influence of various sources of information on children's learning of science. In most elementary science education research the methods of the social sciences are used. Such research studies provide a more solid foundation on which teaching practice can be based.

Research studies in elementary school science are usually reported in such journals as:

Journal of Research in Science Teaching (New York: John Wiley and Sons).

School Science and Mathematics (Kalamazoo, Mich.: Western Michigan University).

Science Education (New York: John Wiley and Sons).

For a summary of some of the research related to elementary school science see: Herbert A. Smith, "Educational Research Related to Science Instruction for the Elementary and Junior High School: A Review and Commentary," *Journal of Research in Science Teaching*, 1:199 (1963).

Science improvement projects are a relatively recent development in the field of elementary school science. In these projects classroom teachers, scientists, science educators, and psychologists are given support to develop new approaches to elementary school science. Usually, the new approaches are subjected to extensive testing in elementary school classrooms before they are released for general use in the schools. A number of the approaches suggested in this book have been influenced by work in these research and development projects.

Among the influential elementary science research and development centers have been:

American Association for the Advancement of Science (AAAS), *Science —A Process Approach* (Washington, D.C.)

Concept Oriented Program in Elementary Science (COPES) (New York: New York University)

Elementary School Science Project (Urbana, Ill.: University of Illinois)

Elementary Science Study (ESS) (Newton, Mass.: Educational Development Corp.)

Minnesota Mathematics and Science Teaching Project (MINNEMAST) (Minneapolis, Minn.: University of Minnesota)

Science Curriculum Improvement Study (SCIS) (Berkeley, Calif.: University of California)

Science Manpower Project (SMP) (New York: Teachers College, Columbia University)

GOALS FOR ELEMENTARY SCHOOL SCIENCE

For effective science instruction in the elementary school we must have a concept of the directions in which we want children to grow. These directions are indicated by our goals. A statement of goals should have operational meanings for our day-to-day work. Too often, our goals become pious platitudes that seem to have little relevance to what goes on in the classroom. In the following statement of goals, concrete examples are given of what these goals can mean in our work with children.

A statement of goals also provides us with yardsticks for the evaluation of our work and the general effectiveness of our program. To what extent have individual children grown in the directions desired? What science experiences seemed to be particularly effective or ineffective?

The following goals are suggested for our work with children in science: (1) to build a rational and consistent view of the natural, physical world; (2) to gain an understanding of the conceptual structures of science; (3) to develop some skill in the use of the methods and processes of science; (4) to prepare for effective citizenship; (5) to gain some understanding of the human body and how to care for it; (6) to develop the ability to participate in exciting new developments in science and technology.

To build a rational and consistent view of the natural, physical world

Children should be encouraged to develop a broad, liberating view of the world consistent with the world view that has been developed in the sciences. This modern, scientific view of the world helps in dealing with the phenomena of the environment. The cosmos is now viewed as being vast in space, containing a tremendous number of stars and, perhaps, planets revolving around many of these stars. This vast universe provides a major challenge for investigation and exploration. Unlike the past, man is now viewed as being a part of the animal kingdom. This view has made possible major advances in medicine, physiology, and our general understanding of the human body and how it works. This modern view of man and his world, liberating him from fear and superstition, has opened new worlds for investigation and exploration. Today's children must have the opportunity to take part in this investigation and exploration.

Teachers can help children to develop a better understanding of the world in which they live by developing some concept of the vast distances involved in the universe. Many youngsters are familiar with travel by jet airliner. How long, for example, would it take for a person, traveling by jet airliner, to reach the sun? Since the distance to the sun is about 93 million miles and a jet airliner travels at about 600 miles per hour, an arithmetic calculation reveals that it would take more than seventeen years to reach the sun. Some children have made the calculations for the time required to make the trip to the nearest stars. Through activities such as this, the teacher helps children to gain a better understanding of the vastness of the universe in which they live.

One of the many ways to develop an understanding of the similarities between living things is to have youngsters try to state the characteristics that differentiate living from non-living things. How does a living thing differ from something such as a candle flame. The candle flame moves, uses oxygen, gives off carbon dioxide, is sensitive, and displays many other characteristics often associated with living things. Such an exercise forces children to consider more carefully the characteristics that are common to living things, including themselves.

To gain an understanding of the conceptual structures of science

A major goal in science is to develop broad generalizations that link together and explain the results of many experiments and observations. For example, the variety among plants and animals is very evident. Fossil evidence indicates that other forms of life have lived in the past but have become extinct. Early in the history of science many plants and animals were studied and carefully described. Later, systems of classification were developed by which plants and animals could be categorized. But, what are the relationships within this great variety of plants and animals? Is there a broad generalization or general theory that could explain this great variety?

The theory of evolution, probably the most basic generalization in the biological sciences, links together and explains the observations of variety among living organisms. Natural selection, which is a part of the theory of evolution, explains how some kinds of organisms have survived through the geological eras, why other kinds of organisms have become extinct, and how new kinds of organisms have evolved. The theory of evolution is used as a base for much of the investigation and experimentation in modern biology.

Young children can begin to formulate conceptual structures. They can describe objects, materials, and living organisms by their physical properties. Systems of classification can be devised for grouping. Sometimes, children can make the imaginative leap to suggest the generalization or theory that will explain the observations and groupings that they have made. As they take part in such activities, they are having experiences in developing conceptual structures somewhat like those in science.

To develop some skill in the use of the methods and processes of science

The methods of science have been employed to give us a better understanding of the basic forces at work in our universe. These understandings have been used to improve our health and build the technology of modern society. These scientific methods and processes can be used to deal with some of the questions and problems that children recognize.

The scientific approach is characterized by the concern for empirical, experiential tests. Einstein's theory of relativity, for example, was subjected to a partial empirical test through the study of the starlight that passed near the sun during a solar eclipse. Also, in science the findings of one scientist or group of scientists are examined, checked, and criticized by other scientists who are competent in that field. This is sometimes called the public dimension of science. A Russian astronomer, for example, reported seeing evidence of volcanic activity on the moon. The existence of volcanic activity on the moon could not be accepted until it had been checked by other experts on vulcanism and lunar surfaces. Although there is still no general agreement, special equipment has been set up to observe flashes on the moon. The controlled experiment is another important method in the sciences. The effect of radioactivity on plants, for example, has been studied by comparing plants that have been exposed to radioactivity with those that have not. These are a few of the characteristics of the methods employed in the sciences. Certainly, one of the most important outcomes of science instruction is that children gain some understanding of these methods and some skill in their use.

A first grade class was studying magnets. They had investigated to find out what kinds of things are attracted to magnets, how compasses are made, and what happens when the ends of a bar magnet are brought near a compass needle. Eventually, they proceeded to make magnets by rubbing iron nails with magnets. One youngster asked, "Does it make any difference which way the nail is rubbed? Would the nail be magnetized if it were rubbed back and forth with a magnet?" The teacher asked, "How can we find out?" The children's immediate response was, "Try it!" However, the teacher hesitated and suggested that they had raised two questions and that they ought to deal with them one at a time. She also suggested that they try to think through what happens when a nail is stroked in one direction by a pole of a permanent magnet. She also asked them to try to describe what happens when a nail is rubbed back and forth with a magnet. In other words, she asked them to use whatever knowledge they had of magnets to formulate hypotheses. The children carried out the operations and stroked a nail in one direction with one pole of a magnet and found that they had succeeded in magnetizing the nail. Another nail was stroked back and forth, and they found that it was not magnetized.

These first grade children had a chance to identify and clarify a problem, use their previous knowledge to suggest hypotheses, and to carry out operations to test these hypotheses. Such experiences help children develop some understanding of the methods used in the sciences.

To prepare for effective citizenship

In a democracy, citizens and their elected representatives have to make decisions concerning public health, transportation, communication, space exploration, national defense, conservation of natural resources, use and control of nuclear energy, agricultural policy, industrial development, and education. Some knowledge of science and technology is essential for intelligent discussion and decision in all of these areas. The elementary school can provide a child with an opportunity to acquire some of this knowledge and understanding with the guidance and help of a teacher. Since the success of a democracy depends upon the wisdom and insight of the citizen, effective elementary science programs are of great importance in an age when so many critical problems are related to science and technology.

One of the important contributions of the elementary school is the development of *scientific literacy*. Special words used in science are terms like mass, isotopes, hybrids, concentrations, and half-life. Some understanding of such terms is necessary in order to evaluate the testimony of experts on various issues and to understand public statements related to science and technology. An understanding of some of these terms is often developed in elementary school science.

Through elementary school science children should also gain some understanding of procedures that can be used to study problems and issues. These procedures are very much like the methods of investigation used in the sciences. Information is sought from a variety of sources: expert opinion, printed documents, and experimentation. The information obtained must be evaluated: checking consistency of statements, recency, and whether there is general agreement among experts. Children use such procedures in their investigations in elementary school science, and they can learn how to use them to deal with public issues and problems.

To gain some understanding of the human body and how to care for it

Through such sciences as anatomy, physiology, nutrition, and public health, a great deal has been learned about the human body and how to care for it. The same general physical principles that have been used to explain phenomena in our environment have been used to study and understand the organization and functioning of the human body. This knowledge has been used to raise the average life expectancy about twenty years in the last half century.

Health is now thought of as more than the mere absence of sickness and disease. Instead, it is a state in which an individual can operate at his optimum effectiveness. Few individuals have attained this state of optimum health. Through a study of the human body and its requirements for healthy living, children can learn how to improve their health.

One of the major factors that influences the state of health is the nourishment that the body receives. Many children have studied the effects of various diets upon the growth and development of laboratory white rats. The laboratory rat has almost the same nutritional requirements as a human being, but the effects of nutritional deprivation are seen about thirty times as fast in white rats as in man. Controlled demonstrations are set up in which one pair of rats is given an adequate diet while another pair of rats is fed a diet deficient in some nutrient. The children set up the demonstration, make the observations, secure and record information, arrange and interpret data. After a period of time, the rats on the deficiency diet are fed an adequate diet to show the changes that take place when the proper nutrients are made available. Through such an experience children discover that what you eat makes a difference and learn more about how to achieve optimum health.

To participate in new developments in science and technology

The grandparents of today's children have seen the development of a relativistic view of the universe, a probing into the nucleus of the atom, and the development of a more profound understanding of the nature of living matter and the mechanism whereby characteristics of living organisms are transmitted from one generation to the next. No other generation in the history of mankind has witnessed such profound scientific developments.

This generation has also seen such technological developments as the efficient automobile, propeller and jet airplanes, rockets that take man into space, radio and television, hybrid seeds that have helped farmers to double and triple production, and public health programs that have helped us to raise the average life expectancy. These important developments have taken place during the lifetimes of many people who are alive today.

The human race is entering an era of research, development, exploration, and discovery never before equaled in history. We are on the brink of a period of exploration in outer space that will rival and surpass in excitement the discovery of the New World. We shall continue to gain a better understanding of the nature of matter to be found throughout the universe and perhaps even of universes made of anti-matter. Certainly, the nature of life will be explored further, and we may find ways to synthesize living matter. A search will be made for evidences of life elsewhere in the universe. These are some of the developments in which our children may take part during their lifetimes.

All of our children have a right to take part in the coming adventures. Obviously, some of our children will be the adventurers who plan and carry out these explorations. However, all of our children should have an opportunity to understand these new developments, to become aware of the implications of new developments, and to share in the thrill of new discoveries. All of our children have a right to a share in this age of investigation, and elementary school science can be one of the keys that unlocks the door to this new age.

To participate in the new developments in science and technology, children will have to gain some mastery of the special languages of science. Again, the need for scientific literacy becomes evident; certainly, our children should gain sufficient command of the terminology of science to read and understand the science articles in our better newspapers and news magazines and to listen to and view with understanding science programs on radio and television. Our children should also gain some understanding of the fundamental principles of science so that reports of scientific developments and controversies over the use of our technology can be evaluated and viewed with some perspective. These are among the important intellectual tools that will enable our children to take part in tomorrow's world of science and technology.

Selected References

CONANT, JAMES B., *Science and Common Sense*. New Haven, Conn.: Yale University Press, 1951.

CRAIG, GERALD S., "Elementary School Science in the Past Century." *The Science Teacher* (February, 1957).

EDUCATIONAL POLICIES COMMISSION, *Education and the Spirit of Science*. Washington, D.C.: National Education Association, 1966.

JACOBSON, WILLARD J., AND TANNENBAUM, HAROLD E., *Modern Elementary School Science*. New York: Teachers College Press, 1961.

LOCKARD, J. DAVID, *Report of the Information Clearinghouse on New Science and Mathematics Curricula*. College Park, Md.: Science Teaching Center, University of Maryland. Issued annually.

UNDERHILL, ORRA E., *The Origins and Development of Elementary School Science*. Chicago, Ill.: Scott, Foresman, 1941.

ZAFFORONI, JOSEPH, AND SELBERG, EDITH, *New Developments in Elementary Science*. Washington, D.C.: National Science Teachers Association, 1963.

2 Teaching and the Nature of Science

Teaching should be consistent with the nature and structure of the subject or discipline being taught. This is of special importance in science, where the freedom to question and the reliability of sources are so important. Experiments, demonstrations, field trips, projects, and discussions should be consistent with the nature and structure of science. In this chapter science as a human endeavor is discussed, using illustrations from the history of science and examples from the experiences of teachers.

METHODS AND PROCESSES OF SCIENCE

The methods and processes used are of critical importance. Astrologers and fortune-tellers make predictions about the natural, physical world, but they are definitely not scientists. Unlike the true scientist, their methods of obtaining data and modes of interpretation are not carefully described; their results cannot be checked and criticized by others. Their interpretations and conclusions, therefore, are unscientific and remain suspect.

The methods and processes of science are among the most powerful intellectual tools of man. These methods are characterized by careful analysis to clarify the nature of the question or problem to be investigated. Children are acting scientifically when they try to clarify the meaning of the questions that they ask. It is not possible to study all of the universe at once. Systems within the universe must be defined and studied. Children define systems when they decide what is and is not pertinent in the study of a problem. Available research must be consulted to see what others have found out about a question or problem. Children do this when they consult science books in the school library or query adults for information or opinions. Possible answers are suggested, and these hypotheses become tools for the investigation of the problem. Experiments and observations are carried out to get the information that will help to determine whether a hypothesis should be accepted or rejected; the acceptability of a hypothesis depends on what actually happens when it is tested, not what we wish would happen. The answers we obtain are checked with the answers that others have reported in books and papers. In our elementary schools, children should begin to have experience in using these methods.

Scientists do not use these methods and approaches at all times in their lives, but they tend to use these methods when they are operating scientifically. Usually, these scientific procedures are used when they are operating in their area specialization. A physicist is more likely to operate scientifically when he is dealing with questions and problems in physics than when he is dealing with difficulties in his home or business, although he may use them under those circumstances as well. The methods and approaches of science are among the most powerful intellectual tools man has developed, and it is especially important that children begin to gain some understanding of these methods.

The following characteristics of science are important. Examples for each of these characteristics have been drawn from the history of science.

Empirical Tests

In science the primary test of an idea is an empirical one—"Does it work when it is tried?" Whenever possible, ideas in the sciences are checked by direct observation or experimentation. Usually, it is desirable that the observations and experiments be checked by a number of qualified scientists.

In the latter part of the seventeenth century, it was commonly believed that dead bodies, filth, or any sort of decayed matter engendered worms. To test this hypothesis, the Italian scientist Francesco Redi placed three dead snakes in a box to decay. Worms soon appeared and began devouring the meat. However, the worms were of different sizes which led him to believe that they had been born on different days. After the meat was devoured, the worms escaped through a hole in the box. In order to find out what happened to the worms, Redi repeated his experiment using a box in which all openings were closed. He noticed the worms changed into egg-shaped objects which we now know as pupa. After a number of days, adult flies emerged from the pupa. Then, Redi had an important idea: "Perhaps all worms found in meat come from flies, and these worms, in turn, develop into new flies!"

Fig. 2-1 Redi tested his hypothesis by covering four flasks and leaving four uncovered. Worms appeared only in the uncovered flasks.

Redi went on to test the idea that all worms found in meat came from flies by conducting a *controlled experiment*. He placed various kinds of meat into eight wide-mouthed flasks. Four of these flasks were sealed so that no flies could get near them, while the four remaining flasks were left open. Worms soon appeared in the open flasks, and flies were seen entering and leaving at will. No worms appeared in the closed flasks. By careful observation and controlled experimentation, Redi obtained empirical evidence to test his hypothesis. The work of Redi and others laid the foundation for the scientific generalization that living things come from other living things.

This insistence upon empirical tests differentiates science from several other areas of human endeavor. For an idea to be consistent with widely held dogma or pervasive beliefs is not an adequate test in the sciences. Similarly, majority vote is of little consequence. To test an idea in the sciences is to subject it to the rugged, demanding check of "Does the idea work when it is tried?"

Children should have an opportunity to consider various kinds of tests of ideas and to experience carrying out empirical tests. For example, hold a heavy steel ball and a light cork of about the same size at the same height above the table. "If they are both dropped at the same time, which will strike the table first?" The teacher may suggest that on the basis of her greater age, college degrees, and other qualifications it is her judgment that the heavy ball will strike the table first. (Reliance on authority for test of an idea.) "Is this a reliable test?" Then, the teacher may ask for a vote. (Majority test.) "Is this a reliable test?" Finally, the empirical test of actually dropping the balls is tried.

Systems Are Selected for Study

In dealing with a question or problem in the sciences, the entire universe is not investigated and analyzed. Instead, systems of objects and structures believed to be pertinent to the question are identified. For some kinds of problems, the solar system may be the object of study. Or, the system may be limited to the chemicals within a test tube. The identification of the pertinent system, an almost automatic response on the part of the trained scientist, makes it possible to deal with the problem with some hope of success.

William Harvey identified a system as he studied the problem of how blood moves in the body. It had been known for a long time that the heart moves blood, but Harvey examined and studied valves in the heart and came to realize that blood could not flow through the heart in both directions. By measuring the capacity of the heart he was able to calculate the amount of blood that went through it at each beat. He found that more blood passed through the heart in one hour than was contained in the entire body. The blood must circulate from the heart throughout the body and back to the heart.

Harvey studied the flow of blood in the heart, arteries, and veins. He did not devote his attention to the brain, the nervous system, or the skeletal system. Instead, he identified those parts of the body that were most pertinent to the problem he was studying.

The identification of systems for study has led to specialization within the sciences. Specialization, in turn, sometimes leads to difficulty of communication between specialists who often use special languages developed within their specialties. Many scientific advances, however, are the result of this specialization which has allowed scientists to devote their energies to the study of particular systems.

Children should practice defining systems. Place a streak of water on the chalkboard. Ask the children to observe carefully what happens, and report their observations. Then have them note the objects they did not mention. Did they mention the clock on the wall? Was the bird that flew by the classroom window part of the system? The children, like scientists, will identify a system of objects that can reasonably seem to be related to the phenomenon under study. By scientists, this is often done almost automatically.

Using and Testing Hypotheses

Hypotheses, or suggested answers, are used as tools in the investigation of questions and problems. Observations, experiments, and investigations are carried out to test hypotheses.

Charles Darwin is reputed to have said, "How odd it is that anyone should not see that all observation must be for or against some view, if it is to be of any service."

An automobile mechanic uses hypotheses to investigate why an automobile will not start. Obviously, he cannot check the entire automobile all at once. Instead, he suggests possible answers and then checks these answers, one by one. For example, he may say, "Perhaps there is no gasoline in the tank." Or, "Perhaps there is dirt in the fuel line." Such suggested answers—hypotheses—help the mechanic to discover what is wrong with the automobile.

The scientist Charles Nicolle often visited a hospital in Tunis where there were patients suffering from many diseases, including typhus. It was well known that while typhus was very contagious outside the hospital, it seldom, if ever, was spread from patient to patient within the hospital. Why? One day Nicolle noticed, at the entrance to the hospital, the body of a man who had died of typhus. What was the difference between the dead man and the patients inside? The patients had been stripped of their clothing, shaved, and washed. Typhus, then, must be carried by something on the outside of the body. The body louse? Once having gained this idea—the hypothesis—Nicolle was able to prove that typhus was transmitted by the body louse and to show how this deadly disease could be controlled.

To formulate a hypothesis, children must use knowledge that they have derived from previous experiences. *If thinking is using what we know to deal with questions and problems*, then this is what children engage in as they strive to suggest useful hypotheses. Actually, one of the great faults with much of our science instruction has been that children seldom use, and thus do not see the value of, anything that they have learned. However, when they are urged to suggest hypotheses, they have to call upon their past experiences and use what they have learned. They are having practice in thinking and, perhaps, learning how to do it.

A fourth grade class had been germinating seeds, and the seeds had been arranged to find out if it made any difference whether the seeds were "right side up, upside down, sideways, or 'kitty-corner'." With little surprise to anyone, the children found that the orientation of the seeds had no effect upon the germination. But, then one child asked, "What would happen if a full grown plant were turned upside down?"

Like many children, these fourth graders were eager to carry out the empirical test. Their first response was, "Let's try it!" But, the teacher insisted that they first suggest hypotheses. "What do you think will happen when you try it?" The responses to this question helped prepare the children better to observe the empirical test.

"The stem of the plant will bend and begin to grow up."
"The plant will grow straight down."
"The plant will die."

You may wish to have your children suggest what they think will happen when a plant is turned upside down. Then, "try it."

Controlled Experiments

Controlled experimental tests are an important means of investigation in the sciences. In the classic type of controlled experiment, all factors but one are controlled. Any changes that take place must be due to the variable factor. When a new kind of seed is being tested, for example, plants from the new seed are compared with plants from other varieties. However, it is important that all varieties be grown under the same conditions of soil, water, sunlight, and cultivation. If all such factors are controlled, any differences in yield must be due to the variety of seed used.

The *control* is an important factor if the experiment is to be a scientific one. A controlled experiment helps to show what factors are causally related to the phenomena being studied.

Children should have many experiences in setting up controlled experiments. For example, one group of youngsters wished to find out whether a dull, dark-colored surface would absorb more heat than a shiny surface. They blackened one test tube by holding it in the flame of a candle. Then they put equal amounts of sand into the black test tube and into a clear test tube. Thermometers were inserted into the sand in both test tubes and the test tubes were supported in front of a gooseneck lamp. All conditions for both test tubes were the same (distance from lamp, amount and kind of sand, etc.) except for the color of the tubes. Any difference in the temperature of the sand must have been due to the color of the tube.

Science Has a Cumulative Dimension

Isaac Newton is reputed to have said, "If I have seen farther, it is because I have stood on the shoulders of giants." Our scientists, today, build on the work of their predecessors. Similarly, in science, our children need not start where the cavemen started. They can make use of the knowledge acquired by scientists who have preceded them.

Michael Faraday discovered how to use magnets to generate electricity. He could not have made this discovery, however, if the following had not already been achieved.

> VOLTA—Developed the voltaic cell which is a source of electric current.

OERSTED—Demonstrated that an electric current flowing through a conductor will affect the magnetic needle of a compass.

ARAGO—Showed how an electromagnet could be made.

AMPÈRE—Showed that two adjacent wires will be affected when electric currents are sent through them.

UNKNOWN—Showed how electric conductors could be insulated.

Children can crawl upon "the shoulders of giants" by using the books and other science materials available to them. A group of fourth graders was studying meteors and meteorites. Although one of the children had a relic of what was supposed to have been a meteorite, there is a limited amount of information that can be gained from the examination of a part of one meteorite. To augment this information, they scoured all the available books in the school and public libraries. Unlike early man who regarded meteors with ignorant awe and fearful superstition, because of their research, these fourth graders were able to view meteors with scientific understanding.

Checking Ideas and Findings

Ideas and findings in science are criticized and checked by others competent in the field. Imaginative, new ideas provide the breakthroughs that lead to new scientific generalizations. But before these ideas can be accepted they must be subjected to the critical scrutiny of other scientists. When Copernicus published his theory that the planets revolve around the sun, the idea was subjected to very severe criticism. Now, however, the heliocentric theory, with some modifications, is generally accepted by all astronomers. This series of checks and balances is known as the public dimension of science. It was not sufficient that Copernicus publish his theory; the theory had to be examined, criticized, and finally accepted by others competent in the field.

Experimental findings must also be checked by other scientists—results of an experiment must be accompanied by descriptions of the experiment that are sufficiently detailed so that other scientists can repeat and check the experiments. The German scientists Hahn and Strassman reported that Uranium 235, when bombarded with atomic particles, split into such elements as barium and krypton. It was quickly realized that if uranium actually fissioned in this way, a great deal of energy would be involved and that this energy might be released in an explosion. When the fissioning of Uranium 235 was reported at a scientific meeting in the United States, it is reported that the scientists didn't wait for the close of the meeting before rushing to their laboratories to begin checking the findings of Hahn and Strassman.

"No one can work as a scientist in complete isolation from other scientists." Ideas and findings are communicated to fellow scientists to be checked and criticized. Obviously, this means that freedom of communication is essential in science, and restrictions of the freedom of speech and publication inhibit the continued progress of science. This is one of the reasons why scientists are often in the forefront in the battle to protect such basic liberties as freedom of speech and press and the right to hold unorthodox opinions.

Children should have a chance to communicate their ideas and the results of their experiments to other children for discussion and criticism. One of the ways to do this is to hold "colloquiums" where children describe their work—whether it be studies of how to grow plants in various kinds of soil or investigations into ways of building telegraph sets—to their schoolmates. The children have to prepare their demonstrations carefully and be ready to answer the probing questions of their colleagues. Usually, the teacher helps to bring out the most important points connected with the demonstrations. This is one way for the children to learn a great deal of science in the traditional sense and, of equal importance, to gain a more profound understanding of the "public dimension" of science.

New Approaches to Problems

One of the important approaches in science is to try to view questions or problems in new and different ways. Irving Langmuir, for example, improved the electric light bulb by approaching the problem in a radically new way.

The first light bulbs were made by putting a carbonized filament inside a glass bulb and evacuating the air from within the bulb. Subsequent attempts to improve the light bulb often took the form of trying to pump a greater fraction of the air out of the bulb. Langmuir considered other ways that the filament could be kept from burning. Rather than pumping air out of the bulb, why not pump into the bulb an inert gas which will not support burning? This was done, and a better light bulb was eventually constructed. Langmuir succeeded because he viewed the problem in a radically new way.

To view questions and problems in new ways is difficult. "In this connection it is not irrelevant to note that, of all forms of mental activity, the most difficult to induce even in the minds of the young, who may be presumed not to have lost their flexibility, is the art of handling the same bundle of data as before, but placing them in a new system of relations with one another by giving them a different framework, all of which virtually means putting on a different kind of thinking-cap for the moment."[1]

The idealized experiment is another important scientific tool. Galileo used such an idealized experiment to achieve a better understanding of motion. If a cart is pushed along a level road, it will continue to roll for a short distance after the pushing has stopped. If the road is very smooth and the bearings well lubricated, the cart will roll farther before it stops. What would happen if the road were perfectly smooth and there were no friction? The cart would continue to roll forever. By using an idealized experiment such as this, Galileo helped achieve a better understanding of the nature of motion. Later, Isaac Newton stated this finding as one of his laws: "A body at rest tends to remain at rest and a body in motion will tend to remain in motion in a straight line unless acted upon by an outside force."

Taking a point of view directly opposite to the prevailing point of view, as Langmuir did, and the idealized experiment of a Galileo are two approaches that we can help our children to use. For example, we can ask children to try to envisage what the sky must look like at noon to children on the opposite side of the earth. Or, "What would our city be like if there were no air pollution?"

Quantitative and Precise Statements

In science an attempt is made to express ideas and findings as precisely as possible. Whenever possible, ideas and findings are stated in mathematical terms.

For example, to answer the question of how many seeds in a package actually germinate, one kind of answer would be "many or most," "few or not many." However, it is more precise to state the actual number, or even better, the fraction or percentage of the seeds that have germinated. These more precise statements can be communicated to and checked by others. Statements such as "many" or "few" are imprecise and depend upon the judgment of the observer or experimenter; obviously, someone may consider "many" to be "few" or vice versa. However, when ideas and results are stated quantitatively, there is greater precision and less room for confusion. Also, more precise statements are more useful. For example, a precise statement of germination rates will help to determine how many seeds should be planted.

New developments in science are sometimes the result of precision of

[1] Herbert Butterfield, *The Origins of Modern Science*. (New York: The Macmillan Co., 1957), p. 1.

statement and measurement. For example, according to the atomic theory of the time, the atomic weights of various elements should be in whole numbers. However, very careful measurements of the atomic weights of elements indicated that many elements apparently had atomic weights that differed slightly from whole numbers. How could this be explained? The measurements were of such accuracy that the discrepancy could not be explained by a lack of precision of measurement. Investigations of these discrepancies led to the discovery of isotopes of elements. Each isotope has an atomic weight that is a whole number. However, the elements as we study them are usually composed of a mixture of various isotopes of the element; the composite weight of these isotopes usually approximates, but is not exactly, a whole number. In this case precision of measurement led to a discovery of tremendous importance.

Children should be encouraged to be as precise as possible in discussing their ideas and reporting their findings. They should learn how to use rulers and measuring tapes, clocks and watches, scales and balances, measuring cups and graduates. As they use these tools for measurement, they will learn the more precise language of science and the importance of precision. More effective ways of reporting can be learned. Graphs, for example, are useful for seeing and showing relationships between data.

THE BROAD GENERALIZATIONS OF SCIENCE

The broad generalizations of science may be considered to be the upright pillars of the structure of science. One of the major aims in working with children is to help them to gain a clearer concept of various broad generalizations of science so that they can use them in their lives.

Science generalizations are the "big ideas" of science. They are based upon the cumulative experience of the scientific community. The law of gravitation—"all matter anywhere in the universe is attracted to all other matter in the universe by a force that is proportional to the product of the masses of the objects and inversely proportional to the square of the distance separating the objects"—is a well-known example of a generalization of science. The child has seen objects fall to the earth; he has had experiences with this generalization.

Science generalizations are broad statements that help to explain phenomena and serve as tools for the investigation of the new and the unknown. An apple falls to the ground, the baseball the outfielder throws to the catcher travels in a certain trajectory, and the planets move around the sun in certain paths. It is the law of gravitation, however, that helps to show and explain the relationships between these phenomena.

The terms "concept" and "generalization" are sometimes used interchangeably. A concept, however, is the individual's view or mental image. For example, a child may have a concept of the distance to the moon, and this concept is peculiar to the individual. Generalizations, on the other hand, are statements based on the cumulative experiences of the scientific community.

In the elementary school children must be helped to develop a more coherent understanding of the broad generalizations of science. The following are examples of important generalizations that should be included in the curriculum.

The Conservation of Matter and Energy

The law of conservation of matter and energy states that *the sum total of matter and energy in a closed system remains constant.* Under ordinary conditions, it can be stated that "matter cannot be created or destroyed" and "energy cannot be created or destroyed." Under unusual circumstances, however, in particle accelerators such as cyclotrons, where particles of matter are accelerated to velocities approaching the speed of light, the particles of matter increase in mass as energy is converted to matter. In nuclear reactions, matter is converted to energy. Except under these extraordinary conditions, matter and energy can be neither created nor destroyed.

The law of conservation of matter and energy means, for example, that when two or more chemicals react in a test tube, in a burning match, or in our bodies, the mass of the products of the reaction will be the same as that of the reactants. A machine will not produce more energy than is put into it. In some ways, the law of conservation of matter and energy indicates some of the limitations to what can be done. It can also be used, however, to predict what will happen when certain operations are carried out.

The law of conservation of matter and energy is often understood in an unsophisticated, but important way, by children when they say, "You can't get something for nothing." The law is used in a more precise way in balancing chemical equations or in calculating the efficiency of machines.

The Second Law of Thermodynamics

The second law of thermodynamics states that *heat energy can never be transferred spontaneously from a colder to a hotter body.* If some object such as a bar of metal is heated, the heat will flow from the hotter region to the colder; it will not move spontaneously from the colder region to the hotter. In refrigerators, air conditioners, and similar devices, heat is "pumped" from a colder region, such as the interior of a refrigerator, to a warmer region, but energy has to be supplied and work done. If a refrigerator is disconnected so that no energy is supplied to operate the compressor, the temperature inside the refrigerator will eventually become the same as that outside.

The science of thermodynamics is largely a study of the application of the second law of thermodynamics. Insulating materials are used in homes and schools to slow down the inexorable transfer of heat from the warmer region to the colder. On the other hand, heating systems are designed to accelerate the process of transfer of heat. Children study this law of thermodynamics as they measure the changes in temperature in solids, liquids, and in the air around them and as they investigate ways that heat is transferred in homes and throughout their environment.

Like the law of conservation of matter and energy, the second law of thermodynamics is a major pillar in the framework of science. It is a law of limitation in that it dictates to us certain operations that cannot be carried out. A spontaneous flow of heat energy from a cold region to a hot region will not occur. To accomplish this, energy must be supplied to the system. In analysis of energy systems, including those in which living matter is involved, the second law of thermodynamics is a valuable tool.

The Law of Mass Production

The law of mass production states that *all living things tend to reproduce at such a rate that the population outstrips the food supply*. The deer in some of our northern forests, for example, reproduce to the point at which they eat all available food. When there is insufficient food for all the deer, many of them will die of starvation. With fewer mouths to feed, the food supply will once again become adequate. Reproduction, however, will continue at such a rate that again there will be an insufficient food supply.

This law of mass production apparently holds for all living things. Among plants there is a struggle for soil minerals, water, and sunlight. Usually, the plant species that is best adapted to survive in a particular environment will be dominant in that environment. Among insects there is a very high reproductive rate. A large fraction of the insect eggs may not even hatch, but the number of eggs is usually so high that the small fraction that hatches usually leads to a total population of such a size that it has an inadequate food supply.

Children can see many evidences of this mass production in the environment. The fluffy tuft of the dandelion contains hundreds of seeds from which new dandelion plants can sprout. Similarly, the female frog can deposit hundreds of eggs which will become tadpoles and adult frogs. Trees produce thousands of seeds that are dispersed in a variety of ways.

TEACHING SCIENCE

As we work with children, we must be concerned with both "how" we teach and "what" we teach. "What" children learn may be largely determined by "how" we teach. On the other hand, "how" we teach, especially in science, should be determined by "what" we are teaching. The teacher endeavors to gain a profound understanding of the "what" and resourcefulness and skill in the "how."

In science the "what" and the "how" of teaching are intimately intermingled. Perhaps the most important goal in working with children in science is to help them acquire a better understanding of the various methods and processes of investigation. However, these understandings can probably only be developed through the demonstration of various approaches and the use of the methods that are characteristic of the sciences. The methods of teaching science must be consistent with the methods and processes of science—to teach science effectively, it must be taught scientifically.

Certainly, one of the best ways to teach science scientifically is to encourage children to identify significant questions and problems in science and then work with them as they investigate these problems. Much of this work can take the form of cooperative investigations in which pupils and teacher work together to clarify questions and solve problems. For example, in one classroom a child demonstrated that when a large glass jar was placed over a burning candle, the candle eventually was extinguished. The child explained that there is a part of the air called oxygen that is necessary for the candle to burn. When much of this oxygen has been "used up," the candle can no longer burn. However, one of the children asked, "What would happen if the glass jar were raised so that some air could enter at the bottom? Would the candle go out?" The teacher asked him to clarify what he meant by his question. He placed the glass jar on two blocks so that air could enter the jar. Next, the teacher asked the class to predict what would happen to the burning candle under these conditions. In other words, she asked the children to use what they knew about gases and the nature of burning to form a hypothesis. They then went ahead, tried the experiment, and tested their hypothesis. After the experiment had been completed, the teacher called the children's attention to the various methods that they had used to investigate and try to answer a

Fig. 2-2 If air can enter the jar, will the candle go out?

question. Through this cooperative investigation of a relatively simple, but important, question, the teacher demonstrated some of the characteristics of a scientific approach.

Teaching science scientifically should help children to develop more sophisticated concepts of the broad generalizations of science. Through their investigation of the burning candle under a glass jar, the children should have developed a clearer understanding of the nature of burning. For example, they can learn that only a fraction of the air is utilized in the burning of the candle. By swishing limewater, which becomes a milky color when exposed to carbon dioxide, around in the jar, they can discover that carbon dioxide, previously not present in very large amounts, was formed as a product of the process of burning. They can also discover that warm gases, in this case gases rich in carbon dioxide, tend to rise, and cooler gases tend to descend. This is probably the principal reason that the candle will be extinguished even though the jar is raised so that fresh air could, but does not, enter through the neck of the jar. These are examples of important generalizations concerning the nature of burning and the behavior of gases. One of the important results of our teaching should be that our children gain a clearer concept of some of these major generalizations.

Selected References

BUTTERFIELD, HERBERT, *The Origins of Modern Science*. New York: The Macmillan Co., 1957.

KUHN, THOMAS S., *The Structure of Scientific Revolutions*. Chicago, Ill.: The University of Chicago Press, 1962.

NAGEL, ERNEST, *The Structure of Science*. New York: Harcourt, Brace and World, Inc., 1961.

PEIERLS, R. E., *The Laws of Nature*. New York: Charles Scribner's Sons, 1956.

ROBINSON, JAMES T., *The Nature of Science and Science Teaching*. Belmont, Calif.: Wadsworth Publishing Co., 1968.

SCHWAB, JOSEPH J., and BRANDWEIN, PAUL F., *The Teaching of Science*. Cambridge, Mass.: Harvard University Press, 1962.

WIGHTMAN, WILLIAM P. D., *The Growth of Scientific Ideas*. New Haven, Conn.: Yale University Press, 1953.

3 Child Development and Elementary Science

The children who sit down in the classroom that first day of school on a September morning may seem to have endless energy, strong drives, pixie mischievousness, and a superficial opposition to learning or an indomitable desire to find out. But regardless of the individual characteristics, almost all of them will have a keen interest in finding out more about themselves and the world in which they live. *This is science.* Science is often such a popular subject with children because it not only allows but encourages their natural curiosity—it sanctions the freedom to question, to explore, to investigate, to find out—and to wonder.

Apparently, almost all children pass through somewhat the same stages of growth and maturation. The particular stage of development of each child should and does influence the areas of study undertaken. Knowledge of each stage of intellectual development influences, of course, the kinds of science activities that are planned. Their stage of physical development, too, may often call for specific kinds of scientific experiences that will help them to meet certain problems that they are encountering.

WORKING WITH CHILDREN IN SCIENCE

A knowledge of child growth and development is essential for successful work with children. The following suggestions for working with children in science are based on our understanding of child development.

Children should be encouraged to wonder and to question

"Do fishes need air in order to live?"
"Why is the sky blue?"

"What makes things stick to magnets?"

"Where did I come from?"

"What happens when I grow?"

These are questions that children have asked, and any teacher can add dozens to the list. These are science questions; they indicate a desire to find out and a yearning to know. Children want to know about the birds in the air, the animals of the field and forest, the fishes and snails in the water, and the insects in their own backyards. They want to find out about electricity, magnetism, and motors. Children can be entranced by the study of how a plant grows from the viable seed to the fruit-bearing adult; they can become engrossed as they use a prism to separate white light into the variegated colors of the rainbow. Children speak of satellites and space probes, brontosaurus and tyrannosaurus, blast-off and burn-out. They follow the exciting course of events in the sciences with the avid interest of devotees and the sincere concern of the young who realize, perhaps better than adults, that they are living in an age of science.

This sense of wonder and urge to question are important in the sciences. Some of the most successful scientists are said to have had a "child-like" inquisitiveness. And it is little wonder that this is so. If science is the investigation and interpretation of the environment, the scientist will be led and guided by the problems that he raises and the questions that he asks. Probably, some of the most important discoveries in the sciences have come about as a result of someone's unsatiated curiosity and persistent desire to find out.

Curiosity, inquisitiveness, and a sense of wonder are precious qualities that should be nurtured. But in many young children, rich in these attributes on that first September morning, the sense of curiosity is deadened and the desire to find out stunted by the time the youngster leaves elementary school. In some cases, this may be the result of maturation, but, too often, it is a result of the kinds of educational experiences children have had. Certainly, every effort should be made to have children's experiences in science nurture their curiosity and inquisitiveness rather than stultify them.

There should be freedom to ask questions, even "silly" questions and questions that don't seem to make sense. True, children may, at times, seem to ask questions that have little meaning and seem to be asked more in a sense of play than from a serious desire to find out. But this in itself may be an important experience. It is becoming apparent that children need the opportunity to play with ideas and questions. Then, too, adults sometimes do not understand the question behind the question—that is, what the child is really trying to find out. The child who asked, "what happens to the water that runs down the drain?" really wasn't asking a question about the community's sewage treatment plant. He thought, with obvious justification, that the water ran into the wall, and was wondering why the wall "didn't get filled up." It is important that teachers understand children's questions; it is even more important that they give children opportunities to ask them.

Children should learn how to use references for information

Many questions that children ask cannot be answered, because there are no answers. Other questions may not be of genuine interest to more than one child in a class. A few questions may serve as springboards for investigation and study for the entire class. Early in the elementary school children should begin to learn how to use textbooks, trade books, encyclopedias, and other references for information. Fortunately, more and more excellent science materials that can be used by children are becoming available. As they learn how to use these materials, they are learning procedures that will be useful to them in their future science studies as they search for information related to questions that, hopefully, they will continue to ask throughout life.

To some, the myriad questions that children ask may seem threatening. "I don't know the answers to all the questions my children will ask." No one does! Even the most learned scientist will not know the answers to all the questions that children will ask, and neither he nor a teacher should be expected to know. This is not sufficient reason to stifle the wondering and questioning of children. In fact, one of the best and most exciting ways to learn science is to work with children as they explore the questions that they ask.

Children's science experiences should be developed in light of the characteristics of their stage of intellectual development

Man is unique in his ability to learn from experience and to communicate this learning to others. To a certain extent, other animals can learn; a dog can learn where he can get food and how he can win favor or disfavor from his master. Other animals can communicate; a crow squawks to warn the rest of the flock of impending danger. (An important finding in the relatively new science of ethology is that many animals are considerably more intelligent than had been thought.) But the dog cannot transmit the knowledge of how to win favor from one's master to the next generation of dogs, and the crow, as far as is known, cannot communicate the nature of the danger to other crows.

Only man is able to use symbols to represent experiences and ideas. It is now known that bees inform other bees of the location of delectable nectar. Such animals as the dog, crow, and bee use "signs" to communicate. But man is able to use "symbols." Symbols, whether they be the spoken word or marks on a piece of paper, can represent experiences and ideas. Symbols can be manipulated and rearranged to indicate new ideas. They can be recorded and used by other humans at great distances. Even more important, the symbols representing ideas and experience can be used by subsequent generations. The symbols are culture, and man is probably the only animal on the planet earth that is capable of developing and transmitting culture.

Science may be viewed as the process of developing an important dimension of man's culture—perhaps the most important dimension. Science includes tested knowledge—tested knowledge of man and the world in which he lives which can often be used for the betterment of man. The study of science, to a large extent, is the acculturation of the child in this dimension of human culture.

The newborn child, weak and utterly defenseless, has certain potentials that are determined largely by the particular genes that he has inherited from his mother and father. It is probable that no one comes close to achieving the genetic potentials with which he is born. The embryonic child is probably affected a number of ways during the nine months that he develops within the womb of the mother, and this possibly critical stage of development is now being studied intensively.

For all practical purposes, as of now, learning begins with birth. A knowledge of how the individual human being learns and his stages of intellectual development have considerable implication for how children should be taught—what methods and what programs for science learning should be used.

STAGES OF DEVELOPMENT

There is apparent agreement among many students of the intellectual development of children that each individual human being passes through four more or less distinct stages of intellectual development.[1] There seems to be a close relationship between physical growth and intellectual development. It is probably significant, for example, that the beginning of one stage of intellectual development seems to coincide with the onset of adolescence.

[1] The delineation of these four stages of intellectual development has largely grown out of the work of the Swiss psychologist Jean Piaget. The existence of these stages appears to have been confirmed by such work as that of the American psychologist Millie Almy.

The Sensory-Motor Stage

The first stage, approximately the first eighteen months of life, has been called the *sensory-motor stage*. Perhaps the most profound discovery of this period is that there is an environment; there is something outside of "me." The infant begins to develop some concept of objects. At first objects exist only when they are perceived. Later, the infant will retain some notion of an object and will try to find it. This young infant is also beginning to develop some concept of space. The child, for example, begins to learn to adjust the movements of his hands as he grasps for objects. The infant also begins to develop some notion of causality. For example, infants have been observed to shake themselves in a bassinet and look at dolls hanging from the bassinet, apparently with some anticipation of their swaying.

There are many students of child psychology who believe that the sensory-motor stage is of critical importance in both the physical and intellectual development of children. Apparently, it is extremely important that infants have the fondling, loving care of parents at this time in order for them to take the physical and intellectual steps that are expected at this stage. Infants in some orphanages, for example, where individual loving care is not possible, often learn to walk two years later than those reared under more fortunate circumstances. There are some indications that similar kinds of situations have a bearing on general development.

The Pre-Operational Stage

The second stage, from approximately eighteen months to six or seven years, has been called the *pre-operational stage*. In this stage the child begins to use the symbols of language. With these symbols he is able to think and probably reconstructs many of the experiences he had on the sensory-motor level. This stage is called pre-operational, because the child cannot yet act or operate on the basis of experience with objects or events. Apparently the child's thought processes are not yet "reversible." The child has a mental image of an object, but he cannot use this image to act or operate on the object.

The basic behavior that defines the pre-operational stage is the young child's inability to "conserve." The following tasks show what is meant by conservation.

1. A child, given two balls containing equal amounts of plasticene, will agree that they both contain the same amount. When one of the balls is rolled into a long thin roll, however, the pre-operational

child will say that one or the other, usually the ball, has more plasticene.

2. A child is given two similar tall containers and asked to fill both so that they contain equal amounts of water. When the contents in one of the containers is poured into a shallow tray such as a cake pan, the pre-operational child will usually say that the taller container has more water.

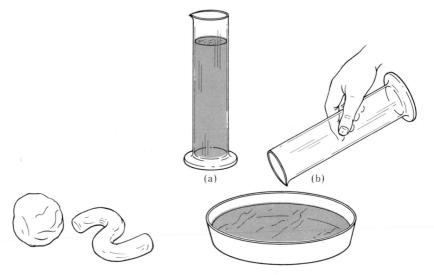

Fig. 3-1   Although there are equal amounts of plasticene in the ball and in the roll, the pre-operational child will usually say there is more in one than the other. There were equal amounts of water in A and B. When water from B is poured into the shallow dish, the pre-operational child will usually say there is now more water in A.

In the pre-operational stage, children should have abundant opportunities for firsthand, primary experiences with the objects of the environment.[2] If the loving, fondling care that was so important for the child in the sensory-motor stage now tends to inhibit and restrict the child's somewhat rambunctious encounters with living-room environment, it may conceivably restrict the intellectual development of the child. The varied activity-oriented nursery school and kindergarten programs are consistent with this view of intellectual development. A science program should emphasize a large number and wide variety of concrete, primary en-

[2] See Chapter 5 for a more detailed discussion of a science program for the pre-operational child.

counters with material objects of the environment even though, of course, the child cannot be expected to conceive sophisticated connections between these objects.[3]

The Stage of Concrete Operations

The third stage is called the stage of *concrete operations*. Usually children from the age of six or seven to about eleven are in the stage of concrete operations, and, therefore, this includes most of the children in the elementary school. Children enter this stage when they are able to "conserve." For example, when equal amounts of water are put into two tall cylinders and then the water in one of the cylinders is poured into a flat pan, children in the stage of concrete operations will say that there is an equal amount of water in each of the containers.

Children in the stage of concrete operations can operate on objects but not on verbal statements. They can describe the physical properties of objects, classify them, and arrange them in order on the basis of some property, and are also beginning to develop more sophisticated concepts of space, time, and number. They can deal with objects in quite sophisticated ways, but they have difficulty in stating hypotheses and making logical deductions from those hypotheses.

In the stage of concrete operations children should continue to have many and far-ranging firsthand experiences with concrete objects. But now they can go a step farther: they can operate with these material objects. They can group objects into various systems and use schemes of classification. They can use materials in experiments, investigations, and projects. Children should be encouraged and helped to verbalize about the material objects and the operations they carry out with them. Activity and language need to be brought together. In fact, it may be that a wide range of concrete operations is essential for future verbal development; it apparently is quite essential in order for the child to move into the fourth stage of intellectual development.

The Stage of Formal Operations

The fourth stage, called the stage of *formal operations*, usually begins at about twelve years, although some children in the upper elementary school will achieve this level. Children can now reason on hypotheses and ideas

---

[3] There are some indications that a child who does not have these primary experiences may be stunted in his intellectual development. For example, it may be that these kinds of primary experiences are an important asset in learning to read.

as well as on objects. In a sense, this might be called the stage of "abstraction." Children in this stage do not have to experience concrete objects but can deal with the abstractions that represent these objects or the actions that they have taken with these objects. A child, or an adult, may revert to the concrete stage of operations when confronted with new and unfamiliar situations, but he has the potential to move into the more efficient and effective formal mode of operations.

Children in the stage of formal operations are able to use general laws. They can carry out logical operations. For example, they can use a law such as Archimedes' Principle (an object placed in a fluid is pushed up by a force equal to the weight of the fluid it displaces) to predict whether or not an object will sink.

In the stage of formal operations, the individual can think of hypothetical situations that are not necessarily related to specific real situations. It has been suggested that this partially explains the adolescent's proclivity for social reform. He is exercising his formal power to hypothesize better worlds.

Some of the characteristics of intellectual behavior in the formal stage of operations, as contrasted to those in the stage of concrete operations, can be seen in the way an experiment in floating is handled.

A large container of water is made available, and a child is asked to classify a variety of objects, such as pebbles, blocks of wood, nails, toothpicks, bottle caps, and hollow metal cylinders, according to whether or not they float. After he has classified them, he is asked to summarize his observations and to look for a law.

Children early in the stage of concrete operations can classify the objects as (1) objects that float, (2) objects that sink, (3) objects (such as the bottle cap and hollow cylinder) that sink or float depending on how they are put into the water. They may explain their classification in such terms as "Light objects float" and "Heavy objects sink." However, they encounter difficulty when they find that a large piece of wood is heavier than a small nail, yet it floats. They do not have operational use of such concepts as *density* and *specific gravity*.

Adolescents in the formal stage of operation can handle this problem in more sophisticated ways. They can make hypotheses about whether or not an object will float and reject hypotheses without necessarily carrying out the concrete operations. Adolescents can view various possibilities. They can arrive at such concepts as specific gravity and density (the same volume of water would not be as heavy as the nail). Adolescents also tend to prove things logically and to take all factors into consideration. They may also be able to carry out mental experiments in which "all things are kept equal but one." This experiment tends to show how the individual in the formal stage of operation is freed from the necessity to rely completely on concrete operations to find out and to test ideas.

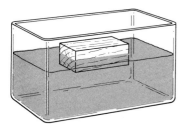 

Fig. 3-2   *A heavy block of wood floats. A light nail sinks.*

Understanding the General Stages of Intellectual Development

The concept of stages of intellectual development should help the teacher to understand children, communicate with them, and work more effectively. These stages should *not* be interpreted as limits to the kinds of experiences planned for children. In fact, teachers and parents too often underestimate children's readiness and capacity to explore and investigate their world. However, an understanding of the general stages of intellectual development can be an important resource in helping children to "stretch" as they explore and investigate.

A major implication of this view of the intellectual development of children is that early experiences—those they should have in elementary school science—are critical for future intellectual development. As children who have been deprived of fond, loving care during the sensory-motor stage are seriously retarded in both physical and intellectual development, children who have been seriously deprived of contact with objects of the environment during the pre-operational and concrete operational stages may never be able to deal with certain kinds of questions and problems on the formal operational level.

A major function of elementary school science is to help youngsters reach the stage of formal operations as they deal with the environment. At the level of formal operations, symbols are used. But if the symbols are to have meaning, they must be related in some way to the concrete, physical environment. As more and more children come to live in urban and suburban environments, they may not have as many unplanned, direct primary experiences with the physical environment as children in rural environments have. It will become increasingly important, therefore, for children to have these experiences in the elementary science program—a program planned to include many firsthand experiences in touching, feeling, handling, smelling, hearing, and observing objects in the class-room and in the natural, physical environment.

SCIENCE LEARNING

Changing Patterns of Behavior

Learning involves changing patterns of behavior. A child who studies the nutritional requirements of the human body and then changes his pattern of eating has definitely learned. Learning is more than memoriza-tion. Youngsters may memorize the parts of a flower, but they will have *learned* the parts of a flower only when they are able to *interpret* the char-acteristics and functions of the parts of a flower in terms of the growth and development of a plant and are able to *use* their knowledge to propagate and care for plants. When children are able to use information, their pat-terns of behavior have changed, and it can be said that they have learned.

In science it is what children actually learn that is important. Un-fortunately, there often is a low correlation between what teachers plan and attempt to teach and what children actually learn. For example, in attempting to demonstrate how a thermostat in an aquarium heater operates, a teacher used a compound bar to illustrate electric circuits. When the compound bar was heated with a candle, it bent so that an electrical circuit was broken and a flashlight bulb ceased to light. When the candle was removed, the compound bar straightened out to close the circuit and the flashlight bulb again gave off light. When asked to explain what the experiment proved, one student said, "When there is light from the candle, the flashlight bulb doesn't have to shine any more, and it goes off. When we take the light from the candle away, the bulb lights up again." To the boy this seemed like a sensible explanation. The teacher, however, had intended that the demonstration would give the children a better understanding of electrical circuits. Since what children actually learn is often quite different from what teachers hope that they will learn, it is essential that what has been learned be determined.

Behavioral Objectives

It is desirable to state what behavior is to be developed. If objectives are stated in behavioral terms, then there is some possibility of evaluation to see whether the objectives have been achieved. For example, in an exercise in which students are to learn how to define "density," it is suggested that they should be able to:

1. Demonstrate a procedure for finding the volume of a solid object by measuring the volume of water it displaces.
2. State an operational definition of density.
3. Demonstrate the computation of the density of an object given the known volume and known mass of the object.
4. Distinguish between objects which will float in water and those which will sink in water on the basis of their density.[4]

Note that each of these objectives is stated in terms of some operation that the child should learn to do. Upon completion of the exercise, it is possible to find out whether or not a student is able to do them.

Of course, the patterns of behavior that are developed should be desirable ones. An important function of the broad goals for elementary school science (see pages 17-23) is to serve as a general guide, as the kinds of changes in patterns of behavior to be achieved are formulated.

Developing Science Concepts Over an Extended Period of Time

Children's concepts, or pictures of themselves and the world in which they live, are limited by their stage of development. At one time, a child's concept of space may be limited to the boundaries of the local neighborhood. Twenty years later, this same individual may have some concept of the vastness of interstellar space. His concept of space has developed over a considerable period of time. Although science instruction is intended to have children develop concepts that are consistent with the broad generalizations of science, the child needs time to conceptualize from the myriad experiences he has with his environment. For example, one young child had the concept that the water used in the home came from the wall.[5] It was only after a considerable period of time during which he saw pipes in the wall and visited a water reservoir that he developed a more sophisticated concept of the source of the water in the home. In some cases, it may be necessary for the child to have time to assimilate a variety of experiences before concepts can be developed.

Apparently, many children's concepts develop gradually. Careful studies of children's concept development show that children come back to

[4] American Association for the Advancement of Science, *Science—A Process Approach*, Part Seven (Washington, D.C.: American Association for the Advancement of Science, 1966), p. 1.

[5] John Gabriel Navarra, *The Development of Scientific Concepts in a Young Child* (New York: Teachers College Press, 1955).

the same ideas after a certain lapse of time, and that each time they return to these concepts, new information and insights refine and extend the concepts. For example, when a group of children had their first experiences with electricity, some commented about the sparks they saw when one end of an electrical circuit was scratched on the other part of a dry cell. Months later, when the children were using flint and steel to make sparks to ignite some tinder, one child asked, "Is the spark that we get when we strike flint against steel the same kind of spark as that which we got from the dry cell?" (On a very sophisticated level there is a relationship.) This youngster was connecting two observations separated by a considerable span of time. The sensitive teacher, who recognizes that children do not develop their scientific concepts "all at once," is able to help them interpret a variety of science experiences so that they can gradually refine and extend their scientific concepts.

An implication of this view is that teaching in science should be "open-ended." Rather than deal with a science generalization as a unit to be studied and completed, it is better to leave matters open-ended to return at later times when the concept can be expanded. Science lessons should not have conclusions in the sense that there will not be further exploration of the subject. Instead, children should have time for digestion and assimilation. Concepts are not closed at the end; they develop as they are nurtured and reconsidered.

Direct Experiences

Children learn as they operate with objects and ideas. It has been said that "We learn as we become aware of what we are doing." In the elementary school there must be a great deal of "doing," and in elementary school science there are rich opportunities for this approach to learning.

Note the differences among three different approaches that are often used in science instruction: "Chalk and talk," teacher or pupil demonstration, and laboratory experience. In chalk and talk, there is almost complete dependence upon the manipulation of symbols. This approach can be very effective when the individuals have already had rich experience in concrete operations, but it is of limited value in the elementary school. Again, in demonstrations, children have an opportunity to observe, but they have limited opportunities to manipulate materials and equipment. There is an important place for demonstration in elementary school science, but only after children have had many firsthand experiences with the equipment and materials used in the demonstrations. It is in the laboratory experience itself, where children actually manipulate materials and equipment, that elementary school science must function if the children are eventually to move on to the formal stage of operations.

In the laboratory approach the classroom becomes the laboratory. Each child pushes and pulls, sets up equipment, experiments with materials, and carries out the classic proposal "Let's try it and see!"[6]

The Discovery Approach

A discovery approach is one in which children find out or discover new relationships—for themselves. Children use materials and equipment and sometimes "play around" with objects of the environment. Suddenly, there is a recognition of a relationship, a new insight. This flash of insight has sometimes been called the "Eureka experience." Archimedes is said to have dashed from his bathtub shouting "Eureka! Eureka!" after having "discovered" and used what is now called Archimedes' Principle. Children also should have opportunities to discover relationships. These relationships may not seem new and unusual to the adult, but to the youngster they are a discovery.

A discovery approach does not imply that the teacher remains out of the picture. Indeed, the teacher's role is a most subtle and important one. In making an assessment of the children's readiness for certain kinds of experiences, in helping to organize the experiences, and sometimes in supplying a boost over a temporary obstacle, the teacher provides a setting in which the Eureka experience can occur. He should not rob the child of the joy of discovery; the opportunity to have the Eureka experience is the child's alone. Promoting it is one of the highest forms of teaching.

Reflection and Generalization

The manipulating of science equipment and materials can become busy work and "meaningless" activity. To derive maximum benefit from an activity, it is important that there be reflection and cognition. Discussions of "What does this mean?" and questions that probe for the possible implications of an activity are examples of how this reflection can be encouraged.

As children mature, they should be encouraged and helped to generalize from their experiences. There is some evidence to indicate that very specific solutions to problems or highly limited experiences can actually block effective action in dealing with a slightly different problem

---

[6] For a more extensive discussion of the laboratory approach, see Chapter 4.

or experience. However, if children learn to generalize from a specific experience, it may help them in dealing with new and unfamiliar situations, as in the following instance:

The children had been studying prehistoric plants and animals. They had read about the nature of plants and animals in earlier geological eras and had seen filmstrips and pictures showing artists' conceptions of the nature of some prehistoric life. This fascinated the children.

The teacher asked the question, "How do scientists learn about the ancient past?" The children studied pictures of life representative of different geological eras and related them to pictures and samples of fossils. They analyzed pictures of fossils taken from rocks formed at different times and tried to describe the changes that had taken place. Not only did these children learn something about the nature of prehistoric life, but they also had the opportunity to learn something of the processes that are used to build a picture of the evolutionary developments in prehistory. This kind of knowledge can have considerable meaning since it can be generalized and used when children encounter similar situations.[7]

While activities such as the manipulation of materials and equipment are essential in an elementary science program, they are not enough; there must be cognition. Play is fun, but a teacher can make it education. The activities become educational as the children reflect upon the activities, relate them to other activities, and conceptualize so that they can use this experience in the future.

Reflection and generalization can help children to achieve the formal level of operations. An action statement such as "Water the plant every day" is indicative of operation on the concrete level. However, if children can state and understand a statement such as "Plants need water" and then explore and state various implications of this statement, they are operating on a more general level. A possible deduction from the general statement is that a particular plant needs to be watered every day. Children should be encouraged and helped to reflect upon their experiences and generalize from them. This is one of the ways that they can be helped to reach the formal level of operations.

Reflection and generalization also tend to leave science experiences "open-ended." In a sense both reflection and generalization lead into the future. They can lead to more intense curiosity and wonder. For example, molds on bread to most people are something undesirable and to be

---

[7] For a description of how such an activity can be carried out and the necessary materials, see Willard J. Jacobson and Harold M. Scott, *Probing into Science Labtext* (New York: American Book Co., 1966), pp. 13–16.

avoided, not to be reflected on, but to the scientist who specializes in the study of molds they are objects of great interest. Reflection makes it possible to see relationships; the scientist who studies molds can see relationships that others cannot. It has been said that one of the major functions of elementary school science is to help children to "*see* where they have only looked before." The process of generalizing leads into the future as the "essences of experience" are made available for use in dealing with problems and learning in the future.

Physical Health Is Important for Learning

Learning, an active, not a passive, process takes place in a whole organism. The learner is not a sponge absorbing knowledge as it is poured onto him by parents and teachers. Instead, the child learns as he reacts in learning situations. This active role of the learner is dependent upon the energy and physical well-being of the learner.

Since learning occurs when a child reacts to a situation, it probably takes place best when the child is healthy, energetic, and achieving optimum growth and development. The amount of energy a child has depends to a large extent upon his nutrition. In one school, it was the practice not to deal with the more demanding school subjects just before or after lunch, because the children just did not seem to have the mental energy needed. A survey showed that about a third of the youngsters were coming to school with little or no breakfast and that a sizable fraction of the children spent the lunch hour on the streets or playground rather than going home for lunch. As results of these findings, the importance of adequate breakfasts was stressed in parent-teacher conferences; a small snack was served all children in the morning, and a "closed school day" was instituted so that all children ate their lunches in the school lunchroom. The children's work improved markedly, and teachers reported that they now could deal with any school subject at any time of the day.

In another school, the principal made a survey of the breakfasts that had been eaten by the children referred to him as disciplinary cases. He reported that 97 per cent of these children had had no breakfast on the morning on which they had been referred to him. Under such conditions, it would be difficult for them to engage in any constructive activities. These are two of the many examples that could be given to show that a child's ability to learn is affected by his nutritional status.

Since physical health and energy are so important for the intellectual, as well as the physical, development of the child, it is essential that children achieve optimum health. This can be approached in many ways in the total school program. Certainly, in elementary school science children should gain an operational understanding of some of the scientific generalizations related to the human body and its care.[8]

A Variety of Educational Resources

It is an educational truism that for effective education an environment that is rich in resources for learning must be provided. If concept development proceeds from the investigations and study of questions and problems, then it follows that children must have the tools and materials needed for such investigations. Such equipment as thermometers, barometers, magnifying glasses, globes, microscopes, graduates, scales, meters, compasses, cameras, metersticks, and maps should be available to children for use in their investigations. It is equally important that children have access to a wide range of information sources such as textbooks, trade books, audio-visual materials, programmed instruction, and a library that is well stocked with science books.

Within the classroom children should have access to aquariums, terrariums, plant-growing areas, and work areas for the construction of science projects. It is also desirable that there should be such outdoor facilities as school gardens, outdoor laboratories, and nature trails. Such facilities and materials help provide a physical environment that is conducive to learning.

The Teacher's Role

It is the child who learns, of course, but it is the sensitive, knowledgeable, highly competent teacher who makes it possible for learning to take place. No teacher can possibly answer all the science questions that children ask, but the teacher skilled in helping children to investigate can provide the opportunity for the children to arrive at their own answers. A teacher cannot accurately predict the future for children, but he can help them to open doors of opportunity by developing a good science program. A teacher who has some background in science, a knowledge of the many resources available in science, and a sagacious understanding of the wide variety of ways that teachers can effectively work with children in science can literally change the lives of children in guiding them to achievements that would otherwise be beyond their grasp.

A profound and subtle dimension of the intricate art of teaching is to know how to stimulate, encourage, help, and guide each youngster to go

---

[8] Scientific generalizations and suggestions for teaching in the fields of health and physiology are developed in Part V of this book.

as far as he can in his exploration of the natural, physical world. Even youngsters with limited potentials in science should go as far as they can. However, to try to jump too far may cause them to slip back rather than to move forward, and this failure may stunt their development in other directions in which they may have more aptitude. Other youngsters, youngsters with potentials to go far, often fail. And this is a tragedy. The gifted teacher makes a profound study of the nature and potentialities of the children whom he teaches, stands beside them in moments of discouragement, supports them in frustration, rejoices with them in their success, and prods them to find new discoveries, new questions, and, perhaps, new answers. It is hoped that this book can help teachers in this profound task.

Selected References

BERELSON, BERNARD, AND STEINER, GARY A., *Human Behavior*. New York: Harcourt, Brace & World, Inc., 1964.

FLAVELL, JOHN H., *The Developmental Psychology of Jean Piaget*. New York: Van Nostrand Reinhold Co., 1963.

HUNT, J. McV., *Intelligence and Experience*. New York: Ronald Press, 1961.

KARPLUS, ROBERT, AND STENDLER, CELIA B., *Piaget's Developmental Theory of Conservation*. San Francisco, Calif.: Davidson Films, 1967. (A film showing how children's conservation abilities can be studied.)

WANN, KENNETH D., DORN, MIRIAM S., AND LIDDLE, ELIZABETH A., *Fostering Intellectual Development in Young Children*. New York: Teachers College Press, 1962.

4 Approaches to Learning and Teaching Science

Variety is the essence of good teaching. Teachers who use a variety of approaches to the teaching of science will have a classroom full of questioners seeking answers—the essence of learning.

Approaches to teaching should be consistent with the nature of the scientific enterprise (see Chapter 2). An attempt should be made to check ideas empirically—"Does it work when it is tried?" The nature of the systems that are being studied should be considered. Hypotheses should be used as intellectual tools in the study of questions and problems. At times, controlled experiments should be carried out. There should be ample opportunities for criticism and exchange of ideas, and ideas should be expressed as precisely as possible. Children should also gain some experience in using the cumulative dimension of science as a resource by relating their findings to those of others. It is important to keep such characteristics of the scientific enterprise in mind in working with children in science.

Each of the approaches to learning and teaching that are discussed in this chapter has inherent advantages and disadvantages. They should be used when they are advantageous. None of these approaches is inherently difficult. However, the possibilities and cautions must be observed if each approach is to be used to its greatest advantage.

THE LABORATORY APPROACH

In the laboratory approach, each child is directly involved in the activity, using materials, handling equipment, and carrying out experiments. The children may work as individuals or in small groups. The important

63

feature of the laboratory approach is that each child has direct, primary experience with the materials and equipment.

Because children do have direct, firsthand experience with materials and equipment, the laboratory approach is of special importance in elementary school science. There are many who would say that a good elementary science program cannot be achieved unless children have frequent experiences in handling materials and equipment and carrying out experiments. Certainly, this view is consistent with current knowledge of child development and learning.

Using the classroom as a laboratory

In the elementary school the classroom can become the laboratory. Desks can be pushed together to form flat surfaces. Rolling labs and table space along the perimeter of the room also make good surfaces on which children can work. Many of the materials that are needed can be found in the local community; more and more equipment can be obtained through special programs such as the National Defense Education Act (NDEA). Children will need water and electricity. While gas is very useful for science experimentation, it is not absolutely essential for most work in elementary school science. When water and other liquids are to be used, paper or fiberboard trays on which children can set up and carry out their experiments have proved helpful.[1]

It is often desirable to have science materials assembled into small kits. For example, when studying magnets, each child is given a small plastic bag containing two ceramic magnets, assorted pieces of metal and other materials, a compass, and a nail. With these materials, each child is able to handle and explore the nature of magnets and to carry out the various experiments that are suggested. Often, these kits can be used in more than one classroom, and, when everyone is finished with the materials, they can be stored for the coming year.

The teacher's role

The teacher's role in the laboratory approach is as critical as in any other approach. The teacher will have to explain, to a certain extent, the nature of the activities to be undertaken. For example, in the work with the magnets, the teacher should explain that the children are to find out as much as they can about the properties of the magnets. However, care should be taken not to give too full an explanation; the children should not

---

[1] For a more extended discussion of science materials and facilities in the elementary school, see Chapter 20.

be robbed of all possibilities of discovery. The teacher may also have to demonstrate how to use certain kinds of equipment. In the study of the magnets, for example, the teacher should demonstrate how a compass can be used to indicate whether or not an object is a magnet. While the children are experimenting, the teacher moves from child to child and from group to group asking questions, leading children to observations that they might otherwise not have made, unobtrusively helping some youngster over an obstacle that seems to have blocked his progress, and helping all children to derive further meanings from the experience.

It has been said that "If laboratory work is worth doing, it is worth discussing." Certainly, with children in elementary school science there should be discussions in which children can compare their findings, explore the meanings and implications of their work, and suggest other lines of investigation that may be of interest and value.

It is important to recognize that laboratory work means activity on the part of the youngsters and inevitably some noise. Children learn when they are actively engaged in a learning activity, when they are acting and reacting in situations. The laboratory is a place where this can happen. And the laboratory approach to teaching science has great potentialities in the elementary school.

COOPERATIVE INVESTIGATIONS

In a sense, cooperative investigation is a laboratory approach in which a group or the entire class works together. Often, what is to be investigated is demonstrated by the teacher. Then there is discussion of it by the entire class. Questions are asked; ways of finding answers are proposed; hypotheses are suggested; operations are carried out by the teacher or one or two pupils; results are obtained, and the implications and significance of the results are discussed.

As an example of a cooperative investigation, a teacher wet her finger, made a streak on the chalkboard, and asked the class to observe what happened. She then asked the class to describe what had happened, and she probed for the meanings of terms, such as "evaporation," that were used. Then the children were asked to list as many explanations as possible for the phenomenon that they had observed. They gave these possible explanations:

"The water went into the air."
"The water went into the chalkboard."

"The water was soaked up in the chalk."
"The water spread out in a very thin film across the board."
"The water just disappeared."

The children then suggested ways that some of these possible explanations could be eliminated. For example, if water disappears from a board on which there is no chalk, it couldn't have been absorbed in the chalk. Then it was suggested that other experiments could be done to "prove" an explanation, For example, one child suggested that if the water goes into the air, then it should disappear into the air faster if more air were moved across it. "How can we find out if this does happen?" Two children put similar streaks on opposite ends of the chalkboard at the same time. One of the streaks was fanned, and the other was not.

Obviously, children cannot be expected to have a sophisticated understanding of experimental procedures, but by involving them in cooperative investigation they can learn some of these procedures as they work with others. They will then be better able to undertake investigations and devise experiments on their own.

DEMONSTRATIONS

Demonstrations in which a teacher, or a pupil, shows how some scientific apparatus works or the operational meaning of some scientific generalization is another experience that children can have in science.

Some demonstrations are carried out to show pupils how to use some tool or piece of equipment. A microscope is an important tool for the study of small objects and organisms. However, there are certain procedures that have to be followed in using a microscope if the pupils are to derive any benefit from its use. Certain cautions must be observed if microscopes, slides, and specimens are not to be harmed. One of the most effective ways to teach children the use of a piece of equipment, such as the microscope, is through demonstration.

Another common use of demonstration is to show the operational meaning of scientific generalizations. For example, one of the most important generalizations in science is Newton's third law, "For every action there is an equal and opposite reaction." But what is the operational meaning of this generalization? A test tube can be suspended horizontally from two wires. A little water can be placed in the test tube and a cork fitted loosely into the neck of the test tube. When the water in the test tube is heated, it changes to steam and forces the cork out. The cork goes in one direction, but the suspended test tube moves in the opposite direction. This is a physical demonstration of an operational meaning of Newton's third law. For elementary school youngsters who are at the stage of concrete operations, such demonstrations are needed for them to derive meaning from generalized statements.

Most generalizations are not difficult to illustrate, and in Parts II, III, IV, and V there are descriptions of many useful demonstrations. The following guidelines will help teachers carry out successful demonstrations.

The demonstration should be as simple as possible

The operational meaning of a generalization will be obscured if the equipment and apparatus used are complicated. Also, children often become so enamored with complicated setups that the central purpose of the demonstration becomes lost.

The demonstration should be visible to all the children

Use large equipment and apparatus for demonstrations. If this can't be done, the children should work in small groups so that all can see.

All parts of the demonstration should be visible to the children

If the most important parts of a demonstration are hidden in a "black box," children may very well attribute magical powers to the black box or to the demonstrator. In either case the value of the demonstration is diminished.

Children should be encouraged to ask questions about the demonstration

In many cases the demonstration can be altered to find answers to the children's questions. The demonstration then evolves into a cooperative investigation.

INVESTIGATIONS

In a sense, investigations might be called "student research"—they are studies of questions and problems to which the answers are not known. In carrying out science investigations students have some of the same kinds of experiences that scientists have as they explore the unknown. Students use the various processes of science, and they find that these are not discrete processes. They learn, instead, that these processes are components of inquiry. Also, students experience some of the frustrations of "things not working as they are supposed to" and the exhilaration of finding ways to overcome obstacles and arrive at tentative answers to knotty questions.

Obviously, children must tackle questions to which answers are not known but lie within their grasp. One such investigation is described in each of the chapters in Parts II, III, IV, and V of this book. In addition, the following are examples of investigations that can be undertaken by children:

1. What kind of stimulus is most likely to make a mealworm (or other worm) reverse its direction of movement?
2. What happens if a full grown plant is turned upside down?
3. What color and angle of roof will keep the interior of a box coolest under intense sunlight?
4. What objects in the environment are magnets?
5. What is the relationship between the length of a pendulum and its period? Will an added weight cause a change in this relationship?
6. What kinds of pigments are found in the leaves of plants? How do various plants differ with regard to pigment?
7. What is the effect of bleaching liquid on different colors of cloth?
8. How does the acidity of soil change with depth?
9. What changes take place in the chick embryo during the period of incubation?
10. What is the magnifying power of a lens?
11. How do various materials rank as conductors of heat?
12. How do shadows change with the day and with the seasons?
13. What kinds of environments do insects prefer?
14. What is our reaction time?
15. What is the relationship between water depth and water pressure?
16. How do plants respond to lights of different colors?
17. What are the effects of water and temperature on seed germination?
18. How far is it across the school grounds? How tall is a tree?
19. How fast do objects fall through different kinds of fluids?
20. What factors affect the rate of fermentation?
21. In what direction does the water tend to swirl when it drains out of a bathtub or wash bowl? What factors appear to affect the direction of swirl?
22. How far can a bath towel be pulled down across a towel rack before it begins to slide off? How is this distance affected by the angle at which the towel is pulled? By the nature of the materials in contact?

Children should communicate their investigations

Since communication is one of the very important processes of science children should begin to have experiences in communicating their investigations and their results to others. The basic test of adequate communication is whether it can be understood by others. Children should be able to take the report of an investigation and carry out a similar investigation to see if they get similar results.

Reports of investigations should include descriptions of how the investigations were carried out and the results. Older children may wish to include some discussion of the meaning and implications of the results. With young children the report may consist primarily of pictures and diagrams of what was done and what the results were.

FIELD EXPERIENCES

Field experiences may be broadly defined as experiences that children have outside their classrooms. The possibilities for field experiences are limitless. They may include: visits to different parts of the school building, studies carried out on the school grounds, projects undertaken in outdoor laboratories, strolls down a nature trail, trips to a farm or a manufacturing plant, visits to museums or planetariums, investigations of nearby biological or geological phenomena, excursions to parks and nature preserves, visits to laboratories and research facilities, and carefully planned school camping experiences. While some field experiences may involve extended and carefully planned field trips, many take the form of short forays to visit a site near at hand or to interview someone who is easily accessible.

Field experiences can provide:

1. Firsthand experiences with materials that cannot be brought into the classroom.
2. The study of plants, animals, and technology in natural settings. This makes it possible to study interrelationships among various elements of the environment.
3. The study of problems related to science and technology in their natural settings.
4. On-the-spot interviews with people in their occupational environment. This helps children to get a better understanding of the nature of their work.
5. Situations in which the applications of science can be studied.

On many field trips, the collection of specimens may be planned. The children should begin to understand conservation considerations. Obviously, the laws designed to protect rare species and property owners should be respected and obeyed. In other cases the basic conservation rule to follow is that *materials and specimens can be collected if this results in no significant change in the environment.* A beaker of sand collected from the beach makes no significant difference. However, the collection of a lone flower from a roadside will make a significant difference and should be avoided.

It is important to recognize that field experiences may take many forms. In some cases, the teacher may take the entire class on a trip. In other cases, the field experience may be undertaken by a single child to whom it is suggested that he "go look at ————— and see it at firsthand after school." Or, it may be small groups that undertake an investigation in the field.

The following are suggestions for planning and conducting field experiences with small and large groups of children:

1. Have the children think through the purposes of the field experience.
   a. What kind of information will be obtained?
   b. What kinds of questions should be asked?
   c. How important is this information? How can it be used?
   d. Will the field experience benefit others as well as ourselves? A community service project, such as a conservation project, can be an important field experience.
2. Reconnoiter the site prior to the visit.
   a. What observations should be stressed?
   b. Where should the groups make stops?
   c. What precautions need to be heeded?
   d. How should the resource people be briefed so that the children will gain the maximum benefit from the experience?
3. Organize carefully for the field experience.
   a. Clear with the school administration. Most school systems have standard policies relating to field experience. These should be adhered to.
   b. Obtain parental permission. Parents have a right to know when their children leave school, and it is usually wise to obtain written permission on simple duplicated forms.
   c. Arrange for transportation. Many school systems have school buses or other modes of transportation that can be used for trips.
   d. Invite other adults, such as parents and other teachers, to accompany the class on the trip.

e. Make advance arrangements for the visit to the park, museum, factory, or farm.

4. Brief the group for the field experience.
   a. Suggest appropriate dress.
   b. Discuss responsibilities for science equipment, first aid kits, maps, cameras, tape recorders, and notebooks that may be brought on the field trip.
   c. Discuss over-all picture of field experience using maps and charts.
   d. Discuss behavioral and safety standards required. Some orientation to conservation aspects of the trip may also be necessary.
   e. Discuss and clarify further the purposes of the trip.

5. Make the field experience as profitable as possible for all children.
   a. Help the students to keep the purposes of the field experience in mind. This will help many children to "see where they have only looked before."
   b. Encourage children to make observations that may not have been anticipated in the previous discussion. At times "free lance browsing" can be quite fruitful.
   c. Make certain that all members of the group hear explanations and discussions. At times, it may be necessary to interpret remarks of experts and relate them to the children's previous experiences.
   d. Check that the planned information, specimens, pictures, recordings, and notes have been obtained.

6. Back in the classroom it is important to help children derive meaning from their field experience. It is important to have the children:
   a. Analyze the data collected.
   b. Discuss the meaning and implications of various observations.
   c. Evaluate the field experience and discuss how future experience can be made more effective.
   d. Express their appreciation, often in the form of thank-you letters, to those who helped them in the field experience.

USING SCIENCE RESOURCES

It has been said that scientific inquiry is "Doing one's utmost with one's mind with no holds barred." If this is true, then there should be no artificial limitations placed on children as they study, investigate, and inquire. In fact, they should learn how to use all of the resources available to them. A standard dictum in teaching is to always use those resources and procedures that are best suited to the goals to be achieved. The following are some of the resources that should be used in an effective elementary school program:

Trade books

There are now many excellent "library" books dealing with a wide range of scientific topics at various levels of reading. These are sources of information, suggestions for experiments and investigations, and places where children can check their findings against those of others. Of special importance, trade books are sources for information about subjects ranging from the interior of the earth to the reaches of outer space that children can not deal with at firsthand.

Textbooks

Textbooks are common sources of information and suggestions available to the children in a class. Like trade books, textbooks should be used within the context of inquiry. They can be a handy reference book and a guide for laboratory and field experiences. They can also provide a broad general outline of a program in science.

Films

Motion picture films can convey motion where this is important in an explanation, such as in the explanation of the electric motor or the slow motions of plants as they grow and orient themselves to light. Films can also be used to develop attitudes and feelings. It is difficult, for example, to view a film such as the classic "The River" without experiencing deep feelings and perhaps changes in attitudes.

Filmstrips

These are excellent mechanisms for bringing a coordinated series of pictures into the classroom. An important advantage of filmstrips is that they can be used at whatever pace the teacher deems desirable, and, sometimes, a prolonged discussion can be carried out over one frame.

Slides

This is another excellent way of bringing pictures into the classroom. Of special importance are the slides brought into the classroom by the teacher, children, and parents. Many of these can deal with unique local features.

Transparencies

Transparencies shown with an overhead projector are a convenient way to show diagrams, sketches, and pictures to an entire class. Since transparencies are relatively easy to make, they can be designed by the teacher, or children, to meet the peculiar instructional needs of a particular classroom.

Television

Through television, distant events and prominent personages can be brought into the classroom. The video tape recorder makes it possible to record television programs and to use them when they best fit into the instructional program.

Telephone

The telephone can be used to interview resource people. In a sense, it is another way of bringing the outside world into the classroom. The conference telephone arrangement is especially useful, since it makes it possible for everyone in a class to take part in the telephone conversation.

PROJECTS

Projects, special undertakings of individual children or groups of children, may take the form of a special study of a selected topic leading to a report. One group of children, for example, made a study of the moon in which they investigated much of the children's literature available dealing with the moon and presented a report of their findings. Other projects might be called construction projects. Many children, for example, have constructed electric motors and in the process have learned a great deal about electricity. Sometimes display projects are made to depict some scientific principle or some procedure that is used in science. One project, for example, depicted the various ways that archaeological artifacts can be dated.

It is important that a science project be a learning experience in science as well as an interesting construction experience. The construction of an electric motor without observation of the scientific principles involved is of little value. An understanding of scientific principles, the most important learning outcome of a science project, is also useful when children encounter setbacks and problems in constructing and operating their projects.

COLLOQUIUMS

Colloquiums are meetings at which children describe and discuss the results of an investigation, a study they have carried out, or a project they have completed. It is desirable that children have some help in organizing their report and planning their presentation. Other children should then have the opportunity to discuss the presentation.

Communication of ideas and the results of investigations are essential components of the scientific enterprise. As they take part in colloquiums held in the classroom or on a school-wide basis, children begin to have experiences with an important dimension of the scientific enterprise.

Selected References

HURD, PAUL DEH., *How to Teach Science Through Field Studies*. Washington, D.C.: National Science Teachers Association, 1965.

JACOBSON, WILLARD J., AND SCOTT, HAROLD M., *Probing Into Science Labtext*. New York: American Book Co., 1966.

JACOBSON, WILLARD J., AND CARR, ALBERT B., *Inquiring Into Science Labtext*. New York: American Book Co., 1966.

JACOBSON, WILLARD J., GROSMARK, JAY, AND SHAPIRO, MARVIN, *Investigating in Science Labtext*. New York: American Book Co., 1966.

MOHR, CHARLES E., *How to Lead a Field Trip*. New York: National Audubon Society, 1957.

NATIONAL SCIENCE TEACHERS ASSOCIATION, *Helping Children Learn Science*. Washington, D.C.: National Science Teachers Association, 1966.

5 Science for the Pre-Reader

"Should there be science *even* in the nursery school and kindergarten?" The answer is an unequivocal *yes*! It may be that science experiences are especially important at this age. As we have seen, there are indications that the physical and intellectual development of children, including the development of reading ability, may be stunted unless certain kinds of primary experiences with the physical and biological environment are undergone. Today, when science and technology are such prominent features of our environment, one of the best ways for children to have such experiences is through science.

FUNCTIONS OF SCIENCE FOR THE PRE-READER

Teachers can use science to achieve the following general goals in the nursery school and kindergarten.

Nurture Intellectual Development

The child in the nursery school and kindergarten is almost always in the pre-operational stage of intellectual development. At this stage it is extremely important that the young child have a wide variety of firsthand, primary experiences with physical objects and living organisms. Because of the young child's inability to "conserve," he cannot be expected to have great facility in relating a science experience he is having here-and-now to one he had yesterday or last week or to project from present experience to experiences he may have tomorrow or next week. But this young child is, nevertheless, building a foundation of experiences for further intellectual development. Will he achieve optimum intellectual development if he doesn't have this base of primary, firsthand experience? Studies in child development seem to say "no"; these primary experiences, of which science experiences are an integral part, are essential for optimum intellectual development.

Build Reading Readiness

Understandably, parents and teachers are concerned with children's learning to read. But what is reading? Certainly, reading involves the interpretation of symbols written or printed on paper. At the pre-operational stage it is probably best to relate these symbols to concrete physical objects and living organisms that can be felt, handled, smelled, and seen. Through early science experiences, the pre-reader can broaden his base of reference for written symbols.

Develop Useful Habits

Habits are more or less fixed patterns of behavior, and many of the habits that persist throughout a lifetime are developed at an early age. Also, it is apparently easier to change undesirable habits when the child is young rather than later. The following are some habits which we can begin to develop in the nursery school and kindergarten:

1. Health and safety habits. For example, it is often possible to broaden the range of foods eaten by a child during this period.
2. The desire to find out. The child's innate desire to find out more about himself and the world in which he lives can be nurtured.
3. Open-mindedness. The child can begin to learn to be receptive to new ideas and to respect the ideas of others.
4. The desire for empirical tests. It is not difficult to foster the attitude of "let's try it and see."

A FLEXIBLE PROGRAM FOR THE NURSERY SCHOOL AND KINDERGARTEN

Out of the rich environment in the nursery school and kindergarten can come a wide variety of exciting and useful science experiences. The following are science experiences that have been developed by alert teachers out of the spontaneous questions and activities of children:

Growing plants from cuttings placed in water.
Germinating a wide variety of seeds. Observing the growth of the new plant.

Observing the behavior of animals in an aquarium.
Observing the daily weather and its effects.
Learning to read a thermometer using a ribbon thermometer.
Study of expansion and contraction of materials.
Study of changes in animal behavior with the seasons.
The study of variety among plants and animals.
Examination of different kinds of soil.
The study of some of the characteristics of air.
Learning how to care for animals and plants.
The study of snowflakes.
The study of shadows.
The study of foods that animals eat.
The study of foods that people eat.
Learning to use simple machines.
Learning about balance of forces on a seesaw or equal arm balance.
Learning to use clocks and calendars.
Observing how different kinds of animals move.
Finding out how wheels are used.
Finding out about sanitary practices in the lunchroom, the lavatory, and at the water fountain, and the reasons for them.
Experimenting to find out how water flows through pipes and rubber tubing.
Developing ideas about land forms using a sandbox.
Making a collection of the various rocks to be found in the community.
Observing the metamorphosis of insects.

Planning the Science Program

The science program for the pre-reader should emphasize the child's direct experience with physical objects and living organisms. Since this can be such an important part of the nursery school and kindergarten program, it is important to make plans for it. These plans are helpful in taking advantage of seasonal opportunities and making certain that the necessary materials are available when needed. The planned program should not become a straitjacket, but should be considered a framework within which the flexible program can also be developed.

In the following science program for the pre-reader, the seasons when the various areas might be considered are suggested. However, most of the areas can be introduced at any time of the school year.[1]

[1] This program is developed in much greater detail with many suggestions for first-hand science experiences by children in Willard J. Jacobson and Eileen Cowe, *Beginning Science* (New York: American Book Co., 1966).

AUTUMN

1. Plants—how they are alike and different, with emphasis on the first-hand study of the variety of plants to be found in the neighborhood.
   a. Where do plants grow?
   b. What parts do plants have?
   c. How are plants alike?
   d. How are plants different?
2. Weather—the observation of weather as experienced by the children.
   a. Does the weather change?
   b. What kinds of weather are there?
   c. What different kinds of clouds can be seen?
   d. How can rain be measured? Snow?
3. The aquarium—setting up an aquarium and the observation of the organisms that live in an aquarium.
   a. What organisms live in water?
   b. How does a fish move?
   c. In what ways are fish different from other animals?

WINTER

4. Objects—a study of the physical properties of objects and materials.
   a. What properties do objects have?
   b. How do our senses help us describe objects?
   c. In what states, or conditions, can matter exist?
5. Food—a consideration of the foods needed for healthy living.
   a. What kinds of materials are used for food?
   b. How can foods be grouped?
   c. How are some foods prepared?
6. Light—a study of some of the characteristics of light.
   a. What gives off light?
   b. How does light travel?
   c. Through what kinds of materials will light pass?
   d. How is light reflected?
   e. How are shadows formed?
7. Sound—a study of some of the characteristics of sound.
   a. What makes sound?
   b. How does sound travel?
   c. What sounds do we hear?
   d. How can different sounds be made?

SPRING

8. Magnets—the study of magnetism through direct experience with magnets.
   a. How can objects be moved with magnets?

   b. What materials does a magnet attract?
   c. What are magnetic poles?
   d. How can a magnet be made?
 9. Water—experimenting with water to find out more about it.
   a. Where does the water we use come from?
   b. What can be done with water?
   c. How can the form of water be changed?
   d. How is water used?
10. Seeds—a study of change in a living organism.
   a. What kinds of plants grow seeds?
   b. How does a seed develop?
   c. What does a plant need to live and grow?

Developing Science Experiences

The responsibilities of a teacher of young children are many, and most of them are not peculiar to a particular area such as science. However, some guidelines are especially important in working with very young children in science.[2]

A rich and stimulating environment is provided

Many of the science activities of the pre-reader grow out of his interactions with his environment. Therefore, the room should provide a rich and stimulating environment. The following facilities and materials will be useful in developing that environment:

 1. Plant trays and potting materials for growing plants.
 2. A large classroom aquarium with smaller ones for projects.
 3. Cages for small animals such as rats, mice, hamsters, and gerbils.
 4. Terrariums and vivariums. Some of these should be arranged so that frogs, toads, turtles, and snakes can be kept periodically in the classroom.
 5. Workbenches with children's tools.
 6. A playhouse area. A number of science activities can be developed from activities related to the playhouse.
 7. Sandbox.
 8. Large blocks and teeter-totter.
 9. Large rolling toys such as tricycles, wagons, barrels, and wheelbarrows.
10. Outdoor areas and nature trails.

[2] Science materials and facilities are discussed in greater detail in Chapter 20.

Children should have opportunities to play with science materials and facilities

Since pre-operational children should have many firsthand experiences with physical objects and living organisms, they should have opportunities to "play around" with science facilities and materials. For example, two boys in kindergarten were observed trying to balance two books on opposite ends of a teeter-totter. They failed to do so and dashed off to some other activity. Two days later they came back to this same activity and had no difficulty in balancing the books. It appeared that they had managed to learn from their experiences in "playing around."

It is perhaps best not to impose an adult integration of the many experiences that children can have in "playing around"; the integration of these experiences takes place within the individual child. The adult helps to provide the setting in which these experiences and integration can take place.

It is important to listen carefully to children's comments

The children were watching an inflated balloon attached to a baby's Pyrex bottle that had been placed in ice water. Several children said, "The balloon is contracting." One boy turned to the teacher and said, "Contract, I thought that was a piece of paper like my father signed." Words sometimes have different meanings, depending on the children's previous experience with them. A sensitive teacher who listens carefully will detect these differences in meaning.

Children's questions and comments can also supply useful leads to science activities. Two teachers worked with two different groups on a similar topic in science. One teacher had a carefully developed plan to which she adhered quite closely. The second teacher had also planned carefully, but her planning might be called "contingency planning." She listened very carefully to the questions and responses of children and planned further activities in light of these responses. Her program was influenced greatly by what she heard, and, of the two programs, there could be little doubt that hers was the most exciting and probably the most effective.

Help children clarify and extend ideas

In science children can often clarify ideas by experimenting with objects in their environment. In one classroom, for example, the children wondered whether air was a real substance like the solids and liquids in their environment. (After all, in most cases they can't see it.) They filled a large plastic bag with air and pushed on it. It seemed as if there was something in the bag. Holding the bag to their faces, they could feel something rush past their faces when the bag was opened and someone squeezed the air out of it. They trapped air in a tumbler under water, and "poured" it into another tumbler. In such ways children can clarify many of their ideas by actually carrying out many such little experiments with objects. One of the advantages of science as an area of study for young children is that they can clarify ideas by doing experiments and manipulating physical objects.

The teacher should help children extend their ideas. A child may admire a flower; a teacher may suggest that he examine it more closely and describe some of the parts of the flower. The child will want to take good care of his pets; he may be led to consider how he should take care of himself. He sees water left in a dish apparently disappear after a while. Is there any connection between this and the fact that water must be added every now and then to the aquarium? By helping young children to see connections between events and to extend their ideas they are helped to reach the stage where they can operate as individuals with the concrete materials of the environment.

Work with children to find some kinds of answers to their questions

The children were concerned about the death of a pet rabbit. One child asked, "Did he die in a statue?" This child thought that people died in statues.[3] Among these children there were many questions concerning death. They were able to resolve them to a certain extent by studying what happens to dead insects and plants. Children want answers to the questions they ask, and, through science, teachers can help children to find some kinds of answers.

In working with young children it should be recognized that they do not always want the "full, complete answer." The classic story is of the young child who asked his parents, "Where did I come from?" These earnest, sincere parents were well prepared for the time their child would ask this question, and they proceeded to give an extended discussion of how humans reproduce. They were quite taken aback when, after the long discourse, the child said, "But, Jimmy came from Cleveland. Where did I come from?" Often, children do not want or need as much as the teacher or parent is prepared to give.

Usually children will come back to the same or a similar question later on. Science experiences, especially for very young children, should open

---

[3] This incident is described in Louis T. Cox, *Working With Kindergarten Children in Science* (Baltimore, Md.: State Teachers College at Towson, 1959).

doors rather than close them. In dealing with questions children ask, the teacher can often suggest observations that they can make, activities they can undertake, and, generally, open doors to further considerations later on.

Children can begin to acquire some basic science skills

In nursery school and kindergarten children can begin to develop and use certain science skills. Ribbon thermometers can be used to help children read thermometers, and this skill can be used as they make daily weather observations. They can begin to measure, using such standards as sticks or pieces of string. This can lead to the use of rulers and measuring tapes. Children gain experiences in telling time by using the classroom clock. Children can compare distances and weights and measure volumes of liquids and granular substances like sand. As science experiences can lead to reading readiness, they can also lead to science skill readiness.

Selected References

ALMY, MILLIE, *Young Children's Thinking*. New York: Teachers College Press, 1966.

JACOBSON, WILLARD J., AND KONDO, ALLAN, *SCIS Elementary Science Sourcebook*. Berkeley, Calif.: University of California Press, 1968.

ROBISON, HELEN F., AND SPODEK, BERNARD, *New Directions in the Kindergarten*. New York: Teachers College Press, 1965.

WANN, KENNETH D., DORN, MIRIAM S., AND LIDDLE, ELIZABETH A., *Fostering Intellectual Development in Young Children*. New York: Teachers College Press, 1962.

85

II

Building a World View

"What would it be like to be an oyster?" Immobile on the floor of some estuary, utterly dependent upon the water that flows by, sensitive to changes in its environment but completely limited to the immediate surroundings, an organism like the oyster is restricted in its "world view" to that part of the environment that flows by it.

Man, with a highly developed nervous system, views a larger world. In fact it almost seems as if man has an innate drive to find out more about himself and the world in which he lives. Certainly, many children have this curiosity, and it should be cultured and nourished so that they will continue to probe and question, to investigate and explore, and to build a view of the world.

In gathering information about the universe beyond the planet earth, man has been, for a long time, in somewhat the same predicament as the sessile oyster—he has been dependent for information upon the matter and energy that flows to him from the vast reaches of the universe. For a long time, he depended almost entirely upon the light given off by the sun and other stars and reflected by the moon and planets. Now the range of information sources is somewhat wider. Radio waves and cosmic rays can be studied, and some of the matter that flows to and by the planet earth can be sampled. Man is also becoming slightly mobile within the solar system as space probes and manned spacecraft are sent out to explore regions within the solar system. However, for knowledge of most of the universe, man is still very much like the oyster—dependent for his information upon the matter and energy that happens to come to him.

Surprisingly, perhaps, man is in very much the same position as the oyster with regard to his knowledge of the interior of the earth. No one has ever probed deep into the earth. Instead, knowledge of the nature of the interior of the earth has been extrapolated from theoretical studies of the solar system and phenomena, such as terrestrial magnetism, that are

87

believed to be due to the nature of the interior of the earth. The heat flow from the interior of the earth and the material that comes to the surface during volcanic eruptions can also be studied. But because there is less information-yielding matter and energy coming from the interior earth than the distant stars, it is probably true that less is known about the nature of the earth one hundred miles beneath the earth's crust than is known of a star a million light-years away.

In the study of the earth's atmosphere, the surface of the earth, and the water of the oceans man has been quite energetic and has not been dependent only on the matter and energy that comes to him; he has gone and seen. Perhaps the greatest handicap in the study of these regions of the world has been the difficulty in interpreting the great masses of data that have been acquired. The models that have been depicted have often not been as imaginative as the means of seeking data. But a great deal has been learned about the environment that is accessible to us, and a much better picture of this part of the world can be built by this generation than by previous generations.

Man also has tried to build a picture of the world of living organisms. Man has studied his relationship to other living organisms, although he has been handicapped by a tendency to set man apart from the rest of the living world. However, the theory of evolution has proved to be a very powerful theoretical tool, and with it man has been able to interpret apparent relationships between living organisms. The study of living organisms has had great practical value in the study and care of the human body.

In this part of elementary school science children develop a *weltanschauung*, a view of the world in which we live. It is essential that children have a chance to take a "scientific" view of their world. Perhaps after having viewed from this vantage point, they will be less prone to superstition and more likely to look for "natural" causes for perplexing events. They should gain a clearer perspective of how they, as individuals, fit into this vast and complex universe.

It may be that man's great adventure is to investigate and explore the universe. Science is an approach, and perhaps the most fruitful, to this investigation and exploration. As children study science, they begin to take part in this great human adventure. They can thrill to new discoveries and be saddened by temporary setbacks. As they build their own world view, they can open the door to participation in mankind's great adventure—the struggle to know and the drive to understand the universe in which we live.

6 The Universe and the Solar System

A child peers out into the dark black sky and sees points of twinkling light. If he is fortunate enough to view the night sky unhampered by the glow of cities, he may be able to see about three thousand stars. If he is aided by a pair of binoculars or a small telescope, he will be able to see many more. And, if he should look at a picture taken of a small portion of the sky using a large astronomical telescope, he will see that the sky is literally filled with stars. This is the world in which children live, and they wonder about it.

As the child watches the stars, he will notice that they seem to move across the sky from east to west. Similarly, the sun seems to move across the sky from east to west as does the moon whenever it is visible. Even the youngest children may take for granted the phenomenon of day and night, but this too is related to the daily appearance and disappearance of the sun. They may notice that the path of the sun, and the length of time that it can be seen, changes with the season.

Careful observation of the night sky will show that there are five objects in the sky that behave differently from the other sources of light. Usually, they do not twinkle as much, but, more importantly, they appear to wander across the sky, appearing and disappearing at different times of the year. The ancients called these objects the *planets* which means "the wanderers." Contemporary man has discovered three more planets, but these cannot be seen with the unaided eye. Including the planet earth, this makes a total of nine planets.

The moon is a favorite for celestial observation. With a small pair of binoculars, the lunar mountains and the broad, level maria or "seas" can be seen. The moon appears to change shape during the course of a month, and for a few days each month it cannot be seen at all.

Stretching across the sky is a cloud of stars that, because of its milky appearance, has been called the Milky Way. An observer watching the sky, may see darts of light often called "shooting stars." Once in a while he may see a comet in the sky. He is much more likely to see points of light move across the sky. These are lights reflected by man-made satellites as they move overhead in their orbits around the earth.

Children, too, observe some of these things as they look at the sky overhead. They should be helped to "see where they may have only looked before." They will *see* as they begin to understand.

THE SOLAR SYSTEM

Man is a space traveler, and his spaceship is the planet earth. From this moving space platform he views the universe. But in order for him to understand what he sees, he must have some inkling of where he is in the universe and from what perspective he is viewing.

The planet earth is one of nine planets in the solar system that revolve around the sun. The sun is a star very much like many of the other stars seen in the sky. Actually, it is a medium-size star, but it appears very bright because the earth is so much closer to it than to any of the other stars. The sun is one of perhaps one hundred billion stars in the Milky Way Galaxy. But the Milky Way Galaxy is only one of several billion galaxies in the universe that can be observed with optical and radio telescopes. The universe is indeed vast; vast almost beyond comprehesion.

In an attempt to comprehend the universe it is perhaps best to start with the solar system—the system to which the planet earth belongs. The solar system is composed of the sun, planets, satellites, asteroids, meteors, comets, and the vast, almost empty space between these objects. As the term solar system implies, the sun dominates this system. The planets, satellites, and other objects can be seen only because of the sunlight that is reflected by them to the earth. The motions of the objects in the solar system are influenced mostly by the gravitational attraction between them and the sun. The sun is probably the most important source of energy for all of the planets. On at least one of the planets, the earth, life is made possible by this solar energy.

The Sun

The sun appears as a bright, yellowish disk in the sky. It is so bright that direct observation is ill-advised; the eyes can be injured by its brightness. This light is so bright that any other star cannot ordinarily be seen as long as the sun is in the visible sky. This light and other forms of solar energy are the major sources of energy on the earth and make life on the earth possible.

The mass of the sun dominates the solar system. Although the sun is only a medium-size star, its mass is 333,420 times that of the earth. Because of its great mass, the gravitational attraction between the sun and the planets holds the planets in orbit around the sun.

The sun radiates energy in all directions. However, because of its relatively small size and because it is some ninety-three million miles away, the earth receives only about two-billionths of the radiation, or energy, emanating from the sun. It is not unlike the light from a distant street light. Because the light is being radiated out in all directions and because of the distance, only a small fraction of the total light given off by a street light will enter a particular bedroom window. Similarly, the earth receives only a very small fraction of the energy given off by the distant sun. However, this small fraction of the total energy from the sun amounts to a great deal of energy. Almost two calories of energy are received per minute per square centimeter. (A calorie is the amount of heat energy that will raise one gram of water one degree Celsius.) However, a great deal more energy is emanated by each square centimeter of the sun. From each square centimeter of the sun's photosphere there is being emanated almost ninety thousand calories of energy per minute.

The only known processes that can yield such prodigious amounts of energy are nuclear reactions such as those that occur in nuclear explosions. In these reactions, matter is converted into energy according to Albert Einstein's famous equation,

$$E = mc^2$$
$$\text{Energy} = \text{mass} \times (\text{speed of light})^2$$

In the nuclear reactions that take place in the sun, atoms of hydrogen combine in a fairly complicated way to form helium atoms. In this process some of the original mass is converted into tremendous amounts of energy.

To generate the enormous quantities of energy that it gives off, the sun's mass is consumed at the rate of five million tons each second. However, the total mass of the sun is so great that it will continue to give off energy in much the same way for hundreds of millions of years.

The Planetary System

Of the nine known planets orbiting the sun, only six can be observed from earth with the unaided eye. These are the six planets that are closest to the sun: Mercury, Venus, Earth, Mars, Jupiter, and Saturn. All of these planets can be seen at one time or other near the path that the sun travels across the sky, the *ecliptic*. Times and positions at which the various planets can be seen are reported by many newspapers and almost all almanacs.

The planets are of varying brightness. Next to the sun and moon, Venus is the brightest object in the sky and often has been called erroneously the morning or evening star. Mars and Jupiter are also quite bright, with Mars having a reddish color which very likely led to its being named after the god of war, Mars. Because of its distance from the earth Saturn is quite faint, and Mercury is difficult to see because it is so close to the sun. In fact, Mercury can be seen only at certain times, a few minutes after sundown or a few minutes before sunup.

Mercury is the planet nearest the sun. Because it is so near the sun, it revolves around the sun much faster than any other planet. Its year is eighty-eight days long. Its rotation period is now known to be fifty-nine earth days, though it was formerly thought that Mercury continually faced the sun. As the planet nearest the sun, its temperature should be very high. We are not certain, however, of the temperature of this planet.

Venus is the brightest of the planets. It is only about two-thirds of the distance of the earth from the sun, and it has a cloud cover that reflects a great deal of the sunlight that strikes it. Since Venus is fairly close to the sun, it is seen in the West after sunset and in the East before sunrise. A great deal has been learned about Venus from space probes. Its atmosphere is largely carbon dioxide with apparently little oxygen or water. Unlike the earth, it does not have a magnetic field or a Van Allen radiation belt. It is reported that Venus has temperatures higher than the melting point of lead. At times it has been thought that some form of life might exist on Venus. However, it would apparently have to be life without oxygen or water and adapted to very high temperatures.

The *earth* is the third planet out from the sun.[1] It has an atmosphere composed largely of nitrogen and oxygen with some water vapor. This, plus the presence of certain essential chemical elements and temperatures that are usually between the freezing and boiling points of water, make life possible on this planet. The earth's atmosphere reflects a great deal of sunlight, and to an observer in space it would appear to be a very bright planet.

Mars, the second brightest planet, is a favorite for study by amateur astronomers. Space probes have indicated that Mars has a very forbidding surface, perhaps something like the moon. Like the earth, it has white polar caps that extend and recede with the seasons. These white polar caps may be composed of ice crystals. This red planet has only about one-

---

[1] The earth is discussed in much greater detail in Chapters 7, 8, and 9.

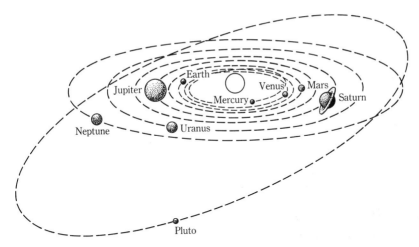

Fig. 6-1 *A modern model of the solar system showing the planets and their orbits.*

tenth as much atmosphere as the earth and it contains little oxygen or water vapor. Mars has been considered to be the most likely place, in addition to the earth, for life to exist in the solar system.

Jupiter is the largest planet, actually larger than all the other planets put together. This planet appears to us brighter than any star except the sun. Jupiter has an atmosphere that is largely composed of methane and ammonia. It is believed that the radio signals that come from Jupiter may be due to electrical storms in this atmosphere. These radio signals can be picked up by modern radio telescopes. As viewed through an optical telescope, Jupiter has brown or deep red bands parallel to its equator. These bands are probably due to currents in Jupiter's atmosphere. Once in a while bright red spots appear and then fade away again. These spots are believed to be due to chemical reactions in the atmosphere caused by the effect of light.

Saturn is also a bright planet, and, viewed through a telescope, it is one of the most beautiful sights in nature. The most fascinating feature of Saturn is its beautiful thin rings, which can be seen through a telescope. These rings make Saturn the most beautiful of all celestial objects. The rings are believed to be composed of very fine particles of dust and ice. Each of these particles acts as a small satellite of Saturn. The rings are extremely thin, being only five to twenty miles thick. Because of their thinness, Saturn's rings can be seen only when they are at an angle to the earth.

Uranus was first recognized as a planet by William Herschel who at the time was a musician who made telescopes and observed the stars as a hobby. Uranus can be observed as a very, very faint object with the unaided eye. However, there are more than five thousand stars that are brighter than Uranus, and earlier observers had considered it to be another star. Through his telescope, Herschel saw the planet and observed that it moved relative to the background stars. One of the unique features of Uranus is that it rotates almost at right angles to the plane in which the planets revolve around the sun.

Neptune can only be seen with the aid of an astronomical telescope. It is thirty times farther from the sun than the earth, and its mass is more than seventeen times as great as that of the earth. It travels around the sun once every 165 years. It has not yet completed an orbit since it was first discovered in 1846.

Pluto is the most distant of the planets, being thirty-nine and a half times as far from the sun as the earth. Appropriately named, the dark and forbidding world of Pluto has very little sunlight and temperatures of about $-213°C$. It probably has no atmosphere, and no satellites have been found. Its period of revolution around the sun is about 248 years.

Asteroids are relatively small planetary bodies revolving around the sun between Mars and Jupiter. There are thousands of them. The largest has a diameter of about 480 miles. It is believed that they may have been formed from the break-up of a planet.

Comets appear quite often, and today's children are likely to see several of the brighter ones in their lifetime. Comets are probably composed of meteoric particles and small flakes of ice. The head of the comet, which probably contains the largest particles in the comet, appears first as a speck in the sky. The tail follows, with such widely spaced particles of dust and ice that it is possible to see background stars through it. The earth has passed through the tail of a comet with no noticeable effect. An important feature of comets to point out to children is that the tail of a comet almost always points away from the sun. This is believed to be the result of the pressures of the radiation from the sun.

Meteors are small particles of interplanetary matter that enter the atmosphere and burn as a result of friction with the air. They are the "shooting stars" that are sometimes seen at night. Meteors that are not completely burned and strike the surface of the earth are called *meteorites*. Most meteorites are very small, but a few large ones have struck the surface of the earth. The Canyon Diablo between Winslow and Flagstaff, Arizona, was undoubtedly formed by the impact of a large meteorite, and in northern Quebec Province there is the Chubb Crater which is even larger. Fortunately large meteorites strike the earth very rarely.

Distances in the Solar System

The distance between objects in the solar system is vast in comparison to any distances known here on the earth. For example, the distance from the earth to the sun is about 3,720 times the distance around the earth at the equator. Sometimes, these distances are thought of in terms of the time it takes to travel them. A jet trip to the sun at a speed of seven hundred miles per hour would take about fifteen years. Even light, which travels at about 186,000 miles per second requires a little more than eight minutes to make the journey from the sun to the earth.

It is difficult for children—and adults—to comprehend the vast distances involved in the solar system. Perhaps, the best way to help children visualize the size of the various objects in the solar system and the distances between them is to use an analogy such as the following.

In a scale model of the solar system the sun could be represented by a ball slightly larger than a basketball. To illustrate the relative size and distance of Mercury, place a grass seed in an orbit 83 feet from the ball. Both Venus and the earth would be the size of a bean. Venus would be 155 feet from the ball and the earth 215 feet. Mars would be a small pea at a distance of 330 feet. Jupiter, the largest planet, would be the size of a small grapefruit at a distance of 1/5 mile. Saturn could be represented by a medium-size apple 2/5 of a mile from the ball, and Uranus would be the size of a large marble 4/5 of a mile away. Neptune would be a little larger than Uranus and at a distance of 1 1/5 miles. Distant Pluto could be represented by a small pea 1 3/5 miles from the ball.

Universal Gravitation and the Study of the Solar System

Newton suggested that there is a force of attraction between all matter in the universe. He called this the *force of gravitation*. It is this force of gravitation that makes an apple fall to the earth and holds the moon and the planets in their orbits. Much is still not known about the nature of this force, but how it acts can be described with a great deal of precision.

Newton stated that the size of the force of gravitation depends upon the sizes of the masses of matter. The larger the masses, the greater the force of attraction. However, the force of gravitation varies inversely as the square of the distance between the objects, that is, if the distance between two objects is doubled, the gravitational force between them will be reduced to one-fourth.

Newton's law of gravitation may be expressed in equation form as follows:

$$F = \frac{G \times m_1 \times m_2}{d^2}$$

Where F is force of gravitation, m_1 and m_2 are the masses of the objects, d^2 is the distance between the objects, and G is a constant used to keep the units of measure in the equation the same.

One of the important tests of any scientific law or theory is whether it can be used to explain known facts. In this respect Newton's law of gravitation has been very effective. It has been of tremendous value in calculating the masses of celestial bodies and their orbits. An even more stringent test is whether or not the law or theory can be used to make accurate predictions and new discoveries. Newton's law of gravitation has also met this test. For example, it was used to discover the planet Neptune.

In the early years of the nineteenth century it was noticed that the planet Uranus deviated from the path predicted. These deviations were small, but there was no doubt of their existence. One possible explanation for these deviations was another planet beyond the orbit of Uranus, which, because of gravitational attraction, would tend to pull Uranus out of its expected orbit.

Two young men, J. C. Adams in England and U. J. Leverrier in France, working independently and unknown to each other, used Newton's law of gravitation to try to calculate the position of the new planet. Adams completed his calculations and sent his results to a noted astronomer, who unfortunately did not try immediately to verify the young man's calculations. Leverrier sent the results of his calculations to the astronomer J. G. Galle in Berlin. After a very short search, Galle found the new planet in practically the position that Leverrier had predicted.

Newton's law of gravitation had been used to find a new planet as well as to explain the motions of those already known. Later, the law was used to explain deviations in the orbit of Neptune by calculating the position of another new planet, Pluto. When a law or theory can be used to predict accurately new phenomena, such as the position of new planets, the authenticity of that law or theory becomes quite certain.

The Moon and Other Satellites

Satellites are objects whose motions are dominated by a planet. The moon's motion is dominated by the earth, and it is the only natural satellite of the earth.

Table 6–1: SATELLITES OF PLANETS

Earth	1
Mars	2
Jupiter	12
Saturn	9
Uranus	5
Neptune	2

Since the earth's satellite, the moon, is the only one that can be observed easily and directly by children, it will be discussed in some detail. Children should be encouraged to observe the features of the moon and the apparent changes in the shape of the moon throughout the month.

The moon can best be seen when it is full. With the unaided eye the dark patches, called the *maria*, can be seen. With the help of a pair of binoculars or a small telescope, the huge *craters* and the light-colored *rays* can be seen.

The moon is visible because it reflects sunlight. At full moon almost all of the moon that is illuminated by sunlight can be seen. At new moon, the illuminated side is away from earth, the dark side toward earth, and it is not visible at that time. At other phases of the moon, only fractions of its illuminated surface can be seen. At certain times a very dimly illuminated portion of the moon is visible. This portion of the moon is being illuminated by *earthshine*. Earthshine is light that has been reflected to the moon and then back again to the earth. The presence of earthshine is excellent evidence to support the view that the earth, and particularly its atmosphere, is a good reflector of light.

With lunar exploration vehicles, more direct observations of the moon and its surface can be made. Not only do these observations reveal more about the nature of the moon, but they also provide clues to the origins of the earth and other parts of the solar system. As they keep informed of explorations of the moon, children become participants in one of the greatest explorations in the history of mankind.

The Earth and Relative Motion

If you are sitting in a train at a railroad station and a train on another track begins to move, you sometimes have the sensation that you are moving rather than the other train. Actually, you are moving relative to the other train, but you are not moving relative to the railroad station. An astronaut in a satellite puts his camera up to his eye to take a picture and then drops it. The camera continues to remain in front of his face. The camera is not moving relative to the astronaut's face or the satellite; it is moving at a tremendous velocity relative to the earth. All motion of any object is relative to some other object. This "relatively" simple statement is one of the central ideas in modern relativity theory.

In most everyday experiences motion is considered relative to the earth. A runner who runs a four-minute mile runs that fast relative to the earth's surface. In the example of the train at the station, you may for a short time consider your motion relative to another train. In the solar system and in space in general, it must be specified to what objects a particular motion is relative. In some of the examples that follow the earth's motion will be considered relative to the sun and other stars. In another example, it will be the moon's motion relative to the earth.

Day and Night

The sun appears to rise in the eastern sky every morning, move across the sky during the day, and set in the west in the evening. During the night, the stars also appear to move across the sky.

Two of the possible explanations for these phenomena are: (1) The sun and other stars do actually move across the sky to set and reappear again the following morning, and (2) the sun and stars are relatively stationary while the earth spins around on its axis once each day. The first alternative, the more obvious, was believed by the ancients. Now, however, it is known that the earth rotates on its axis once each day and that it is this that makes the sun and other stars appear to move.

The earth rotates from west to east. If an observer could look down on the earth from the North Star (Polaris), it would appear to be spinning in a counterclockwise direction. The stars are stationary relative to each other, but, because the earth is rotating, they appear to be moving relative to the earth. The sun is also practically stationary relative to the stars; the spinning of the earth makes the sun appear to move across the sky thus creating day and night.

The Seasons

Like almost all other bodies in the solar system, including man-made satellites, the earth travels around the sun in an ellipse with the sun at one focus of the ellipse. For a long time most learned men believed that the sun revolved around the earth. It was not until Copernicus published his heliocentric (sun-centered) theory of the solar system that scholars began to consider seriously the theory that the earth and the other planets revolve around the sun.

The early Greek astronomer-mathematician Aristarchus of Samos, in the third century before Christ, suggested that the sun was at the center of the solar system and that the earth revolved around it. He also correctly suggested that the apparent relative positions of the stars should change if the earth revolved around the sun. This change is called the *parallax effect*. If you view distant objects while standing at one end of the school building, they will appear to be in certain positions in relationship to each other. But, when you have walked around the building to the other side, the distant objects appear to be in a different relationship. Similarly, the stars should appear in a different relationship to each other when viewed from different positions on the earth's path around the sun. However, the early viewers of the stars could not see this parallax effect and, therefore, believed that the earth did not revolve around the sun.

The early observers did not see the parallax effect because the stars are much, much more distant from earth than the Greeks conceived. You will notice, too, that the parallax effect for distant objects is much less than for objects that are near at hand. In fact, the parallax effect was not detected for some of the nearer stars until 1838. A telescope is needed to observe it, and usually the measurements on the photographic plates are made with the aid of a microscope. Now this parallax effect is considered to be one of the evidences of the revolution of the earth around the sun.

Other evidence for the earth's revolution is the *aberration of starlight*. Like the parallax effect, children cannot observe this aberration of starlight directly, but it can be explained with the help of an analogy. During a rainstorm, when there is no wind, raindrops will appear to be falling straight down. On a parked car the raindrops will leave trails straight up and down on the windows. When the car is moving, however, the rain-drops will appear to be falling toward the car and will leave oblique streaks on the windows of the car. Similarly, the light from stars directly overhead will appear to be displaced because of the movement of the earth in its orbit, and the direction and amount of displacement will depend on the direction and speed of the earth's motion.

The axis of the earth, that is, the imaginary line around which it spins, is tipped at an angle of about twenty-three and a half degrees from the perpendicular to the plane of its orbit around the sun. For example, the earth can be compared to a spinning top moving in a path or *orbit* on the floor around some object representing the sun. In this case, the floor is the plane of the top's orbit. To carry the comparison further, the axis of the top should be tipped to an angle of twenty-three and a half degrees from a line straight up-and-down from the floor. Another way to explain this is to say that the North Pole of the earth is always pointed in the direc-tion of the North Star. This tilt of the earth's axis is one of the basic factors leading to the seasons.

The earth revolves around the sun once every 365 1/4 days. On Decem-ber 21, the *winter solstice*, the North Pole is pointing away from the sun, and, although the earth is then closest to the sun, the winter season begins in the Northern Hemisphere and the summer season in the Southern Hemisphere. By March 21, the *spring equinox*, the earth has moved about a quarter of the way around its orbit. On June 21, the *summer solstice*, the North Pole is pointing in the direction of the sun, and the Northern Hemisphere begins its summer and the Southern Hemisphere its winter.

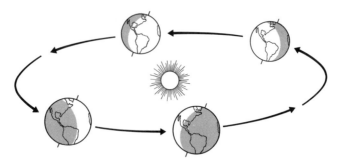

Fig. 6-2 *The axis of the earth is tipped. Solar radiation intensity on different parts of the earth changes as it revolves around the sun.*

By September 23, the *autumnal equinox*, the earth has completed three-quarters of its annual orbit. Then, the North Pole begins again to point away from the sun.

The basic reason for seasons is that the amount of solar energy received at any particular place on the earth varies throughout the year. The amount of solar energy received will depend upon the length of the day and the intensity of the sunlight.

By checking with almanacs or by direct observation, children can determine the number of hours of sunlight at various seasons. Often, it is helpful to organize this data in graph form. Obviously, there are more hours of daylight in the summer than in the winter. The actual number of hours will depend upon location; within the Arctic and Antarctic circles there are short periods of time when there are twenty-four hours of sunlight every day.

The amount of solar energy received also depends upon the angle at which the sun's rays strike the earth. When the sun's rays strike the earth at an oblique angle, the solar energy received during any given period of time is spread out over a larger area than when the incoming sunlight is perpendicular to the surface. A similar effect can be observed with the light from a flashlight. When the flashlight is beamed directly onto a surface, the light covers a relatively small area. When the flashlight shines at an oblique angle to the surface, the same amount of light is spread out over a larger area. Similarly, during the winter season when the sun appears relatively low in the sky, the sun's rays are spread over a larger area than during the summer when the sun may be almost directly overhead.

Surprisingly, the fact that the earth is closer to the sun in the Northern Hemisphere in winter than in the summer has very little effect. It might be expected that summers in the Southern Hemisphere would be somewhat warmer than those of the Northern. One of the reasons why this is not true is that the Southern Hemisphere is largely covered by water, and it takes more energy to raise the temperature of water than that of an equal amount of rock and soil.

The Phases of the Moon

As the earth revolves around the sun, its satellite, the moon, revolves around the earth. Actually the moon is carried along by the earth as it revolves around the sun.

Each time the moon revolves around the earth, it rotates once on its axis. This means that the moon always keeps the same side toward the earth. It is somewhat as if you are walking around some other person always keeping your face in the direction of that person. In the process of walking around the person once, you will have turned or rotated once on your axis. Since the moon always keeps the same side toward the earth, in order to see the other side of the moon, man-made satellites must be sent around the moon to take pictures of it.

Half of the moon, except when there is an eclipse of the moon, is illuminated by sunlight. However, all of this illuminated half cannot always be seen. During the new moon the moon is between the earth and the sun, and not any part of the moon is visible on earth. Soon a tiny sliver of the moon can be seen in the western sky just after sundown. In about seven days the moon will be at first quarter, and about one-quarter of the moon's surface (about half of the illuminated half of the moon) can be seen. In about another seven days, the full moon (all of the illuminated half of the moon) is visible as it rises in the east early in the evening. In another seven

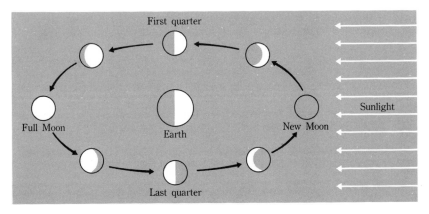

Fig. 6-3 The phases of the moon.

days, the moon will be at last quarter and it will be rising later and later in the evening. Finally only a thin sliver of a moon will be seen rising before sunrise, and then the moon will be invisible again as a new moon.

These changes in the appearance of the moon are called its *phases*, and these different phases all occur in one month. It takes the moon about 27 1/3 days to revolve around the earth as determined by the background stars (sidereal period). However, during this time the earth-moon system is revolving around the sun so that the moon has to revolve a little farther before it appears to be again in the same relationship with the sun (*synodic period*). The synodic month is about 29 1/2 days long and corresponds very closely to a calendar month.

Eclipses

The *eclipses* are due to the shadows of such objects as the moon and the earth. When the moon passes between the sun and the earth so that its shadow falls on part of the earth, that part of the earth's surface has a *solar eclipse*. On the regions of the earth having a solar eclipse part or all of the sun cannot be seen because the moon is between those positions and the sun. When the earth passes between the moon and the sun, part of its shadow may fall on the moon, and there is a *lunar eclipse*. During a lunar eclipse, anyone on the surface of the moon would be unable to see the sun because the earth would be between him and the sun.

Basically, shadows, and hence eclipses, occur because light travels in a straight line. Also, because light travels in a straight line, the shadow of an object has some resemblance to the shape of the object casting the shadow. An interesting observation for children to make is to note the shape of the edge of the earth's shadow as it moves across the moon. The edge of the shadow is curved and this is part of the evidence that the earth is round.

The only time it is possible to have an eclipse of the sun is during the new moon when the moon is between the sun and the earth. On the other hand, the only time there can be a lunar eclipse is during the full moon when the earth is between the sun and the moon.

Why isn't there a lunar and solar eclipse each month? This would seem to be reasonable, since the moon revolves around the earth about once a month. Actually, however, the moon's plane of revolution is inclined at an angle of five degrees to that of the earth's. This means that there can be an eclipse less frequently than once a revolution.

A total eclipse of the sun is an important astronomical event, and very often scientific expeditions are sent to those places on the earth where it can be viewed. At this time the sun's corona can be seen. Scientists are also interested in finding out what kinds of radiation and cosmic particles are blocked off by the moon. To view a solar eclipse, several dark photographic negatives should be placed in front of the eyes.

The Formation of the Solar System

Men have long wondered how the sun and the planets may have been formed. Certainly, this is a question about which children are often concerned. To develop some concept of how the solar system may have been formed is an important aspect of developing a consistent, defensible view of the world in which we live.

In a sense, the question of how the solar system may have been formed is a historical question. Since there was no witness to report the event, however, the laws and principles of science must be used to develop some hypothesis concerning the origin of the solar system. Also, any hypothesis must be consistent with the known characteristics and features of the solar system. It is important to emphasize with children how hypotheses are developed concerning an event that took place so long ago and of which there were no observers.

Any defensible hypothesis concerning the origins of the solar system must take into account such features as the following:

1. Most of the mass of the solar system is concentrated in the sun.
2. The sun is the only object in the solar system that gives off light and other forms of energy in any appreciable amounts.
3. All of the planets revolve around the sun in the same direction and in practically the same plane.
4. All of the planets, except Uranus, rotate in the same direction as they revolve around the sun. Uranus is tipped so that it rotates at almost a right angle to the plane of revolution.
5. Most of the satellites of the planets, but not all, revolve around the planet in the same direction in which the planet revolves around the sun.
6. The hypothesis also has to explain the asteroids, comets, meteors, etc.

All of these demands have taxed the imagination and ingenuity of astronomers. However, they help explain the insistence that explanations of the origins of the solar system be termed hypotheses or "educated guesses."

The dust cloud hypothesis

One of the most widely held hypotheses is the *dust cloud hypothesis*. Throughout the universe there are great clouds of gas and dust. Earth

satellites and space probes have encountered such dust as they have ven-
tured into interplanetary space. The great dark areas to be seen in many
photographs of the sky are probably the result of dust clouds through which
starlight cannot penetrate. Although there may be only one very small
particle of dust per cubic yard of space, space is so vast that the total
amount of dust and gas in space becomes very great. In fact, it has been
estimated that there is as much matter scattered throughout space, as dust
or as gas, as there is in all stars and planets in the universe. It is hypothesized that the solar system was formed out of such interstellar gas and
dust.

Particles of dust in space would tend to be attracted to each other
because of the pressure of starlight and the force of gravitation. It is known
that light exerts pressure on matter. The tails of comets usually point away
from the sun because of the pressure of sunlight. Also, the orbits of earth
satellites that remain in space for some time are shifted by the pressure of
sunlight. A particle of dust would be affected by the pressure of starlight.
Also, each particle would cast a small shadow. Two particles that passed
into each other's shadow zones would tend to be pushed together. As the
particles moved closer together, the gravitational force of attraction between the particles would increase and the particles would tend to push or
pull the particles of dust and gas together to form a huge cloud.

Within clouds of dust and gas there is swirling, and whirls of gas and
dust are formed. For example, if a cloud of smoke is enclosed in a glass
bottle and strong light is directed at the smoke, the swirling of the smoke
can be seen. Usually, the entire cloud of dust and gas begins rotating, and
within the cloud there are smaller cloudlets that also revolve.

As the cloud and the smaller cloudlets continue to contract, the rate of
rotation increases. This is like the figure skater who starts spinning slowly.
When she places her arms and hands close to her chest, she begins to
rotate much faster. This can be demonstrated to children by having them
sit on a piano stool with their arms outstretched and holding small weights
in their hands. After they are given a slight turn, ask them to pull the
weights in, and they will begin to turn much faster. This is how the rotational speed of the cloud of dust increased as the cloud contracted.

As the clouds of dust and gas contracted, their temperatures increased.
As air is compressed in a bicycle pump while being used to pump up a tire,
the pump sometimes becomes too hot to touch. The largest cloudlet within
the dust cloud contracted to form the sun. The temperatures in this cloud
were raised to the point where certain nuclear reactions that give off
energy could begin. Other cloudlets were left in space revolving around
the central cloud. These cloudlets contracted to form the planets and
some of the satellites. However, these cloudlets were much smaller than

the one that formed the sun, and the temperatures never reached the point where nuclear reactions could begin.

This dust cloud hypothesis explains most of the characteristics of the solar system. It explains the rotation and revolution of the planets and why only the sun gives off energy. The satellites that revolve in a direction opposite to the rotation of the planets are assumed not to have been formed with the rest of the solar system but to have been "captured" by the planets when they passed nearby. Obviously, the hypothesis needs to be extended to explain in greater detail the formation of the planets and the sun.

One of the interesting implications of the dust cloud theory is that there may be other solar systems in the universe similar to the earth's. Perhaps other stars were formed in the same way that the earth's star, the sun, was, and the chances are great that many other stars would also have planetary systems. Among these many solar systems, perhaps, there will be many planets where conditions will be somewhat similar to those on earth. This would suggest that there may be life in many other solar systems in the universe.

THE MILKY WAY AND THE UNIVERSE

Observers of the sky have long known of spiral-shaped sources of light known as "spiral nebulas." For a long time it had been assumed that these spiral nebulas, along with the sun and other stars, were members of the Milky Way system, and many thought that the Milky Way Galaxy was like an island in the universe—an island that encompassed almost all known celestial objects.

In 1924, Edwin P. Hubble trained the new one-hundred-inch Mount Wilson telescope on one of the spiral nebulas and resolved the glow of the nebula into points of light that undoubtedly were stars. In other words, the spiral nebula was not an amorphous, glowing cloud but was composed of large numbers of individual stars. Later, another astronomer working at Mount Wilson, Walter Baade, was able to detect individual stars in the center of the Andromeda Nebula. Actually, this nebula is another galaxy, very much like our own, containing hundreds of millions of stars. On the basis of their studies, Hubble and other astronomers have estimated that there are hundreds of millions of such galaxies in the universe. The old folk saying may be truer than we think; there may be "as many stars in the sky as there are grains of sand on the beach."

In the Andromeda Galaxy, Hubble also noticed certain stars that varied in their brightness. It was already known that the brightness of such a variable star could be determined by the time it takes for it to change from bright to dim to bright again. The greater the intrinsic brightness of a variable star the longer it takes for the star to pass through this cycle. Once the intrinsic brightness of a star is known, it can be compared with its actual brightness on earth, and its distance from the earth can be calculated. When Hubble found that the distance to Andromeda Galaxy was almost a million light-years, the great vastness of the universe became apparent. Later, galaxies that were as much as two billion light-years away were discovered.

This vast universe is a challenge to children. Almost all children, at some time or other, wonder about the nature of the universe. "How big is the universe?" "Of what is it composed?" "What are stars?" "Where does their light come from?" "How did the universe begin?" "How do we fit into this universe?" These are the kinds of questions astronomers deal with in the study of the Milky Way and the universe.

How the Universe Is Studied

Although the stars are very distant from earth, a great deal has been learned about them. An important approach to the study of stars is the investigation of the radiation that comes to earth from the stars in the form of light and radio waves. A careful analysis of this radiation can reveal a great deal about the stars that are the source of this radiation. Another important approach to the study of the stars is to apply the basic laws that have been developed on earth to the universe at large. This is the approach that is used in the very important science of astrophysics.

Spectral analysis

It has been said that more is known about the stars, even though they are so very distant from the earth, than is known about the earth a few hundred miles below. The main reason for this is that radiation, including light, is received from the stars. This radiation can be analyzed in several important ways. No similar form of radiation is received from the interior of the earth.

A crude estimate of the temperature of a star can be made by noting its color. If a nail is held in a flame for a short time and then taken out, the heat being given off by the hot nail can be felt. The hot nail is giving off infared radiation of long wavelength which can be felt but cannot be seen. As the nail is held in the flame, its color will change from red to orange to yellow to white as its temperature increases. Similarly, a very hot star will give off white light. There are stars that are not hot enough to give off visible light. Some of these can be detected with radio telescopes. The wavelengths of the radiation from a star indicate the temperature of a star.

The chemical elements present in a star can be determined by studying the spectrum formed when the starlight is passed through a prism. Each of the chemical elements has a characteristic spectrum. These have been produced and studied in the laboratory. The spectra of stars can be compared with the spectra of various elements to see whether the specific lines that are characteristic of various elements are present in the light from the stars.

If a hot source of light is surrounded by a cool gas, light of certain wavelengths will be absorbed by the gas. The spectrum will now have dark lines in it. The position of the dark lines will depend upon the chemical elements in the gas. The spectra of light from many stars have dark lines in them. These dark lines are due to the absorption of light by the relatively cool atmosphere that surrounds the star. In the spectrum of Sirius, which is the second brightest star, the characteristic lines of hydrogen are found. Sirius is a hot star whose atmosphere would not contain the gases that would absorb the light from hydrogen. Betelgeuse, the red star found in the constellation Orion (The Hunter), has a spectrum in which the hydrogen lines are not prominent. Betelgeuse has a reddish color and, therefore, is a relatively cool star that can have an atmosphere that absorbs the hydrogen lines. Thus, through the careful analysis of the spectra of starlight, some understanding of stellar atmospheres as well as the composition of the light-emitting parts of the stars can be gained.

Stellar spectra also indicate the relative motions of stars. The positions of the spectral lines for various chemical elements are known with great precision. However, in the spectra from distant stars, these lines have been shifted a little to the red end of the spectrum. The more distant the stars the greater is the shift toward the red end of the spectrum. This shift is believed to be due to the *Doppler effect*. The frequency of wave motions is increased when the object emitting the wave motion is moving toward the earth and is reduced when the emitter is moving away. The sound of an automobile horn that is coming toward you has a relatively high frequency, while that from an automobile moving away from you has a lower frequency. It is suggested that the frequency of the light from the stars receding from the earth will have a lower frequency and, therefore, be shifted toward the red end of the spectrum. Since the light from very distant stars shows the greatest shift, they are assumed to be traveling away from the earth at much greater speeds than those relatively nearby. The red shift of spectral lines is the most important evidence of an expanding universe.

Much information about the nature of the universe has been obtained through the analysis of starlight, particularly through the study of stellar spectra. This is such an important source of information that much of the time of the most important telescopes, such as the two-hundred-inch telescope on Mount Palomar, is devoted to obtaining spectra of the light from stars.

Radio astronomy

Another important approach to the study of the universe is *radio astronomy*. In 1931 a Bell Telephone engineer, Karl Jansky, attempted to find the source of static and other forms of interference with radio communications. His reason was to find some way of eliminating unwanted interference. It was known that lightning, high voltage power lines, and various kinds of electrical equipment create static. However, after eliminating these sources of static, Jansky found that there was still considerable radio noise. When he searched for the origin of this noise, he discovered that some of this static was coming from outer space. Here was another source of information about the universe. The study of these radio signals is called radio astronomy.

Radio waves are much longer than light waves. A very important radio signal, that given off by hydrogen, is twenty-one centimeters (about eight inches) long. Radio waves emitted by celestial objects that may not be hot enough to give off visible light are about the only source of information about these dark objects. Also, since radio waves are of longer wavelength, they will penetrate clouds of dust and gas that block the passage of light. Children know that they can receive radio signals through the walls of their homes while the passage of the shorter wavelength light waves is blocked. Of great importance, hydrogen gas gives off a characteristic radiation with a wavelength of twenty-one centimeters. By noting the strength of this signal in various regions of the sky, it is possible to map the distribution of gas and dust. This is especially important because hydrogen is believed to be the most abundant element in the universe, and it probably is the building block from which other chemical elements are formed. These are some of the important avenues of study that have been opened up by radio astronomy.

The Milky Way Galaxy

Stretching across the sky is a luminous band of stars called the Milky Way. At some time, everyone should have a chance to view the Milky Way on a clear moonless night at a place where there is little light from artificial sources. Then, the Milky Way is one of the most beautiful sights to be seen in the sky. Early in the evening during late summer, it can be seen stretched across the sky from northeast to southwest. In the late winter the Milky Way arches across the sky from northwest to southeast in the early evening. The Milky Way is composed of one hundred billion or more stars. The sun is one of these stars, and, therefore, this *galaxy* of stars is of special interest.

The basic problem in studying the Milky Way stems from the fact that the earth is located in the Milky Way and it is impossible to get an over-all picture of it. Children might be asked how they would go about making a map of a city if they were enclosed in a room in the residential section, had never seen a map of another city, and could only view the city through a small window. In addition, the weather is always hazy and cloudy so that it is difficult to see. Under these conditions it would be hard to make a map of the city. The astronomer faces similar problems when he tries to map the Milky Way.

Observations of the Galaxy

A considerable amount about the Milky Way can be learned from observations made with the unaided eye. The stars seem to be concentrated along an imaginary line that can be drawn across the sky through the center of the Milky Way. Spreading out from this line, the number of stars diminishes. This observation suggests that the galaxy is flattened in shape. More stars can be seen in the Milky Way of the southern sky, particularly in the summer, than in the northern sky. When an observer looks at the bright section of the Milky Way, it is believed he is looking toward the center of the galaxy. When he looks toward the part of the Milky Way that has fewer stars, he is looking away from the center of the galaxy and toward the outside. This observation also suggests that the earth is located at some distance from the center of the galaxy.

Pictures of other galaxies that are believed to be similar to the Milky Way have helped to achieve a better understanding of the earth's galaxy. It would be a help in mapping a city to have a map of another city. For example, it might be assumed that the grid pattern of streets and avenues that is seen from the window prevails for much of the city. Of particular value to astronomers have been the pictures of the galaxy in Andromeda which fortunately can be viewed at an angle so that its spiral arms and central core are visible.

The *radio telescope* has been of special importance in the study of the galaxy. The clouds of gas and dust block off the light from many regions of the galaxy, but radio waves penetrate these clouds as easily as they do

Fig. 6-4 *Our Milky Way Galaxy may be like this Andromeda Galaxy.*

rain clouds. Radio telescopes have provided information about the deepest reaches of the galaxy. Much information about the spiral arms of the galaxy comes from this source.

Distances, motions, and structure of the galaxy

The Milky Way Galaxy is believed to be a flattened spiral. The distance across the galaxy is believed to be about eighty thousand light-years, that is, it takes light eighty thousand years to traverse the distance from one edge of the galaxy to the other. The galaxy has a core region where a large number of stars are concentrated. Trailing around the core are three or more complicated spiral arms.

The sun is located in one of the spiral arms at a distance of about twenty-seven thousand light-years from the center. This means that the sun, one of the medium-size stars in the galaxy, is about two-thirds of the way out from the center.

The entire galaxy rotates around its center. The central regions are believed to rotate faster than the trailing spiral arms. By earthly standards, the speed of rotation is very fast. The sun and its planets, for example, are moving around the center of the galaxy at a rate of 140 miles a second. So vast is the galaxy, however, that it takes two hundred million years to complete one rotation.

In the spiral arms of galaxies such as the Milky Way there are dark patches. These dark patches are believed to be composed of interstellar gas, which is probably the raw material from which new stars are formed. No such clouds are visible near the core of the galaxy. Here, the stars are probably older, and no new stars are being formed. In the spiral arms, however, many of the stars are younger. In fact some of the stars are probably still in the process of being formed. It is believed that they are being formed as described in the dust cloud hypothesis, used to explain the formation of the solar system. At least one astronomer has reported seeing stars on photographs that were not present on photographs of the same regions taken years ago. Perhaps they are stars that have been formed since the earlier photograph was taken. Probably new stars are also being formed in the Milky Way Galaxy. As stars age they move gradually toward the core of the galaxy. It should be emphasized that this process takes place over billions of years.

A Universe of Galaxies

Hubble's discovery that the spiral nebulas visible in the sky actually were gigantic galaxies of stars enlarged enormously the concept of the size of the universe. There are perhaps one hundred million galaxies within the purview of the two-hundred-inch telescope on Mount Palomar, which has a range of about two billion light-years. Undoubtedly, there are many galaxies beyond this range. There may be hundreds of millions, if not billions, of galaxies in the universe. Since the known universe is so large, is there any limit to it? This is one of the unanswered questions about the universe. Is it finite or infinite?

DISTANCES IN SPACE

One of the most important tasks to be performed in astronomy is to determine the distances to the planets and stars. Ordinarily, we measure distance using a ruler or tape measure. Obviously, we cannot use these out in the universe because the distances are too great, and we cannot reach the stars. Instead, astronomers have to use indirect methods. Four methods that astronomers use for measuring distances are: triangulation, parallax, spectral analysis, and the use of variable stars.

Triangulation

Triangulation is the method used by the surveyor to measure the distance to an inaccessible place, such as a place on the other side of a river. For example, if a surveyor wishes to find the distance across a river from point A to X, he can carefully measure a line AB. He can then sight at both points A and B to determine the angle that a straight line to X will make with line AB. Knowing the distance AB and the size of angles A and B, he can calculate the distance to X. This method is used in the calculation of distances to planets. A planet is observed simultaneously from two observatories a known distance apart and the distance to the planet calculated. Because any base line on earth is very small as compared to distances in space, the triangulation method cannot be used to measure distances to stars.

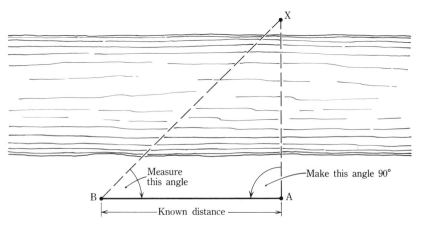

Fig. 6-5 *Measure the angle at B. Then make a scale drawing of the triangle and measure the distance from A to X on the drawing.*

Parallax

In the *parallax* method of measuring astronomical distances, the base line is the distance across the earth's path around the sun (about 2 × 93 million miles). Pictures are taken of the star and the stars in its background at six-month intervals when the earth is at opposite points in its orbit. The background stars are so far away that they can be assumed to be stationary. By noting the shift of the nearby star against the background stars, the angle of parallax can be measured and the distance to the star calculated. Because the distances to the stars are so great, the amount of parallax is very small and difficult to measure. Even the nearest star has an angle of parallax only as large as that of a flat penny if viewed from a distance of one and a half miles. Because measurement of parallax is difficult and requires such fine tools, it was not until 1838, after many attempts by many observers, that the astronomer F. W. Bessel was able to observe and measure the parallax to one of the stars. Now, parallax measurements have been made to several thousand stars, and these measurements are very important as a means of calibrating methods of measuring distances to more distant stars.

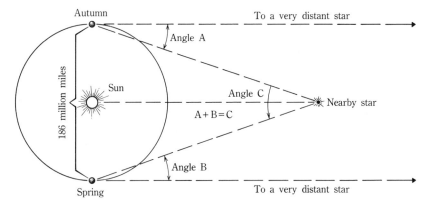

Fig. 6-6   *The base line is the distance across the earth's orbit. By measuring angle A in the autumn and angle B in the spring, angle C can be calculated. A scale drawing can thus be made and the distance to the nearby star measured.*

Relative brightness

Parallax measurements of distance are possible only for the nearest stars. However, it is important to have reliable means of determining the distances to much more distant stars. Perhaps the best way of explaining the methods that are used is to compare them to the way the distance to a set of automobile headlights is judged. If the headlights appear bright, they are probably nearby, but if they appear dim, they are probably more distant. These qualitative judgments of the distance to a set of headlights are based on the assumption that they have a certain intrinsic brightness. If the headlights were intrinsically very dim or extraordinarily bright, the judgments would be faulty.

The distances to the very remote stars are measured in terms of their apparent brightness. Unlike the case of the automobile headlights, it cannot be assumed that all stars are of equal intrinsic brightness. Instead, some means must be found to determine the intrinsic brightness of the stars so that the measurements of their brightness on the earth can be used to calculate their distance. The actual brightness of starlight on the earth can be measured with great accuracy using an instrument called the photo-electric photometer.

Spectral Analysis

One way of determining the intrinsic brightness of stars is through *spectral analysis*. The light from a star is passed through the slit of a spectrograph that has been placed at the focus of a large telescope. The starlight is dispersed into a spectrum. The spectrum of the star is then classified on the basis of the presence or absence and comparative strength of various spectral lines. With this classification, the position of the star can be denoted on a special diagram called the Hertzsprung–Russell Diagram and the intrinsic brightness of the star determined. This diagram was first worked out using stars whose distances were known as a result of parallax measurements.

For example, as a result of spectral analysis, the sun is classified as a G star type. A vertical line from G up to the curve designating the main sequence of stars and then across to the left side of the diagram shows that the sun has an intrinsic brightness of the absolute magnitude of +5. Strange as it may seem, stars with a negative absolute magnitude have the highest intrinsic brightness. The star with the highest known brightness is Rigel at −6. The numbering system, of course, is arbitrary and is based upon the system used by the early Egyptian astronomer Ptolemy.

After the absolute magnitude of a star has been determined by spectral analysis and the Hertzsprung–Russell Diagram, the apparent magnitude of the star on earth is measured with a photoelectric photometer. The astronomer can then calculate the distance the star must be in order to give the measured apparent magnitude. The spectral analysis method of measuring stellar distance can be used for any star for which it is possible to obtain a spectrum. It has been especially valuable in determining distances within the Milky Way Galaxy.

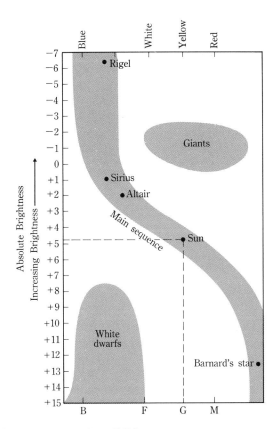

Fig. 6-7   *The Hertzsprung-Russell Diagram.*

Variable Stars

Another way to determine the intrinsic brightness of stars is to observe the rate at which they vary in brightness. Certain stars called *Cepheid variables* vary in brightness over periods ranging from one day to fifty days. Cepheid variables that belong to the same cloud can be assumed to be at equal distances from the earth because the distance from the earth is so great that the comparatively short distance between them can be ignored. Among such variable stars it has been found that the slower the rate at which the star varies the greater is its average brightness. The faster the rate at which it varies the smaller is its brightness. This is a powerful tool for determining the absolute magnitude of a variable star. All that is needed is to determine the length of time that is required to fluctuate from maximum brightness through minimum brightness and back to maximum again. Cepheid variables have been isolated in other galaxies such as the galaxy in Andromeda and have provided a way of determining the distances to these galaxies.

Units of Distance in Astronomy

The distances involved in studying the universe are so great that the usual units of distance used on the earth are clumsy and unwieldy. An often-used unit in astronomy is the *light-year*, that is, the distance light travels in a year. Light travels at about 186,000 miles per second or in the metric system 3×10^{10} centimeters per second. Children sometimes enjoy calculating the length of a light-year in miles.

The problem would look like this: $186,000 \times 60 \times 60 \times 24 \times 365\,1/4$ = 1 light-year = 5,869,713,600,000 miles. Some concept of the distances in space can be gained when it is realized that, after the sun, the nearest star, Proxima Centauri, is about $4\,1/3$ light-years away.

An Expanding Universe

When the spectra from various galaxies are analyzed, it is found that certain characteristic lines are often shifted toward the red end of the spectrum. This is the famous *red shift* of spectral lines. Furthermore, it has been found that the more distant the galaxies the more pronounced is the red shift.

It is believed that this red shift is due to the movement of the galaxies away from the earth. Apparently, the farther away the galaxies are the faster they are moving away. The red shift is the basic evidence to support the view that the universe is expanding. The relationship between the observed red shift and distance has been checked for galaxies whose distances are known. When the distances to the *quasars* (quasi-stellar sources) are determined by this method, however, the distances turn out to be so great that the basic red shift-galactic distance relationship is being questioned. The investigation of the red shift of quasars and their distances is an important frontier in astronomical studies.

The galaxies are moving away from each other. The expanding universe is a matter of galaxies and groups of galaxies, not of planets or individual stars. The planets remain in their respective orbits and the stars in their motions in the galaxies, but the galaxies are rushing away from each other at great speeds. In fact, the speed of the most distant galaxies approaches the speed of light which theoretically is the greatest speed that can be achieved by any matter in the universe.

It should not be assumed that all the galaxies are rushing away from

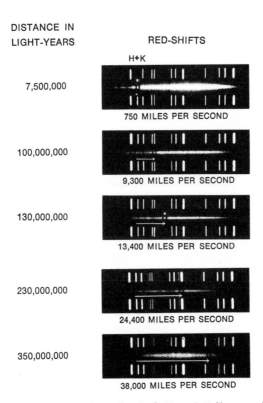

DISTANCE IN
LIGHT-YEARS   RED-SHIFTS

H+K

7,500,000

750 MILES PER SECOND

100,000,000

9,300 MILES PER SECOND

130,000,000

13,400 MILES PER SECOND

230,000,000

24,400 MILES PER SECOND

350,000,000

38,000 MILES PER SECOND

Fig. 6-8   The red shift. Note how the dark H and K lines at the head of the arrows are further to the right in the spectra from galaxies at great distances.

the Milky Way Galaxy alone. There is no need for a sense of rejection because all the galaxies would appear to be moving away regardless of the point in the universe from which the expansion is viewed. This expansion has been compared to that of an expanding, transparent balloon. Make a series of marks on the surface of a balloon. Imagine yourself as an observer at any one of these points. As the balloon is inflated, regardless of which point you observe from, it would appear that all other points are moving away from you. Similarly, regardless of the galaxy from which the universe is viewed, it would appear that all other galaxies are moving away.

Is the universe finite or infinite? Does it have an end or does it go on forever? It is difficult to tackle this question. To date, however, no edge or end to the universe has been found, although the large radio telescopes are beginning to probe the regions where astronomers might, from a theoretical point of view, expect to find an end. One observation that everyone can make has been used to support the idea of a finite universe: namely, if the universe were infinite, the night sky should be as bright as day. Since it isn't, it has been reasoned that the universe is finite. However, the dark of night can be explained in other ways. Undoubtedly, one of the most fascinating questions with which scientists deal is whether or not there is a limit to the universe.

The Earth's Place in the Universe

One of the important goals of elementary school science is to help children build a view of the world that is consistent with the best scientific evidence available. Here is a review of the earth's place in the universe.

The earth is one of the nine known planets that circle the nearest star, the sun. The earth is a medium-size planet and is the third planet out from the sun. The outstanding characteristic of planet earth is that it has the conditions that are necessary for life.

The sun is a medium-size star that gives off a great deal of energy, a very small part of which is received on earth. The sun is one of perhaps one hundred billion or more stars in a giant galaxy of stars called the Milky Way Galaxy. The earth is located about two-thirds of the way out from the core of the Milky Way Galaxy and is moving around the core of the galaxy at a rate of 140 miles a second.

The Milky Way Galaxy is one of perhaps billions of galaxies in the universe. These galaxies are rushing away from each other in a universe that may or may not have a finite limit.

The universe is vast. The distances involved are almost incomprehensible. There is also a tremendous amount of matter in the universe in the form of stars and possibly planets circling the stars, and clouds of gas and dust. One of the great challenges that faces the human race is to gain a better understanding of this great, vast universe.

THE FORMATION OF THE UNIVERSE

Man has always been interested in beginnings. "How did this world in which we live begin?" Imaginations have been stirred by this question, and a variety of intriguing hypotheses have been suggested. However, all hypotheses, if they are to be accepted, must be consistent with the observations that can be made of the universe. As observations have been extended and refined, many of the esoteric hypotheses concerning beginnings have had to be rejected. A hypothesis that is consistent with many observations may be called "The Hypothesis of a Beginning." Other imaginative hypotheses may be developed in the future.

The Hypothesis of a Beginning

The Hypothesis of a Beginning has sometimes been called the evolutionary hypothesis. According to this hypothesis, the universe did have a beginning several billion years ago and since that time has evolved into its present state. It will continue to evolve, perhaps infinitely.

In the beginning, all matter in the universe was collapsing rather than expanding. As a result of this collapse a great "squeeze" took place in which all matter in the universe was compressed into a very dense mass. This matter was broken up into atomic particles such as electrons, protons, and neutrons. Much of what is now matter was at that time in the form of radiant energy. After reaching a stage of great compression, there was a gigantic explosion. The expanding universe is a result of that explosion, and man is living in the aftermath of it.

One of the surprising features of this hypothesis is that the atoms in the universe are conceived of as having been formed during the first hour or so of the expansion from the primordial electrons, protons, and neutrons. Some elements heavier than uranium undoubtedly were formed, but these have long since decayed radioactively. Hydrogen, the simplest element, consisting of only an electron and proton, is understandably the most abundant element in the universe. As the universe evolved, a great deal of radiant energy was converted into matter, and matter became dominant in the universe.

The matter that existed was affected by gravitational forces and radiation pressure. The effects of these forces have been carefully worked out from experiments with them in the laboratory. It has been shown, for example, that a gas in an unlimited space will, inevitably, develop regions where the gas is relatively condensed. Because of the gravitational attraction between particles of gas, the regions of condensation do not dilute again but form gigantic clouds of gas. The gases in these clouds will be in motion as a result of the original explosion. Since there is nothing to impede this motion, the clouds of gas will tend to rotate somewhat as the galaxies now do.

These clouds of gas will divide into smaller clouds, and these clouds may form into even smaller cloudlets. Eventually, some of the clouds will condense to form stars. As the gases condense, the temperature is raised to the point where the stellar nuclear reactions can begin, and the process of converting matter in the stars into light and other radiant energy is under way. In smaller cloudlets, the temperatures were not raised to the point where nuclear reactions could take place. These cloudlets formed planets that are believed to circle many stars. This process of star and planet formation was discussed in greater detail as the dust cloud hypothesis (see pages 105–107).

The process of star formation is still going on. The dark patches in the spiral arms of the galaxy are believed to be clouds of gas and dust. These clouds may be the raw material for the formation of new stars. In intergalactic space there is also gas, and this may eventually form new galaxies. Thus, the process of stellar and galactic evolution continues.

According to this hypothesis, the universe had a beginning. Strange as it may seem it may be possible to see this beginning, or at least the stages that followed soon after the beginning. Light from very distant sources started on its journey many years ago. When a star that is two billion light-years away is seen with the two-hundred-inch telescope, the star is as it was two billion years ago. If we could increase the range of observational devices to several billion light-years, it might be possible to see part of the universe as it was just after the beginning.

Since very distant parts of the universe are seen as they were a very long time ago, there should appear to be a greater density of matter in these distant regions of the universe. It should be possible to see things as they were soon after the great explosion. This may prove to be an important check on the validity of this hypothesis. Some of the most important research in astronomy involves checking whether or not there actually is a greater density of matter at great distances.

Life Elsewhere in the Universe

Is there life elsewhere in the universe? This is a question of great interest. However, a definite answer to the question is not yet possible. All that can be done is to analyze the physical requirements for life and investigate the possibilities that these conditions exist elsewhere in the universe.

In order for life to exist, at least as man knows it, the chemical elements that make up living things must be present. The human body and the bodies of other living things are made up largely of oxygen, carbon, hydrogen, nitrogen, and calcium with traces of such elements as silicon, iron, phosphorus, sulfur, and sodium. All of these elements are found in the earth's crust. However, they also seem to be present in the sun, many other stars, and probably in the invisible matter in the regions around stars.

The chemical elements that are needed for life appear to be present throughout the universe.

Life can probably exist only within a certain temperature range. Life is found in the hot waters of geysers and hot springs as well as in the cold arctic and antarctic. However, life could not exist in the great heat on or near the stars; the complex molecules that make up living matter would be broken up. On the other hand, a certain temperature is needed to keep the biochemical operations in living systems operating. Thus, the zones where life can exist are limited somewhat by the fact that life cannot exist on the stars or at distances from the stars that are too great to receive a certain minimum amount of energy.

Apparently, living things also need an atmosphere to protect them from deadly radiation from the stars. On planet earth, the atmosphere is also the most important source of the oxygen and carbon dioxide taken into living systems. Atmospheres are retained by celestial objects by the force of gravitation, and they have to be of a certain size in order to retain an atmosphere. The moon, for example, is too small to retain an atmosphere. The necessity for an atmosphere rules out smaller celestial objects such as meteors, comets, satellites of planets, and the smaller planets as possible habitats of life.

A consideration of the requirements for life suggests that life is most likely to be found, perhaps can only be found, on planets or stars somewhat like the sun. These planets must have the necessary chemical elements, an atmosphere, and satisfactory temperature conditions. Since the temperature range cannot be too great, the planets must revolve around a star in orbits that do not carry them too close or too far away from the energy-giving star. How many such planets are there in the universe?

Modern theories of star formation, such as the dust cloud hypothesis, suggest that many stars have planetary systems. Only a small fraction of these planetary systems will have the requirements to sustain life. However, the number of stars in the universe is so large that even a small fraction constitutes a tremendous number. It has been conservatively estimated that there are more than one hundred million planetary systems in the known universe that have conditions suitable for life. With this many possibilities it is difficult to believe that life would arise on only one planet in one planetary system. The possibilities that there is life elsewhere in the universe are very great indeed.

Recent laboratory experiments have shown how living matter might originate. A mixture of ammonia, methane, hydrogen, and water vapor— gases that were probably present in the early atmosphere of the earth and are found in the atmospheres of some other planets—was subjected to electrical discharges much like lightning. Some amino acids were formed;

amino acids are the building blocks for the formation of proteins. Given long periods of time, these proteins would probably become living matter. This evidence from the laboratory also suggests that life may be found many places in the universe.

Other Universes

It has been suggested that there may be universes in addition to this one. This, of course, assumes that this universe has a finite limit.

One of the reasons for suggesting that there may be at least one more universe is the *principle of symmetry*. Throughout the environment there is general symmetry. The human body is largely symmetrical, with left and right hands, legs, eyes, ears, and lungs. There are positive and negative charges of electricity and north and south magnetic poles. With symmetry so general throughout the environment, perhaps there is symmetry on the scale of universes as well.

Since this universe is characterized by matter, it has been suggested that there may be another universe of *anti-matter*. In anti-matter, the basic particles have an electric charge opposite to the basic particles of matter. An electron has a negative charge; an anti-electron has a positive electric charge. Similarly, a proton has a positive charge while an anti-proton has a negative charge. A universe of anti-matter is theoretically possible. Perhaps, it will be found.

APPROACHES TO TEACHING

One of the problems in teaching *The Universe and Solar System* is that so much of the evidence on which the modern view of the universe is built is not directly obtainable by children or by most adults. The modern view of the universe has been built upon evidence garnered through the use of large telescopes, sophisticated spectrographs, radio telescopes, radar, and highly sophisticated theoretical tools. These cannot be used directly by children, and yet it is important that children begin to build a view of the world in which they live.

It is possible for children to have some firsthand experiences in the study of the sun, moon, and stars, and it is strongly urged that every effort be made to do this. Have them locate constellations, use a prism to examine sunlight, look at and map the moon, and observe the visible planets and stars.

However, children should also begin to build mental models with which to think about the nature of the earth-moon system, the solar system, and the universe. A number of the activities that follow are demonstrations in which models of such systems are developed. Whenever possible, the children should participate actively in these demonstrations. It is important for the teacher to repeatedly relate the demonstrations to the phenomena they are intended to help explain. These kinds of demonstrations will become increasingly important as more and more areas of science become increasingly abstracted from the common, everyday experiences of children and adults.

How can various constellations be located?

The constellations can best be seen on a clear, moonless night. If possible, it is desirable to find a spot where there is a minimum of distracting light from cities and highways. You should have a star map and a red light with which to check the map. (A few sheets of red cellophane fastened over the glass of a flashlight makes a fine source of red light.) Orient your map so that it is in the correct position in terms of date and time of night.

Perhaps the best way to start is to find an easily recognizable constellation such as the Big Dipper which appears in the northern sky. Many other

Fig. 6-9 *Winter constellations. Hold this chart vertically so that the horizon you are facing is down. Constellations at the lower edge will be near the horizon and those in the center of chart will be overhead.*

constellations can be found in terms of their location with respect to the Big Dipper.

Be sure to point out to the children how Polaris can be located. The two stars in the Big Dipper opposite the handle are called the "pointers." Imagine a line between the two pointers and extend it to a distance about five times the distance separating the pointers. The star at the end of this imaginary line is Polaris. Having found Polaris, you have the direction of true north.

Polaris is at the end of the handle of the Little Dipper. On the side of Polaris opposite the Big Dipper is a W-shaped constellation called Cassiopeia. With these constellations as reference points, many other constellations can be found.

If possible, view the constellations at different times of the night. How do they appear to move during the night?

How does the rotation of the earth lead to day and night?

Have the children relate their observations concerning the occurrence of day and night and the apparent movement of the sun, moon, and stars across the sky from east to west. How can this be explained? Two possible explanations are: (1) The sun, moon, and stars all actually move across the sky and (2) the earth rotates on its axis so that the objects in the sky appear to be moving by the earth. The following demonstration shows how day and night and the movement of sun, moon, and stars across the sky can be explained by the conception of a rotating earth.

Shine the light from a flashlight or slide projector on a globe that is free to spin on its axis. (Make certain that the children realize the sun,

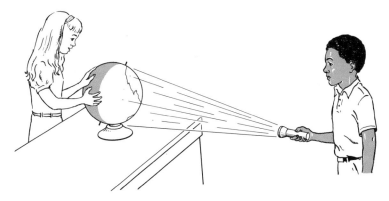

Fig. 6-10 *Children carry out a demonstration of how the rotation of the earth leads to day and night.*

unlike the flashlight or projector, shines in all directions.) Put a dab of clay or piece of tape on the globe indicating "home," and ask the children to imagine how the light would appear if they were at that spot.

Why can't the sun be seen at night? To see it we would have to look through the earth, and the earth is made up of opaque material. If the classroom is darkened, the side of the globe opposite the light will be dark because it will be in the globe's shadow.

As the globe is slowly spun counterclockwise, the children can imagine that they see the sun appear in the east. As the globe turns, the sun would appear directly overhead, and finally disappear in the west.

With some children this may be the time to raise the question, "What is motion?" Motion is the change of position of objects relative to other objects. To us, the sun, moon, and stars seem to be moving. But, to an observer out in space, it would certainly appear that the earth is rotating.

What is an explanation of the earth's seasons?

The earth's seasons are due to the earth's annual revolution around the sun and the tilt of the earth's axis. The effect of these two factors can be demonstrated by carrying a globe in an orbit around a light representing the sun in a darkened room.

It is important that the globe always be tilted so that the North Pole of the globe points toward the north. Again, a piece of plasticene may be stuck on the globe to indicate the location of "home."

As the globe is carried around the light, stops should be made at points representing each of the four seasons. For example, when the north pole of the globe is pointing away from the sun, it is winter; when the North Pole is pointing toward the sun, it is summer. Between these two positions

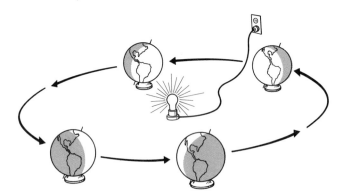

Fig. 6-11 *This arrangement is effective in demonstrating how the revolution of the earth around the sun produces the seasons.*

are spring and fall. At each of the stops, the children should be asked to consider such questions as the following:

Where would the sun be seen during this season at the North Pole?
Where would the sun be seen this season at the South Pole?
Where would the sun be seen at "home"?
Would the sun's rays at "home" be slanting or direct?
Where on the earth's surface would the sun be seen directly overhead at noon?
Where would you look to see the sun at noon at the Tropic of Cancer? The Tropic of Capricorn?

(Note that in this demonstration the children are viewing the earth from positions near the sun within the earth's orbit.) After the youngsters have a clear understanding of the factors that lead to the seasons, carry the globe around the orbit with the axis held at right angles to the plane of the orbit to show that, if the earth's orbit were like this, we would not have the kinds of seasons that we now have.

*How can the apparent change in shape of the moon
during a month be explained?*

Half of the moon is always illuminated by sunlight. The apparent changes in the shape of the moon can be explained in terms of the revolution of the moon around the earth. As the moon revolves around the earth the changing fractions of the illuminated half of the moon can be seen.

For this demonstration use a projector and a large ball that has been painted with aluminum paint. The aluminized ball is carried around two or three children who are placed in the position of the earth. These chil-

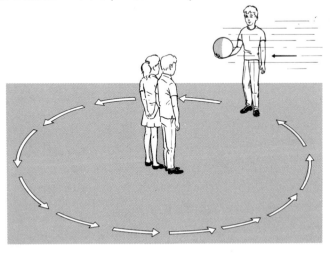

Fig. 6-12 *Children can demonstrate how the revolution of the moon around the earth leads to the phases of the moon.*

dren should report what parts of the ball they see illuminated by light from the projector as the ball is carried around them.

Start by holding the ball between the children and projector. This is the position of the moon at new moon. How much of the illuminated half of the ball can be seen by the children in the earth position?

Now move the ball in a counterclockwise path (as viewed from above) around the children. When do they first see a little light reflected from the ball? Stop at each quarter and ask the children to report how much of the illuminated half of the ball they see. Also ask which direction the "horns" of the moon are pointing. (Note that in this demonstration most of the children are viewing the moon from a position near the sun. Only the children within the orbit of the moon can see the moon as it might be seen on the earth.)

Under what conditions do eclipses occur?

A lunar eclipse occurs when the moon passes through the shadow of the earth. A solar eclipse happens when the earth passes through the shadow of the moon.

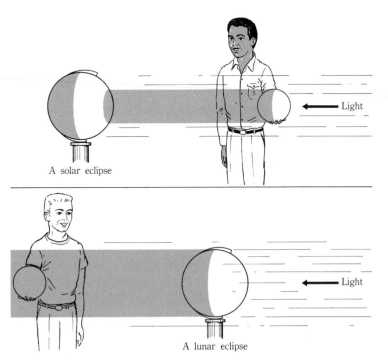

Fig. 6-13 *A child holding a ball, together with a source of bright light and a globe, can demonstrate how solar and lunar eclipses are produced.*

Have a projector represent the sun, a volleyball or basketball represent the earth, and a tennis ball or baseball represent the moon. Place the volleyball at a distance of ten or fifteen feet from the projector and carry the baseball around it very much as the moon revolves around the earth. Note that at certain times the shadow of the baseball falls on the volleyball and at that time on the surface of the volleyball there is an eclipse of the projection light. Similarly, as the shadow of the moon passes over a portion of the earth's surface, those areas experience a solar eclipse.

As the baseball is carried around the volleyball, it sometimes passes through the shadow of the volleyball and the baseball is eclipsed. Similarly, when the moon passes through the shadow of the earth an eclipse of the moon occurs. Ask the children, "How would the sun appear to anyone on the moon during an eclipse of the moon?" At those times, to a person on the moon, the sun would appear very much as it does to us during a solar eclipse.

How can light from the sun be examined?

Sunlight can be examined by using a prism in somewhat the same way that sunlight and starlight are examined with a spectroscope.

Arrange the shades in the room so that a very thin beam of sunlight enters. This is critical if a good spectrum is to be obtained. One way to get a thin beam is to cover an opening between the curtain and the wall with opaque paper and then cut a thin slit in the paper.

Hold a glass prism so that the beam of light passes through it. This should produce a spectrum on one of the walls of the room. What colors are in the spectrum of sunlight? Hold a sheet of paper so that one spectrum is projected onto it. What is the width of the total spectrum? What is the width of each of the colors that make up the spectrum?

Make a small loop in a wire and place some grains of salt in the loop. Hold the salt in the flame of a burner. The flame that is produced is characteristic of the element sodium in the salt. Pass a beam of this light through

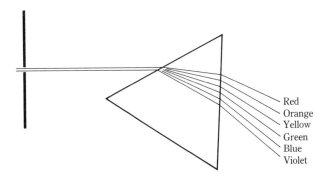

Fig. 6-14 *When a thin beam of light shines through a prism, a spectrum should be projected.*

a prism to get its spectrum. Compare this spectrum with that of sunlight. Are any of the characteristics of the sodium spectrum seen in the spectrum of sunlight?

If possible, it may be desirable to obtain the spectrum from a neon light or from tubes filled with other gases and made to glow with a spark coil. Are any evidences of these gases seen in the spectrum of sunlight?

How can a map of the moon be made?

It is possible to make a map of the moon that is quite consistent with maps made using large telescopes. The mapping can best be done on a clear night when the moon is full. It is helpful to have a large piece of sturdy paper supported on an easel and a small telescope or pair of binoculars.

Before mapping, draw a large circle on the paper to represent the moon. With the help of the telescope or binoculars, view the moon and try to locate dark and light areas. Try to sketch these in the right positions and to scale on the map. Perhaps, some craters can be seen. If so, locate these on the map.

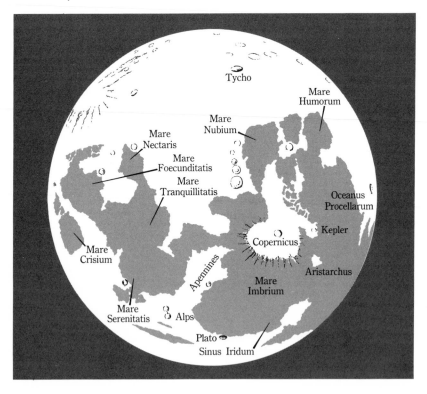

Fig. 6-15   *A map of the moon.*

When the map is completed, compare it with the map of the moon included in this book. What are the names of the various features that you have mapped?

Investigation

How do shadows change during the day and during the seasons?

To study the apparent movement of the sun across the sky and record the change of shadows during the course of a day without looking directly at the sun, place a stick upright on a flat piece of ground. (One way to arrange for this study is to fasten a short stick at one side of a piece of plywood.) Hold a string with a weight at the end next to the upright stick and adjust the stick so that it is parallel to the string. This upright stick is called a *gnomon*. Fasten a piece of paper on the north side of the upright stick on which the shadows can be marked.

Start making observations as early as possible in the morning. Mark the position of the shadow of the gnomon, and at every hour mark the position of the tip of the shadow and note the time. Continue making observations until sunset. It is especially important to get the length and the position of the shadow at noon.

Measure the length of the shadow at various times of the day and record them for future reference.

Measure and record the angles between the shadow at 9 A.M. and noon and between noon and 3 P.M.

Sketch a smooth curve between the various points, denoting the tip of the shadow at various times. How does this curve compare to the apparent path of the sun across the sky?

Carry out this study of shadows in the autumn, winter, and spring. Compare the lengths of the shadows at noon at each of these seasons. Also, compare the angles between the shadows at 9 A.M. and noon and between noon and 3 P.M.

How do the curves connecting the tips of the shadows at different times of the day at the different seasons compare? What does this investigation indicate about the path of the sun across the sky at different seasons?

Selected References

BERNHARD, HERBERT J., BENNETT, DOROTHY A., AND RICE, HUGH S., *New Handbook of the Heavens*. New York: New American Library, 1950.

BONDI, HERMAN, *The Universe at Large*. Garden City, N.Y.: Doubleday & Co., Inc., 1960.

HYNEK, ALLEN J., AND ANDERSON, NORMAN P., *Challenge of the Universe*. New York: McGraw-Hill Book Co., Inc., 1962.

JACOBSON, WILLARD J., KLEINMAN, GLADYS S., SUGARBAKER, JOHN, HIACK, PAUL, AND CARR, ALBERT, *The Universe and Solar System*. New York: American Book Co., 1968.

WATSON, FLETCHER G., *Between the Planets*. Garden City, N.Y.: Doubleday & Co., Inc., 1962.

READINGS FOR THE PRIMARY GRADES

ASIMOV, ISAAC, *The Moon*. Chicago: Follett Publishing Co., 1966.

JACOBSON, WILLARD J., LAUBY, CECILIA J., AND KONICEK, RICHARD D., *Day and Night*. New York: American Book Co., 1968.

JACOBSON, WILLARD J., LAUBY, CECILIA J., AND KONICEK, RICHARD D., *Earth Satellites*. New York: American Book Co., 1968.

JACOBSON, WILLARD J., LAUBY, CECILIA J., AND KONICEK, RICHARD D., *Exploring the Solar System*. New York: American Book Co., 1968.

JACOBSON, WILLARD J., LAUBY, CECILIA J., AND KONICEK, RICHARD D., *Exploring Space*. New York: American Book Co., 1968.

JACOBSON, WILLARD J., LAUBY, CECILIA J., AND KONICEK, RICHARD D., *The Moon*. New York: American Book Co., 1968.

JACOBSON, WILLARD J., LAUBY, CECILIA J., AND KONICEK, RICHARD D., *Rockets*. New York: American Book Co., 1968.

POLGREEN, JOHN AND CATHLEEN, *The Earth in Space*. New York: Random House, Inc., 1963.

SONNEBORN, RUTH A., *The Question and Answer Book of Space*. New York: Random House, Inc., 1965.

SUTTON, FELIX, *The How and Why Wonder Book of the Moon*. New York: Grosset & Dunlap, 1963.

READINGS FOR THE INTERMEDIATE GRADES

CLARKE, ARTHUR C., AND THE EDITORS OF LIFE, *Man and Space*. New York: Time, Inc., 1966.

GURNEY, GENE, *Walk in Space: the Story of Project Gemini*. New York: Random House, Inc., 1967.

JACOBSON, WILLARD J., LAUBY, CECILIA J., AND KONICEK, RICHARD D., *Exploring the Universe*. New York: American Book Co., 1968.

JACOBSON, WILLARD J., LAUBY, CECILIA J., AND KONICEK, RICHARD D., *The Milky Way and the Universe*. New York: American Book Co., 1968.

JOSEPH, JOSEPH MARON, AND LIPPINCOTT, SARAH LEE, *Point to the Stars*. New York: McGraw-Hill Book Co., Inc., 1963.

KNIGHT, DAVID C., *The First Book of Mars*. New York: Franklin Watts, Inc., 1966.

MYRUS, DON, *Keeping Up With the Astronauts*. New York: Grosset & Dunlap, 1963.

WYLER, ROSE, AND AMES, GERALD, *The Golden Book of Astronomy*. New York: Golden Press, Inc., 1955.

7 The Earth
on Which We Live

In 1785 a Scottish geologist named James Hutton published a paper entitled "The Theory of the Earth." In this paper Hutton stated his belief that the geological processes now at work could be used to explain how all of the geologic features of the earth had been formed. This became known as the *theory of uniformitarianism*, and it is now almost universally accepted by geologists and other students of the earth. The belief that we can understand geological events of the past by studying the processes at work today is one of the fundamental assumptions of historical geology.

A basic assumption of the theory of uniformitarianism is that the earth is very old. The Hawaiian Islands, for example, have been built up from the lava flows of volcanoes. This process is still at work on the island of Hawaii. Here, lava flows occur once every twenty years or so. Each flow adds a few feet to one relatively small section of the island. Clearly, the island of Hawaii must have been built up over a very long period of time. In terms of the total age of the earth, however, the Hawaiian Islands are relatively young. Elsewhere in the Pacific there are volcanic islands that have been built up and almost completely eroded away again. However, it is now known that the earth is at least 4.5 billion years old, and this is sufficient time for the various geological features to have been formed by the geological processes that can be observed in action today.

The theory of uniformitarianism is a powerful tool for the study of the history of the earth. After a rain, small rivulets can be seen emptying into a mud puddle. These small rivulets carry sand and silt. However, as the water enters the mud puddle, its velocity is decreased, and it can no longer carry as much sand and silt. These sediments are deposited at the mouth of the rivulet to form small deltas. The processes at work in this mud puddle are the same as those that have been at work over long periods of time to form large deltas such as those at the mouths of the Nile and Mississippi rivers. By observing delta formation on a small scale in a mud puddle, the history of large deltas can be studied. Many other geological features can be studied in a similar way.

THE HISTORY OF THE EARTH

Men have speculated about the age of the earth for a long time. In 1642 a distinguished scholar, John Lightfoot, stated that the earth was created at nine o'clock in the morning on September 17, 3928 B.C. In the latter part of the nineteenth century the famous physicist Lord Kelvin attempted to deduce the age of the earth from the rate at which the earth has been cooling and decided that the earth was twenty to forty million years old. Based on data from the radioactive dating of rocks, it is now believed that the earth is at least 4.5 billion years old with a possibility that it may be somewhat older.

It is very difficult for children, or adults, to develop a working concept of such a long period of time. The basic difficulty is in relating the unknown to the known. Six years is a lifetime to a six-year-old. Older people have a longer period of time in which to relate, but the longest life span is infinitesimal compared to the age of the earth. One approach to developing some concept of great periods of time is to study some geological process in action. For example, a stream flowing over a solid rock bottom will probably erode away only a small fraction of an inch in the course of a year. Still, an entire canyon, such as the Grand Canyon of the Colorado, has been cut by the running water of the streams, and since most of the North American continent has been uplifted and worn down several times, the cutting of such a canyon may have been repeated several times. By studying geological processes in action, the child may develop some concept of a fairly long period of time in which the much longer period of time that the earth has existed can be compared.

The great age of the earth is an important factor in our theories explaining the earth and its inhabitants. For example, one of the puzzling observations for early students of the earth were fossils of sea organisms that were found on tops of high hills and mountains. How could they have gotten there? If the earth were only a few thousand years old, perhaps it was some catastrophe that deposited these fossils on the tops of mountains. It is now known, however, that during some periods of the earth's long history what are now mountaintops were actually under water and the remains of sea organisms were deposited at that time. Similarly, the great age of the earth helps to explain the great variations among living things. If the earth were young, it would almost have to be assumed that all kinds of living things had come into being at about the same time. But how then would fossils of animals and plants that must once have existed but are now extinct be explained? Of course, it is now believed that the various kinds of living things that are now on the earth have evolved over a long period of time. The finding that the earth is very old makes it possible to explain the earth and its history in terms of physical and biological processes that are at work today.

A Geological Time Scale

Much information about the history of the earth and the living things that have inhabited it has come from the study of *sedimentary rocks*. Sedimentary rocks are formed from layers of sediment that are deposited usually at the bottom of bodies of water. Unless there has been severe tipping and twisting of rock formations, the layers of sedimentary rock are arranged in order of their age, with the oldest rocks on the bottom. The layers of sedimentary rocks can be compared to a history book. Starting at the bottom of a sedimentary formation, a chronological history of at least part of the history of the earth can be read. Often buried in these "books" of sediments are "illustrations" or fossils that reveal a great deal about the living things that inhabited the earth at a particular time.

One of the first men to grasp the significance of the sedimentary layers and their fossils was the English surveyor-scientist William Smith. In his surveying, Smith had a chance to study the strata and fossils to be found throughout England, Wales, and much of Scotland. Of greatest importance, he recognized that strata could be distinguished from each other by the kinds of fossils to be found in them. Smith published a detailed map of the geology of most of Britain. Because of his great interest in strata of sedimentary rock, he became known as "Strata" Smith. He has sometimes been called the Father of the Science of Stratigraphy.

Each geological age was characterized by a certain distribution of living things. In fact, certain fossils called *index fossils* lived only during certain geological ages. The fossils that are characteristic of a given geological age are usually found in many places throughout the world. A trained geologist can often determine the geological age in which a rock was formed by examining the fossils found in the rock.

In places such as the Grand Canyon of the Colorado River, as much as a mile of the earth's crust is exposed to view, providing a fine opportunity to piece together several chapters of earth history. At the bottom of the Grand Canyon, the Colorado River is cutting through granite rocks that are the roots of mountains that existed long before the sedimentary rocks

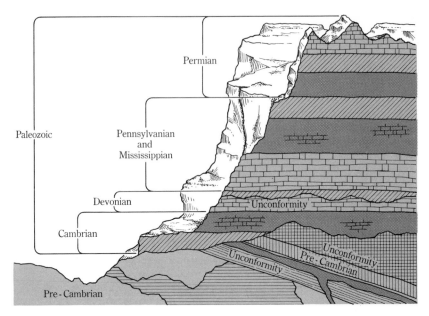

Fig. 7-1   Rocks exposed in the Grand Canyon.

that make up the cliffs were laid down. These mountains were worn down
to a plain. The plain subsided and was covered with water. Perhaps as
much as twelve thousand feet of sediment were deposited during this
period. These sedimentary rocks were pushed up into another series of
mountains. Again, the mountains were worn down to a plain, subsided
and were covered with water. The sediments that formed the rocks of the
present canyon walls were then deposited. These sediments have been
uplifted, and since that time, the Colorado River has cut its awe-inspiring
gorge.

The rocks at the bottom of the Grand Canyon are more than a billion
years old. In that time three mountain systems have been formed. There
are traces of the roots of two of them and the third is now being worn down.
In the walls of the Grand Canyon there are excellent stratigraphic records
of about one hundred million years of the earth's history. At other places
in the earth's crust there are records of even earlier geological ages than
those represented by the sedimentary mountains of the Grand Canyon
region.

The history of the earth has been divided into eras, periods, and epochs.
The greatest division is between the phase of earth history for which there
is little fossil record and that following the onset of the Cambrian Period
when fossils became abundant. There is no doubt that life existed in the

Precambrian Era, but there are few fossil records of it. The Precambrian Era probably encompassed more than 85 per cent of geologic time, and ended about six hundred million years ago. Because more information about the eras following the Precambrian is available, most study in earth history is devoted to them.

The Study of Fossils

Fossils are traces of living things left in rocks. Fossils can be formed in several ways. Perhaps the most common fossils are those of marine animals formed under water in sedimentary rock. Usually it is the hard parts of the animals, such as shells and bones, that are preserved. In some cases mineral matter fills up the porous holes of the bones or shells and preserves them. In other cases, all of the remains of a living thing may be actually replaced by mineral matter. One example of fossilization by replacement is petrified wood. In some cases the finest details of the living things are preserved. In other instances only the rough outlines are preserved. Along the coasts of the Baltic Sea, insects have been fossilized in the amber that has been formed from the resins given off by evergreen trees. In places such as the Big Bone Lick bog deposit south of Cincinnati and the tar pits at Rancho La Brea in Los Angeles living things have been preserved by quick burial in quicksands or tar pits. The tracks of animals, such as the famous dinosaur tracks of the Connecticut Valley, have been preserved in rocks formed from mud. Perhaps the most famous fossils are those of the mastodons that were buried in ice in Siberia. In some of these specimens the actual muscles and meat as well as the bones were preserved.

Most fossils form under shallow seas. Many groups of animals such as brachiopods, cephalopods, and corals lived only in the sea. Fossils of these animals are found in many places, such as in the Midwest, that are now dry land. They are clear evidence that these areas were once covered by water. Because some organisms live only in warm waters and others in cold, a more careful analysis of the fossil record will reveal considerable information about the nature of the seas that covered the land. Similarly, the study of fossils reveals whether there were water connections between various oceans. For example, the discovery of fossil mammoths in North America indicates that there must, at one time, have been a land connection between Asia and North America on which the Asian elephant could have crossed.

Fossils can be used to link various rock formations throughout the world. The rocks of various geologic ages contain certain distinctive types of fossils that are not found in rocks of any other age. These fossils are called index fossils. For example, the trilobites lived only during the Paleozoic

Table 7-1: A HISTORY OF THE EARTH

Geological Unit	Number of Years Ago	Geological Events	Biological Events
CENOZOIC ERA:			
Tertiary Period			
Pleistocene Epoch	Present	Glaciers. Form great glacial advances.	Age of man and mammals
Pliocene Epoch	1 million	Continual elevation	Horses and elephants become modern
Miocene Epoch	13 million	Mountain formation: Alps, Himalayas, Cascades	Apes appear
Oligocene Epoch	25 million	Tremendous lava flows in the Northwest	Hoofed animals become established
Eocene Epoch	36 million	Land bridge between Asia and America	Mammals begin to dominate
Paleocene Epoch	58 million	Rocky Mountains continue to rise. Active volcanoes in Western North America	Monkeys and whales appear
MESOZOIC ERA:			
Cretaceous Period	63 million	Rocky Mountains formed. Large chalk deposits	Flowering plants appear. Dinosaurs near extinction. Deciduous trees. Modern mammals
Jurassic Period	135 million	Colorado Plateau. Dinosaur fossils. Sierra Nevadas begin to form	Birds appear. Many dinosaurs. Mammals appear
Triassic Period	181 million 200 million	Large red sandstone deposits. Climate probably very dry	Age of reptiles

Table 7-1: Continued

Geological Unit	Number of Years Ago	Geological Events	Biological Events
PALEOZOIC ERA:			
Permian Period	230 million	Appalachian folding. Great glaciation. Continents emerge	Trilobites become extinct. Reduction in number of types of life
Pennsylvanian Period	280 million	Large coal deposits formed	Earliest reptiles. Coal-forming vegetation. Insects appear
Mississippian Period	310 million	Mississippi Valley continuously submerged. Indiana limestone formed	Sharks. Amphibians become well established
Devonian Period	345 million	Core of White Mountains, Acadian Mountains formed. Great sand deposits formed by erosion of mountains	Amphibians appear. Large numbers of brachiopods. First forests
Silurian Period	405 million	Niagara Falls rock formations. New York and Ohio salt beds	Corals and coral reefs. Land plants appear
Ordovician Period	425 million	Most of North America under water. Vermont marble formed	Vertebrates appear. Large numbers of trilobites, brachiopods, cephalopods
Cambrian	500 million	Fossils become abundant	Large numbers of trilobites
PRECAMBRIAN ERA:	600 million	This era encompasses the bulk of geologic time. However, there is only a scanty fossil record.	

Era. Any rock found anywhere in the world containing trilobite fossils must be a Paleozoic rock. Similarly index fossils have been found for other geologic ages. Through an examination of the fossils in rock samples, it is possible to determine the geologic age to which it belongs. The recognition and study of index fossils has made it possible to link rocks found in many places on earth and to build a history of the earth as a whole.

The study of fossils has provided evidence for the gradual evolution of organic life on the earth from the relatively simple forms to the more complex. The oldest fossil-bearing rocks contain the fossils of only the very simple forms of life. As ever younger rocks are examined, the fossils that are formed indicate the presence of more complicated forms of life. The fossil evidence provides strong support for the modern theory of evolution.

Paleontology is the science that deals with the study of fossils. Paleontologists help reconstruct the history of the earth and, perhaps even more importantly, the history of living things that inhabit the earth.

THE SHAPE AND SIZE OF THE EARTH

What is the shape of the earth? Early Europeans believed the earth to be flat. To sail too far out on the ocean might mean precipitously falling off the edge. The early Polynesians, on the other hand, believed that the sea and the sky joined, and if you could sail far enough, it might mean that you could sail into the sky. This view of the shape of the earth probably explains why the Polynesians were venturing thousands of miles over the Pacific while the Europeans were still hesitant to sail much beyond the point where they lost sight of land.

We are now certain that the earth is shaped very much like a round ball. Because it is spinning on its axis somewhat like a top, it bulges slightly at the equator. The distance through the earth (the diameter) at the equator is about 27 miles greater than at the poles. Evidence obtained from earth satellites indicates that the earth bulges a little more in the Northern Hemisphere than in the Southern which suggests an earth that is somewhat pear-shaped. This slight bulging may be due to the fact that most of the earth's land mass is found in the Northern Hemisphere. These deviations from the shape of a sphere are very small, and for all practical purposes, the earth may be considered to be the shape of a round ball.

The Problem of Mapping a Sphere

Because the earth is sphere-like, it is impossible to show the surface of the earth on a flat map without some distortion. To illustrate this, peel an orange so that all of the skin is in one peel. Now try to press the orange peel down flat. It is impossible to do so without stretching or tearing the orange skin. Similarly, some errors are introduced whenever the surface of the earth is portrayed on a flat map.

Flat maps of the earth's surface can be made by projecting a light through a transparent globe or wire grid system representing a globe and marking the shadows of the land surfaces or grids as they fall on paper. The paper may be a flat surface or be wrapped around the globe as a cylinder or as a cone. The light may be located at the center of the globe, at the surface, or outside the globe. There are also mathematical ways of constructing flat maps.

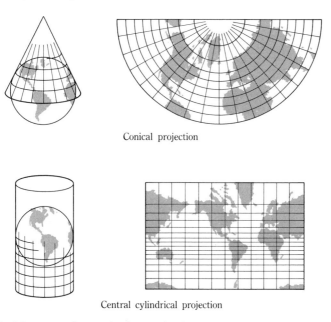

Conical projection

Central cylindrical projection

Fig. 7-2 *Maps can be made by projecting features from a sphere onto cones, cylinders, or other shapes.*

The Size of the Earth

One of the ways of determining the distance around the earth involves astronomy. This method was used by the early Greeks, and they arrived at an answer that is surprisingly close to the figure of today.

The distance between two astronomical observatories is measured very carefully. (The discrepancy between the early Greek results and modern findings were probably due to errors in measuring the distance between two observatories.) In this example suppose the distance is exactly 1,050 miles. At both observatories plumb bobs are suspended to indicate the direction of the center of the earth. A telescope at the first observatory is

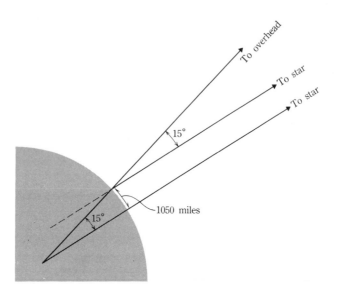

Fig. 7-3   *This is one way to determine the circumference of the earth.*

pointed at a star directly overhead. At the same time, a telescope at the second observatory is pointed at the same star. Since the second observatory is 1,050 miles from the place where the star is directly overhead, the telescope makes an angle of 15 degrees with an extension of the string leading to the plumb bob. Since the distance to the star is so great, the imaginary lines from the two observatories to the star may be considered to be parallel. Therefore, the 15-degree-angle at the second observatory is equal to the angle at the center of the earth that subtends an arc of 1,050 miles. If we divide 1,050 by 15, we find that an angle of 1 degree would subtend an arc of 70 miles. Multiply the 70 by 360, the number of degrees in a complete circle, and we find the circumference of the earth to be 25,200 miles.

The mass of the earth has been determined by measuring the gravitational force of attraction between the earth and a small object of known mass. This is a delicate measurement demanding very sensitive instruments. The mass of the earth has been found to be about 6.6×10^{21} tons. (This number means 6 followed by 21 zeros.)

Table 7-2: SIZE AND SHAPE OF THE EARTH

shape	round, almost a sphere
circumference, average	24,800 miles
mass	6×10^{21} tons
average diameter	7,910 miles
average density	5.5 times that of water

THE STRUCTURE OF THE EARTH

It has been difficult to learn about the nature of the interior of the earth because there is no direct source of information, such as light, radio waves, or other kinds of radiation, coming to us from the interior of the earth. Deep holes have been drilled, but even these have probed a very small fraction of the 4,000 odd miles to the center of the earth. Water from hot springs and geysers and lava from volcanoes come from within a few miles of the surface of the earth. However, these scanty sources of information are about the limit of direct information about the interior of the earth.

Most knowledge of the interior of the earth has been derived by indirect means. Since both the volume and the mass of the earth is known, it has been possible to calculate the average density

$$\text{average density} = \frac{\text{mass}}{\text{volume}}$$

of the earth, and it has been found to be about 5.5 times the density of water. Since the average density of rocks found in the earth's crust is less than 3, the materials in the interior of the earth must have a density considerably greater than 5.5.

The most important sources of indirect information about the structure of the interior of the earth are the earthquake waves which serve somewhat as X rays to reveal the structure of the earth's interior. Earthquake waves have revealed a picture of the layers that make up the earth's interior.

"X-raying" the Earth

Although the physician cannot see the bones in a patient's leg, he can study them through the use of X rays that penetrate matter that is opaque. A somewhat similar approach is used to study the interior of the earth. Instead of X rays, the waves that are set up by earthquakes are used. A great deal has been learned about the structure of the earth by studying how these *seismic waves* travel through various parts of the earth. The science dealing with earthquakes and earthquake waves is called *seismology*.

Earthquake waves are generated by a sudden shearing of part of the earth's crust, volcanic eruptions, or large man-made explosions. The shearing of the earth's crust may be either vertical or horizontal. Often this shearing action takes place deep within the crust. However, the movement of the earth after an earthquake at such places as the famous San Andreas fault in California is visible at the surface. Here the shearing is in a horizontal direction and has led to such famous earthquakes as the one in 1906 that caused great damage in San Francisco. Violent volcanic explosions, such as those that have occurred at Vesuvius, Parícutin, and Krakatoa, also set up earthquake waves. Although small in comparison to many natural earthquakes, man-made explosions, such as nuclear detonations, also set up earthquake waves. In fact, the earthquake waves set up by these underground nuclear explosions usually make possible their detection. One of the advantages of using nuclear explosions for seismic study is that the exact point where the explosion takes place is known. This is often not the case with earthquakes of natural origin.

Earthquakes set up two types of waves that travel through the interior of the earth: primary or "P" waves and secondary or "S" waves. The primary waves travel faster through the earth and therefore arrive at some seismological station first. The "S" waves travel at slower speeds and therefore arrive later at a recording station.

"P" waves are *compression waves*. If a helical spring or "Slinky" is stretched out and then a few coils are pinched together and released, the compression will move along the coil. The coils move in the same line as the waves. Sound waves are also compression waves. Compression waves can travel through both solids and liquids.

"S" waves are *transverse waves*. If the end of a slack rope is jerked quickly up and down, a wave will be seen to travel down the rope. This is a transverse wave. In a transverse wave, the particles in the medium, whether it be a rope or rock, move in directions that are at right angles to the direction that the waves are moving. In general, transverse waves can travel through solids but not liquids.

Strong earthquake waves may cause buildings to sway, even fall. A nearby explosion may cause windows and Venetian blinds to rattle. Distant or small earthquakes, however, can only be detected by sensitive instruments called *seismographs*.

Basically, a seismograph consists of a heavy mass of metal and a recording device. The mass of metal is suspended somewhat like a pendulum. Because of its inertia, the metal tends to remain at rest even though the earth underneath it may be moving. The recording device is anchored in

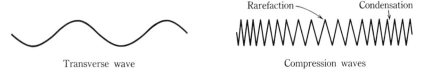

Rarefaction   Condensation

Transverse wave   Compression waves

Fig. 7-4 *In transverse waves the vibrations are at right angles to the directions in which the wave moves. In compression waves the vibrations are back and forth in the same line as that along which the wave moves.*

bedrock. The recording device has a clockwork mechanism which keeps a drum rotating. Whenever there is a tremor in the bedrock, the recording device also moves. The mass of metal, however, remains relatively motionless. A small beam of light is projected from the metal mass and this records the movements of the bedrock and rotating drum.

The earth is believed to be made up of three great layers: a relatively thin *outer crust* that is 0 to 25 miles thick, the *mantle*, beneath the crust, which is about 1,800 miles thick, and at the center, the *core*, which has a diameter of about 4,320 miles.

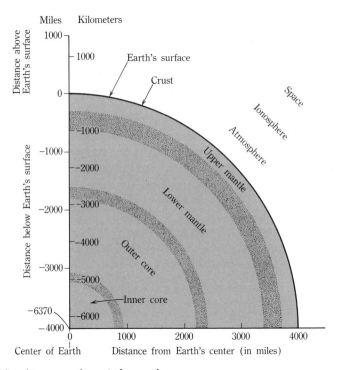

Fig. 7-5 *A cross-section of the earth.*

The Crust

The relatively thin crust is the only part of the earth with which we have direct contact. It is essential to living organisms, since it is the source of all the minerals needed and used by plants and animals. The depth of this crust varies, being thickest on the continents but practically nonexistent at the bottoms of some oceans.

Imagine standing at the bottom of an empty ocean basin such as the Pacific or the Atlantic. At various places, huge mountains loom above the ocean floor. Some of these mountains now stick up above the surface of the oceans and form islands such as the Hawaiian Islands and the Azores, but some of the highest and longest mountain chains are now completely submerged. In various places relatively large land masses, the continents, appear as high plateaus. How were these mountains and plateaus, or continents, formed?

According to one theory that has considerable acceptance, all of the material that makes up the earth's crust has been spewed out as volcanic lava and then altered in many different ways. It has been estimated that on the average, about one-fifth of a cubic mile of lava is poured out each year from existing volcanoes. In light of recent outpourings in the Hawaiian Islands and Central America, this would appear to be a very conservative estimate. However, lava flowing at this rate throughout the history of the earth would have produced enough materials to have formed the crust.

Once rocks and soil are elevated above the level of the oceans, the process of erosion begins. The sediment from the erosion is deposited at the bottom of the oceans and forms sedimentary rocks. These sedimentary rocks are subjected to heat, pressure, and chemical change to produce many of the materials that make up the earth's crust. In fact, the mountain-forming granites all may have been formed originally from these early sedimentary rocks.

The ocean basins cover more than 70 per cent of the earth's crust. Here, the overlying crustal material is very thin. In fact, in some places it may be almost nonexistent, and mantle rock may be near the surface at some places on the ocean bottom. This is why drillings into the mantle are made under the ocean.

It has been found that the force of gravity is slightly less on the continents than over the oceans. A pendulum suspended over the Bay of Biscay was found to be deflected very slightly toward the ocean bottom rather than toward the nearby Pyrenees Mountains, as had been expected. Similar results have been obtained from pendulums suspended near the Himalayas, the Andes, and other mountain chains. The most obvious explanation for these observations is that the mountains are composed of materials that are less dense than those underneath the oceans.

We believe that the rocks that form the mountains and the continents are relatively light, with granite being of special importance. The granites may have been formed from sedimentary rocks which at some time in the distant past were formed from particles eroded away from the original volcanic materials that formed the continents. The granitic base of mountains and continents is probably pressed down into the rock of the mantle, in a sense, to form roots for the continents and mountains.

It is believed that, on a large scale, the lighter materials that compose the continents tend to be supported at a higher level by the rock of the earth's interior than do the heavier rocks of the ocean bottom. This is somewhat like a ship floating in water. If the ship is empty, it will float relatively high in the water, but if it is heavily laden it will sink lower in the water. At a depth of several miles, rocks are under such great pressure that they act somewhat as a viscous plastic. Over long periods of time the heights of crustal materials are adjusted according to their weights. Heavy materials are balanced by larger volumes of lighter materials. This balance within the crust of the earth is called *isostasy*, meaning "equal standing."

Most of the chemical elements used by plants and animals are obtained from the crust. The relative abundance of the most common chemical elements in the earth's crust is given in the following table. It should be remembered that certain elements are more common in some regions than in others. Although their total amounts are small, most of the other 92 naturally occurring chemical elements also are found in the crust.

Table 7–3: ELEMENTS IN THE EARTH'S CRUST

Element	Weight %
Oxygen	46.6
Silicon	27.7
Aluminum	8.1
Iron	5.0
Magnesium	2.1
Calcium	3.6
Sodium	2.8
Potassium	2.6

The Mantle

At a depth of 25 to 1,800 miles earthquake waves travel in a more consistent manner. In fact, their speeds remain fairly constant throughout this part of the earth's interior called the mantle. The line of demarcation between the mantle and the crust is now called the *Moho* after the Yugoslavian seismologist A. Mohorovicic, who discovered it.

The mantle is believed to be composed of rocks such as the greenish rock called *olivine*. Greenish grains of olivine are often found in volcanic lava. The condition of the mantle probably varies with depth as the temperature and pressure in the mantle changes. In certain places near the top of the mantle there probably are great underground pools of molten rock.

Periodically, some of this molten material is forced up through cracks in the crust and flows out as molten lava or is spewed out as volcanic ash and dust.

Children often ask, "Why not drill to the center of the earth?" A line, drawn to scale, representing our deepest drillings can be compared to a line representing the distance to the center of the earth. If the drilling was to a depth of five miles, then a line representing the distance to the center of the earth (4,000 miles) would be eight hundred times as long as a line representing the depth of drilling. From this, children can see that the deepest drillings are mere pin pricks into the interior of the earth.

The Core

The transverse "S" waves set up by an earthquake are not transmitted through liquids. Since it has been discovered that "S" waves do not travel through the central portion of the earth, this is strong evidence to support the theory that the earth's core is in liquid form. The bending (refraction) of "P" waves when they reach the core supplies additional evidence that at least part of the core of the earth is liquid. The behavior of the "P" waves suggests that the outer part of the core is liquid. This outer core would block the transmission of the "S" waves. But inside the liquid outer core there may be a solid inner core with a thickness of about eight hundred miles.

The core is believed to be made up of nickel and iron. We know that the materials that make up the earth's core must be quite dense, because the over-all density is considerably greater than that of the comparatively light rocks in the earth's crust. Both nickel and iron meet this requirement of density. Also, both nickel and iron are magnetic materials, and this is helpful in explaining the earth's magnetic properties.

The temperatures and pressures in the core are very high. The temperature of the core is believed to be about 4,000° Celsius. The pressures may be as great as three or four million atmospheres. (One atmosphere of pressure of air at sea level under standard conditions is about fifteen pounds per square inch.) We are handicapped in our study of the earth's core by the difficulty of producing and maintaining these temperatures and pressures in the laboratory.

THE ROCKS OF THE EARTH'S CRUST

Rocks are the "books" from which the history of the earth is read. Since no observer was present to record the events of the distant past, we infer the events of the past from evidence left in rocks.

Rocks Formed from Molten Material

The original rocks of the earth were probably formed from hot molten material. As this liquid rock material cooled, it solidified into solid rock. When this liquid material cooled quickly, it sometimes formed a glassy material that has very small crystals or no crystals at all. In fact, glass is made by cooling hot, molten material quickly. At times hot, molten material is pushed in between layers of rock deep within the earth. Under these conditions, the molten material cools very slowly, and relatively large crystals are formed. By examining a rock that has been formed from molten material, it is possible to determine the relative rate at which it cooled and, to a certain extent, where the cooling took place.

Sometimes the comparative ages of rocks can be determined by noting how liquid rock was pushed into other rocks. In a given location, for example, a rock mass formed from hot molten material can be assumed with little doubt to be younger than rock masses into which it appears to have pushed. Since the age of rocks formed from molten material often can be determined by radioactive dating, the approximate ages of nearby rocks can also be determined.

Rocks Formed from Sediments

The rains that fall upon the land carry away small particles of sand, silt, and clay. These particles are deposited at the bottoms of lakes and oceans. Particles of lime and the remains of plants and animals are also deposited. As layer upon layer of sediment is deposited, the pressure, together with certain natural cements to be found in these materials, presses these materials into *sedimentary rocks*. From a study of these sedimentary rocks, a great deal can be learned about the conditions at the bottom of the oceans and also about the land from which the sediments came.

When particles of soil are washed into oceans, the largest particles settle out first while the smaller particles are deposited farther out in the oceans. By noting the sizes of the particles in sedimentary rocks in various places, it is possible to determine the direction of the shoreline at the time the rocks were formed. With the help of other evidence, such as actual ripple marks in sedimentary rocks, it is sometimes possible to locate boundaries of ancient lakes and seas.

The character of the sediments reveals something about the nature of the land where the soil particles originated. The composition of the sediment indicates a great deal about the nature of the soil on the dry land. Because swift waters can carry larger particles than slow-moving streams, the size of the particles in sedimentary rock is an indication of the relative steepness of the topography of the ancient land.

Sedimentary rocks also indicate the nature of the climate at the time the sediments were deposited. Some sedimentary rocks show alternating bands of coarse- and fine-grained sediment. Sometimes, these bands are of different colors. These bands suggest a climate in which there was a rainy season and a dry season. During the rainy season, coarse-grained particles were swept out to sea by seasonal floods. During the dry season, the sluggish streams could only carry the fine soil particles. Certain clays, called *varve clays*, that were deposited by streams flowing out of a glacier, show very clearly summer and winter layers. These layers can be counted very much like tree rings and analyzed to get a better indication of the climate at the time they were formed.

The study of stratified rocks is the science of *stratigraphy*. In places such as the Grand Canyon, it is possible to study strata to a depth of more than a mile. In these layers there is source material for the study of more than one hundred million years of earth history. In deep drillings it is possible to bring up rock particles from strata that are more deeply buried.

Changes in Rocks

Over long periods of time many rocks are subjected to heat, pressure, and chemical action which change the nature of the rocks. Rocks that have been changed in this way are called *metamorphic rocks*. Metamorphic rocks, which often have a banded appearance, may have been formed from sedimentary, igneous, or other metamorphic rocks.

Sedimentary rocks may eventually be deeply buried. The overlying sediments will exert great pressure, and the temperatures may become almost as high as those of the pools of magma that later form igneous rocks. Under such conditions the grains of quartz in sandstone may become welded and cemented together to form *quartzite*, one of our hardest rocks. In quartzite the sand grains have lost their identity, and when quartzite breaks, it may actually fracture across the grains.

Similarly, limestone under pressure and cementation forms *marble*. In marble, too, the individual grains of lime have lost their identity. Marble, one of our most beautiful rocks, is used extensively for buildings and memorials. Like limestone, it can be identified by the bubbles that form when dilute hydrochloric acid is applied to a scratched surface.

Shale that has been subjected to pressure and some heat forms *slate*. The small flakes of mica in slate make it possible to split slate into thin sheets. Because of this property, slate can be used as a roofing material and for chalkboards. The flakes of mica in slate tend to lie at right angles to the direction of the pressure. Therefore, the direction that slate splits is often at right angles to the layered structure of the original shale.

If slate is subjected to additional heat and pressure, *schist* will be formed. The most conspicuous feature of schist is the mica that usually makes it possible to split off parts of the schist. Schist is the final product of a series of metamorphic changes.

$$\text{clay} \xrightarrow{\text{pressure}} \text{shale} \xrightarrow{\text{pressure}} \text{slate} \xrightarrow[\text{heat}]{\text{pressure}} \text{schist}$$

Gneiss is a metamorphic rock having distinct bands. There is less mica in gneiss than in schist. Some gneisses probably were formed from shaly sandstone or sandy shale. Igneous granite is sometimes also converted into gneiss. The distinguishing feature of the gneisses is their banded structure.

The Rock Cycle

Many materials in nature are involved in cycles. There is, for example, the water cycle. All surface water—whether in rain, streams, lakes and oceans, or as water vapor—is in some phase of this cycle. Sometimes a particular drop of water may pass through this entire water cycle in a matter of days. At other times, particularly if the water enters the ground water supply, many years may be required to complete the cycle. There are other cycles involving oxygen, carbon dioxide, and nitrogen. The changes that occur in the materials in the environment often can be interpreted as being a part of a cycle of changes.

Rocks may also be considered as being part of a cycle of changes called the *rock cycle*. This cycle of changes is depicted in the following diagram.

The original rock material probably often came from the mantle in a liquid, molten state. Upon cooling, the magma hardened to form igneous rock. In some cases, this rock may be remelted to form magma again. But if the igneous rock is eventually exposed to the work of the elements, weathering takes place, and small particles of the rock are broken off and carried away by wind and water. The sediments are eventually deposited, often under the waters of the oceans, and harden to form sedimentary rocks. Sedimentary rocks that are acted upon by heat and pressure or undergo chemical reactions form metamorphic rocks. Under high temperature conditions, the metamorphic rocks may again become magma. Sediments may be formed directly from both sedimentary and metamorphic rocks if they are exposed to the elements.

The rock cycle is not a completely closed cycle. Certainly, material enters the cycle from the mantle. A small amount of material comes from the meteorites that enter the earth's atmosphere. It has been estimated that more than a million tons of meteoric dust are deposited on the earth each year. This dust has been found in samples of the ocean bottom in regions where there is very little sedimentation. Also, it may be that some particles of dust from the earth's surface eventually escape from the earth's atmosphere.

The rock cycle is a broad generalization that ties together a large number of discrete facts about rocks and minerals. This is one of the "big ideas" of science of which children should develop some concept. When they examine a rock found in their neighborhood, they can try to analyze the rock in terms of its place in the rock cycle. By consulting the diagram of the cycle, they can gain some idea of history of the rock and predict some of the changes that may eventually take place in it.

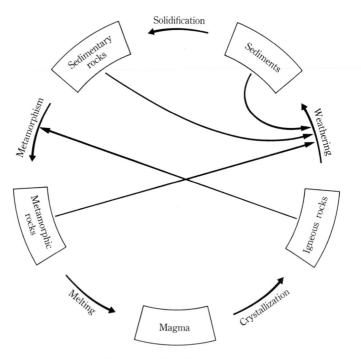

Fig. 7-6   *All rocks are in some stage of the rock cycle.*

APPROACHES TO TEACHING

Among the more difficult concepts to develop in the teaching of *The Earth on Which We Live* are those of space and time. These are difficult concepts for children because the magnitudes of space and time are far beyond those that are normally experienced. Maps, models, and analogies can be used to help develop these concepts.

What kinds of maps can be used?

Every classroom should have access to a globe. The globe is a fairly accurate model of the earth. A globe can be used to show the relationships between various land masses and oceans. It can be used in measurements of distances between points on the earth's surface and for demonstrations of the relationships between the earth, the moon, and the sun as described in the previous chapter.

The following maps of the local region are very useful and easily obtainable.

Index map. An index map of each state is available free from the United States Geological Survey, Washington, D.C. The index map can be used to select the topographical map quadrangles for your region.

Topographical maps. These are extremely useful maps for local regions and are available at low cost from the U.S. Geological Survey. Three-dimensional maps of some quadrangles are available from commercial suppliers.

Road maps. Useful maps available from local gasoline stations.

What kinds of models can be used?

A wide range of models of geologic features and rock structures are available commercially. Many useful models can be made by simply arranging different colored pieces of plasticene between pieces of glass.

How can the geologic time scale be explained?

Because the span of geologic time is so great, as compared to any span of time that we experience, it is helpful to use an analogy to convey the comparative length of various eras and periods. A useful analogy is the face of a clock and the twelve-hour time span between noon and midnight.

If the earth is considered to be about 4.5 billion years old and this is represented by the twelve hours on the face of a clock, then the Pre-cambrian Era, which encompasses all but 600 million years of the earth's history, would last from noon till about 10:30. The Paleozoic Era of ancient life lasted about 370 million years and on the clock ended at about 11:25. The Mesozoic Era of middle life lasted for about 170 million years and closed about 11:50. The remaining ten minutes of the geologic clock analogy are accorded to the Cenozoic Era of recent life. Since man probably appeared on the earth about 2 million years ago, on the clock time scale man came on the scene at about twenty seconds before midnight.

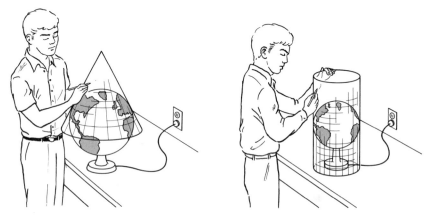

Fig. 7-7 *Shadows of features on the globes can be projected onto paper, making it possible to draw a flat map of the surface of the globe.*

How can a flat map of the surface of a sphere be made?

A transparent globe with a small light at the center and a large sheet of fairly stiff, translucent paper are needed. It is easier to see the projection in a darkened room.

Wrap the paper around the globe as a cylinder touching the globe at the equator. Switch on the light inside the globe, and the outlines of the land features and the geographical grid will be projected onto the paper. These lines can be traced lightly on the paper and reinforced after the paper is removed from the globe.

Maps can also be made by rolling the paper into the shape of a cone and fitting it onto the transparent globe. How do the conical projections compare with the cylindrical?

How are different layers of sediment deposited beneath water?

Using a large jar full of water and two different kinds of soil, show how particles are sorted as they settle out of water. It is more effective to have soils that are contrasting colors such as black and white.

Take a handful of one soil sample and sprinkle it over the water. Watch the particles settle through the water. Do they settle at the same rate?

Take a handful of the other soil sample and sprinkle it over the water. Watch it settle. Alternately sprinkle handfuls from each of the samples into the water.

How are the sediments deposited at the bottom of the jar? Is there any difference in the size of particles deposited at the bottom of a layer as compared with those at the top of a layer? Are there particles that remain suspended in the water? If there are, allow the jar to stand for a few days to see if they eventually settle out.

If a little cement is added to the soil samples, the sediments will actually harden to form sedimentary rock.

What are some things that can be learned from the study of a rock?

Obtain some samples of local rocks. Break them with a hammer so that a fresh surface can be examined. (To prevent chips from flying into the face and eyes, place the rock in a sack or other container before hitting it.) A small magnifying glass will help in the examination of the rock.

The first step is to determine how the rocks were formed. If the rock contains small grains of sand, lime, or clay, it is a sedimentary rock which was most likely formed under water. If the rock contains crystals or is glassy it was formed through the cooling of hot, molten material. Sometimes the fire-formed rocks and the sedimentary rocks have been altered after they were formed by heat and pressure. If this occurred, some evidence of it usually can be seen in the rock sample.

If the rock was formed from molten materials, examine it to find answers to such questions as the following:

Does the rock contain crystals?

If it has crystals, are they comparatively large or small?

Are all the crystals composed of the same materials?

Were the rock crystals formed quickly or slowly?

Were all the rocks in the place where this rock was found of a similar nature?

Was there any evidence to indicate whether some of the rocks were younger than the other rocks?

If the rock was formed from sediments, examine it to find answers to such questions as the following:

Are the grains large or small as compared to the grains in a piece of chalk?

Were the sediments deposited near the mouth of a river or farther out at sea?

Are the sediments of sand, lime, or clay? (A drop of dilute hydrochloric acid dropped on lime will cause it to effervesce. If a rock formed of clayey material is wetted, it will usually have a slight smell of mud.)

Are there layers in the rock? If so, are the layers of equal width? Composed of the same materials?

Are there fossils in the rock? If so, what kind of living thing formed the fossil?

How can crystals be grown?

Excellent crystals can be grown from any one of such common substances as salt, copper sulfate, or alum. The crystals grow as water evaporates from saturated solutions of these materials.

The salt solution can be prepared by dissolving as much of the salt as possible in hot water. This solution usually should be filtered into a clean container to remove foreign substances. When the hot solution cools, some crystals will be formed on the bottom of the container, and the solution will be saturated. This is the stock solution which will be used for filling the evaporation dish.

A ring of vaseline should be smeared around the evaporation dish at the level to which it will be filled with liquid. The vaseline will prevent the solution from "creeping" up the sides of the container, evaporating, and leaving a troublesome crust of salt.

Some of the stock salt solution should be poured into the evaporation dish up to the level of the vaseline ring. As the water evaporates, crystals are formed at the bottom. One or two of the best crystals should be left on the bottom as "seed" crystals and the others removed with forceps.

As water evaporates at the surface of the solution, that part of the solution becomes saturated and somewhat heavier than the rest of the solution. It sinks to the bottom of the dish, and some of the material is deposited on a seed crystal.

The growth of the crystal should be watched carefully. Nearly constant temperature should be maintained. To get symmetrical crystals, the crystal should be turned onto a different face each day. Abnormal growths or "suckers" should be removed from the crystal. Occasionally, fresh stock solution will have to be added to the solution in the evaporation dish. To prevent a shower of crystals at this time, it is usually desirable to add a few drops of water to the evaporation dish before pouring in the stock solution.

With a little care, children can grow large, beautifully shaped crystals. The crystal should be examined every day, turned, and any deformities removed. Children may wish to grow large crystals of different substances and compare their shapes.

Most substances change when exposed to the air. To protect crystals when stored, coat them with a clear nail polish.

What can be learned from fossils found in rocks?

Obtain a fossil-bearing rock. If possible, it is desirable to use local rocks. In some regions, however, fossil-bearing rocks are scarce or not to be found at all. In these places samples will have to be obtained from outside sources such as scientific supply houses.

Examine the fossils to find answers to such questions as the following:

In what kinds of rock are fossils found?
Are all the fossils in the sample of a single type organism?
Was the organism a plant or an animal?
Was it a type of organism that probably lived under water?
What parts of the organism were fossilized?
How was the organism fossilized? By mineralization of body parts or by complete replacement with mineral matter?

With the aid of a handbook on fossils,[1] it may be possible to identify the fossils in the rock samples and learn a great deal more about the conditions under which the organisms lived.

Investigation

What minerals are in rocks found in the local area?

There are many places in most areas where samples of local rocks can be obtained. Bedrock can be sampled in roadcuts, stream beds or banks, quarries, and excavations for buildings.

In some cases, rocks may have to be examined in the field, but in most cases it is preferable to bring samples back to the home, school, or laboratory for closer examination. However, the locations where various rocks

[1] An excellent handbook on fossils is Richard Casanova's *An Illustrated Guide to Fossil Collecting* (San Martin, Calif.: Naturegraph Co., 1957).

were obtained should be noted. Pebbles and other rock samples should be broken in order to see the minerals better. A magnifying glass will be helpful in examining the rock samples.

In order to recognize common rock-forming minerals, children should have experiences in examining good samples[2] of quartz, feldspar, mica (white and black), calcite, and hornblende. Children should describe their mineral samples in terms of such physical characteristics as hardness, streak, color, and luster. In addition, such guides as those listed at the end of this chapter should be available for children to consult.

By hardness is meant the relative ability of a substance to scratch other substances. The harder substances can scratch all softer substances. A scale of one to ten is used to indicate hardness, and the hardness of most minerals can be tested with a fingernail, a copper coin, a knife, and a piece of glass. The following hardness scale is commonly used:

Table 7–4: WORKING SCALE FOR HARDNESS

1. Very soft and greasy. Can be scratched with a fingernail. Example: talc.
2. Soft but not greasy. Just barely scratched with fingernail. Example: gypsum.
3. Can be scratched with the edge of a penny. Easily scratched with a knife. Example: calcite.
4. Can be scratched with a knife blade, but the mineral will not scratch glass. Example: fluorite.
5. Can be scratched with difficulty with a knife. Barely scratches glass. Example: apatite.
6. Scratches glass but cannot be scratched with knife. Example: feldspar.
7. Scratches glass easily. Hardest common mineral. Example: quartz.
8. Scratches quartz. Example: topaz (rare).
9. Scratches topaz. Example: corundum (rare).
10. Scratches corundum. Example: diamond (very rare).

When a soft mineral is scraped on a piece of unglazed porcelain, a piece of flower pot, or a ceramic tile, a *streak* is left that may help in identifying a mineral. The color of the streak is not always the same as the color of the mineral. Note that hard minerals will scratch the streak plate and not leave a streak. A common streak is that of chalk on a blackboard and graphite in pencils on paper.

Minerals reflect light in different ways. Two common types of *luster* are metallic and nonmetallic.

---

[2] Excellent samples of minerals can be obtained from such commercial suppliers as Ward's Natural Science Establishment, Inc., P.O. Box 1712, Rochester, N.Y.

The various minerals to be found in local rocks can be listed and described in a table such as the one below.

Name of Mineral	Color	Streak	Hardness	Luster	Other Properties

Selected References

DUNBAR, CARL O., *Historical Geology*. New York: John Wiley & Sons, Inc., 1961.

HELLER, ROBERT L. (ED.), *Geology and Earth Sciences Sourcebook for Elementary and Secondary Schools*. New York: Holt, Rinehart & Winston, 1962.

JACOBSON, WILLARD J., KLEINMAN, GLADYS, HIACK, PAUL S., SUGARBAKER, JOHN, AND CARR, ALBERT, *The Earth and Its Surface*. New York: American Book Co., 1968.

WHITE, J. F. (ED.), *Study of the Earth*. Englewood Cliffs, N.J.: Prentice-Hall, Inc., 1962.

ZIM, HERBERT A., SHAFFER, P. R., AND PERLMAN, R., *Rocks and Minerals*. New York: Simon & Schuster, Inc., 1957.

READINGS FOR THE PRIMARY GRADES

ALLEN, HAZEL, *Up From the Sea Came an Island*. New York: Charles Scribner's Sons, 1962.

BENDICK, JEANNE, *The Shape of the Earth*. Chicago: Rand McNally & Co., 1965.

ELTING, MARY, AND FOLSOM, MICHAEL, *The Secret Story of Pueblo Bonito*. Irvington-on-Hudson, N.Y.: Harvey House, Inc., Publishers, 1963.

JACOBSON, WILLARD J., LAUBY, CECILIA J., AND KONICEK, RICHARD D., *The Earth and Its History*. New York: American Book Co., 1968.

JACOBSON, WILLARD J., LAUBY, CECILIA J., AND KONICEK, RICHARD D., *Rocks*. New York: American Book Co., 1968.

RUCHLIS, HY, *Your Changing Earth.* Irvington-on-Hudson, N.Y.: Harvey House, Inc., Publishers, 1963.

READINGS FOR THE INTERMEDIATE GRADES

AMES, GERALD, AND WYLER, ROSE, *Planet Earth.* New York: Golden Press, Inc., 1963.

CHANDLER, M. H., *Man's Home: The Earth.* Chicago: Rand McNally & Co., 1964.

JACOBSON, WILLARD J., LAUBY, CECILIA J., AND KONICEK, RICHARD D., *The Earth and Its Changing Surface.* New York: American Book Co., 1968.

STONE, A. HARRIS, AND INGMANSON, DALE, *Rocks and Rills: A Look at Geology.* Englewood Cliffs, N.J.: Prentice-Hall, Inc., 1967.

WHITAKER, GEORGE O., AND MEYERS, JOAN, *Dinosaur Hunt.* New York: Harcourt, Brace & World, Inc., 1965.

8 The Air and the Atmosphere

One of the most important features of the planet earth is the relatively thin envelope of gases that covers it. This envelope of gases is called the *atmosphere*. Without this atmosphere, life probably could not exist on this planet. An understanding of the earth's atmosphere is an understanding of one dimension of a world view.

THE NATURE OF THE ATMOSPHERE

Compared to the eight-thousand-mile diameter of the solid part of the earth, the atmospheric envelope is quite thin. Half of the materials in the atmosphere are to be found within three and a half miles of the surface of the earth. Although there is no definite boundary line between the atmosphere and interplanetary space, practically all of the atmosphere is within six hundred miles of the surface. The gases of the atmosphere are held in this region by the gravitational field of the earth. Some gas particles do escape into interplanetary space, but probably about an equal number of particles are captured by the earth's gravitational field.

Although the atmosphere is a relatively thin envelope, it is absolutely essential for life on this planet. All living things on this planet require oxygen, and almost all living things obtain this oxygen directly from the atmosphere. The atmosphere also serves as a sort of greenhouse to trap solar energy and to keep the temperature in most places within the fairly narrow range that is conducive to life. The atmosphere also shields the earth from X rays and other kinds of harmful radiations that bombard the upper layers of the atmosphere. The millions of small meteors that would otherwise strike the earth's surface each day burn and disintegrate because of the heat generated by friction as they pass through the atmosphere.

167

The Troposphere

The lower layer of the atmosphere is called the troposphere. In the troposphere, the air temperature decreases with height. The top of the troposphere is called the *tropopause*. Above the tropopause temperatures cease to diminish with height and may even increase slightly. The troposphere extends to about sixty thousand feet over the equator while over the poles it may be as low as twenty-three thousand feet. The troposphere extends out farther in the summer than in the winter.

Almost all weather occurs in the troposphere. The prefix "tropo" indicates turning or turbulent air. This turbulence, of course, is due largely to the heating of lower regions of the atmosphere. Moisture, smoke, and dust particles that originate on the earth do not ordinarily go beyond the troposphere. Since these are critical materials in weather formation, it is not surprising that weather in the ordinary sense is not found beyond the troposphere.

The Stratosphere

Extending from the troposphere out to a distance of about twenty miles is the stratosphere. Within the stratosphere the temperatures remain fairly constant or may even increase slightly with increasing heights. There is very little upward transfer of heat by convection above the troposphere. This makes the stratosphere, as its prefix "strato" suggests, a layer of stable stratified air.

The Ozonosphere

Above the stratosphere is a layer of atmosphere characterized by the gas ozone and called the ozonosphere. Ozone, a form of oxygen formed when oxygen is bombarded with radiation, can often be smelled after a series of electrical sparks. Ozone is an efficient absorber of solar radiation, particularly ultraviolet radiation, and serves to protect life on the earth from this harmful radiation.

The Ionosphere

Above the ozonosphere is a layer that contains electrically charged particles—ions—and is called the ionosphere. The layer of electrically charged particles is important because it reflects radio waves. Long distance radio transmission is made possible by the fact that radio waves can be bounced off the ionosphere to places at a considerable distance from the radio station. Television signals, on the other hand, are not reflected by the ionosphere and cannot be broadcast long distances in this way.

The electrically charged particles in the ionosphere are probably formed by bombardment of various gases with solar radiation.

The Exosphere

The region beyond the ionosphere and extending as far as the atmosphere extends is called the exosphere. The exosphere is very rarefied, being an almost perfect vacuum but containing small amounts of hydrogen and helium. The temperatures in the exosphere are very high, 10,000 degrees or more, but because there is so little matter there, the amount of heat present is very small.

The atmosphere is composed of a mixture of gases. As children study the atmosphere they are dealing with matter, but this matter is in a phase that seems quite different from the liquids and solids with which they are familiar. Usually, the air in the atmosphere is colorless, odorless, and tasteless. Yet, it is matter, and there are a number of ways that children can detect and study it.

What Is Weather?

Weather may be defined as the condition of the atmosphere at a given time. Most changes in the atmosphere take place in the lower regions. Children can study these changes directly. They can gather data related to temperatures, pressure, humidity, winds, and precipitation. Cloud formations are among the best indicators of future weather. Stress should be placed on trying to understand the atmospheric conditions that lead to certain cloud formations. Thus, when these cloud formations are observed, something is learned about conditions in the atmosphere. In a somewhat similar fashion the speed and direction of winds can be indicative of future weather conditions. As part of their study in this area, children can keep records of clouds and winds to see with what kinds of weather they are associated.

However, to understand the atmosphere and the changes that take place in it, it is helpful to develop a conceptual model of the atmosphere. It is possible to obtain tremendous quantities of information about the atmosphere; such information is gathered at hundreds of meteorological stations and supplemented by cloud pictures from weather satellites. But this information must be interpreted if it is to be useful, and conceptual models provide a framework for such interpretation.

In the study of the air and the atmosphere there is a great variety of experiments, demonstrations, and investigations through which children can have firsthand experiences with the air and the atmosphere. They are enveloped in air, and it is readily studied. Because there are such rich opportunities for firsthand study of air, much of the text of this chapter is written in terms of activities that can be undertaken with children.

AIR

Although ordinarily air cannot be seen, smelled, or tasted, it is a material substance. It is a mixture of nitrogen, oxygen, argon, carbon dioxide, water vapor, small quantities of certain rare gases, and almost always some pollutants such as dust and smoke. About 78 per cent of air is nitrogen and 21 per cent oxygen. The remaining one per cent is composed of the other gases. In the atmosphere, the amounts of water vapor and dust vary greatly, and these variations have great influence on the weather.

Air is a gas, and it has the same characteristics as other gases. It has no definite shape or size but will fill its container. Therefore, a bottle cannot be half full of air because the air will move throughout the bottle. Like other gases, air will expand and can be compressed. The air over a burning candle will expand as it is heated. Air can be compressed with a bicycle pump.

The kinetic-molecular theory of matter is very useful in explaining the behavior of air and other gases. According to the kinetic-molecular theory, all substances, including air, are made up of large numbers of very small particles that are constantly in motion. These particles are traveling in all directions. They travel at many different speeds, but their average speed depends upon their temperature. In fact, temperature is a measure of the average kinetic energy (energy of motion) of the particles of a substance.

Consider the air in a balloon. The balloon remains inflated because there are trillions of particles of air bouncing against its rubber sides. If the balloon is heated, the balloon will expand because the particles have more kinetic energy and are striking the balloon at higher speeds. If the balloon is cooled, it will contract, because the particles are now traveling at lower average speeds. The kinetic-molecular theory will be referred to as the nature of air as material is considered.

Air Occupies Space

Pull the open end of a clear plastic bag through the air and then close it. Can the air in the bag be seen? Push on the side of the bag with a finger. Can the matter inside the bag be felt? Open the bag next to your face. Can you feel some material move past your face?

Crumple up a piece of paper and push it down into the bottom of a glass tumbler. Turn the tumbler upside down and push it down into a container of water. Pull the tumbler straight out again and feel the paper. Did it become wet? Place a cork on the water and push the tumbler down over the cork. What happens to the cork and the level of water in the tumbler?

Fill one tumbler with water and place it upside down in water in an aquarium. Invert another tumbler and push it straight down into the water. Tip this tumbler under the water-filled tumbler so that bubbles will flow into the water-filled tumbler. Note that as bubbles flow into this tumbler the other tumbler becomes filled with water. The bubbles, of course, are air. With care the air can be poured back-and-forth between the tumblers many times.

Since air is a material substance, it does occupy space. The activities that have been described are ways that we can detect the presence of air.

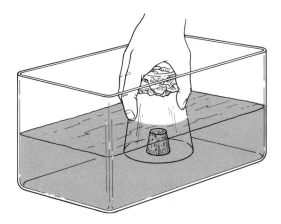

Fig. 8-1   Air occupies space.

The Weight of Air

Weigh a deflated basketball or volleyball on a platform balance. Then pump it full of air and weigh it again. The increase in weight is due to the air that has been pumped into the ball.

The weight of air, as with all other materials, is due to the gravitational attraction between it and the earth. The air in a ball or automobile tire is considerably denser than the air in the atmosphere. A cubic foot of air at atmospheric pressure at sea level weighs about 1.2 ounces or 34 grams.

However, the volume of air in the atmosphere is so tremendous that the total weight of the air in the atmosphere is approximately 11,850,000,-000,000,000,000 pounds. The weight of the air over one square foot of surface is about 2,117 pounds and over one square inch about 14.7 pounds. It is the relatively great weight of the atmosphere over the earth's surface that makes air pressure a very significant factor.

Air Pressure

Place one end of a piece of glass tubing in water. Cover the other end of the glass tubing with a finger. When you pull the glass tubing out of the water, you will notice that water will remain in the glass tubing. What holds the water in the glass tubing? What happens when you remove your finger?

Fill a metal can, such as a duplicating fluid can, with water. Insert a one-holed rubber stopper with a piece of glass tubing into the opening of the can. Fill a long piece of rubber tubing with water and attach one end to the glass tubing. Toss the other end of the rubber tubing out the window or in some way allow the water in it to fall a considerable height. What happens as the water from the can flows out the rubber tubing? How can this be explained?

Because of the weight of the atmosphere, pressure is exerted against the earth and other surfaces. This pressure is exerted in all directions. Press on

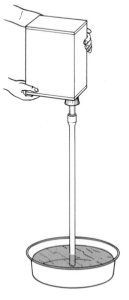

Fig. 8-2 *As water flows out of the can, the pressure of air outside the can will press in on the can.*

one part of an inflated balloon. Note that the pressure is transmitted to all parts of the balloon. In the case of the water in the glass tubing, the pressure is exerted upward to hold the water in the tube.

If a tumbler is filled with water and a paper card is placed over the top, the water will remain in the tumbler even though it is tipped upside down. The air pressure upward on the card is much greater than the downward pressure of the water, and, therefore, the card continues to be pressed against the tumbler.

Since air pressure is so great and acts in all directions, why aren't all objects crushed? In the case of the metal can, as long as it was filled with air or with water, the pressure on the outside was balanced by pressure on the inside. But when some of the water was allowed to run out, there was

Fig. 8-3 Here, air pressure upward is greater than the downward pressure of the water.

less counteracting pressure on the inside of the can, and the air pressure on the outside crushed it.

The pressure on the surface of the human body is tremendous. But there is air inside the body, and the pressure on the inside counteracts that on the outside.

This balance of inner and outer air pressures is evident when there are rapid changes in the outside air pressure. When we are taken up in an elevator or in an unpressurized airplane, the outside air pressure diminishes. However, the pressure on the inside remains the same until some air is forced out of a body opening. For example, we often swallow or yawn to equalize the inside and outside air pressure on our eardrums. Persons who, because of a cold or some other reason, are unable to equalize the pressure, sometimes suffer considerable pain. Upon descending, air is swallowed in order to increase the inside air pressure to counterbalance the increased outside air pressure.

Air pressure is measured with a barometer. If a glass tube closed at one end is filled with mercury and inverted so that the open end is immersed in a jar of mercury, the mercury will fall to a certain level. The column of mercury in the glass tube is supported by the outside air pressure. The height of the column will vary with changes in air pressure. This is a *mercury barometer*, one of the most important weather instruments.

The *aneroid barometer* consists basically of an evacuated corrugated metal box. The box expands and contracts with changes in air pressure. These variations are transmitted by a system of levers to a needle that indicates the air pressure. The aneroid barometer has the advantage of being easily portable and is often used in homes and schools.

Atmospheric pressure is affected by temperature. If the air in an automobile tire is heated, the pressure is increased. But the air in the atmosphere, unlike the air in a tire, is not in a closed system. When the air in the atmosphere is heated, it expands. Hence, there will be less air over that part of the earth's surface, and the barometer reading will decline. Declining barometer readings often indicate that warmer air is moving in.

Atmospheric pressure is also affected by the amount of water vapor in the air. Contrary to common belief, water in its vapor form is only about three-fifths as heavy as dry air. Therefore, a mass of air that contains considerable water vapor will weigh less than a comparable mass of dry air. Declining barometer readings often indicate that a mass of air containing more water vapor is moving in.

Because of the indications that changes in air pressure give of the nature of the air that is moving in, the barometer is one of the most useful instruments for short-range weather forecasting. The changes in barometric readings are more important than the actual readings. Declining barometric readings may indicate that a relatively warm air mass containing water vapor is moving in. This often results in bad weather, for slight cooling or contact with a colder air mass may cause condensation of water vapor and precipitation. A "falling barometer" usually indicates bad weather is on the way. Conversely, rising barometric readings indicate that cold dry air may be moving in, and this usually means fair weather.

There is a general flow of air from regions of high pressure to regions of low pressure. This flow of air is *wind*. Any factor, such as differences in temperatures of the surface of the ground, that causes differences in air pressure helps start wind. The greater the difference in pressure between the low- and high-pressure regions, the higher the wind velocity.

Heating and Cooling of Air

Warm a Pyrex flask or infant's feeding bottle slightly and then stretch the mouth of a balloon across the top of the flask. Place the flask in a pan of hot water. As the air in the flask and balloon is heated, it expands, and the balloon is inflated.

When the flask is placed in cold water, the air contracts, and the balloon is deflated. As the pressure within the balloon and flask becomes less and less, the balloon may actually be pushed down into the flask by the outside air pressure.

This demonstration of what happens when air in a closed system is heated can be explained by the kinetic-molecular theory of gases. When the air is heated, the average velocity of the particles in the air is increased.

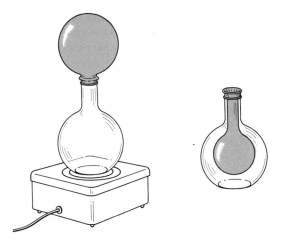

Fig. 8-4 *As air is heated it expands, so that the balloon is inflated. When air is cooled it contracts—deflating the balloon.*

These bombard the inner surface of the balloon with greater energy, causing the balloon to be inflated. Conversely, when air is cooled, the average velocity of the particles is reduced and the elasticity of the balloon and the outside air pressure cause the balloon to become deflated.

In the atmosphere masses of air also expand when heated and contract when cooled. However, a segment of the atmosphere is not a closed system like the flask and balloon. When a mass of air is heated, it expands. But this means that there will be less air, fewer particles over a given area of surface in this region, and the air pressure will drop. A falling barometric pressure often indicates that a warm mass of air is moving into the region. Conversely, when a mass of air is cooled, it contracts, and more air will be concentrated over a given surface. This leads to a rise in the barometric pressure.

Winds are movements of air, and, in general, winds blow from regions of high pressure to regions of low pressure. How the heating and cooling of masses of air lead to winds can be illustrated by the land and sea breezes that occur at the seashore.

In the daytime, the land along the seacoast warms more rapidly than the water. The air over the land is heated, expands, and rises. The colder air from above the water flows in over the coast to displace the warmed air. This flow of air from off the water is called the sea breeze, and it is the primary reason that the regions along the coast are considerably cooler than those inland. The sea breezes are important along the California and Long Island coasts. The lake breezes along the Great Lakes are similar in nature to the sea breezes. The coastal areas of Chicago and Milwaukee on Lake Michigan are kept relatively cool by such breezes.

At night the land cools more quickly than the water, and the air over the land is cooled. As the air cools, it contracts, becomes denser and flows out to sea to displace the warmer air over the water. This evening flow of air from land to sea is called the land breeze. Because the temperature differences at night are less than in the daytime, the velocity of the land breeze is usually less than the sea breeze. The sea and land breezes combine to give coastal regions pleasant summers at the same time that temperatures inland may range from hot to torrid.

Water in the Air

Fill a shiny metal can with a mixture of ice and water. Usually, drops of water can be seen forming on the outside of the can. Where did these drops of water come from? They did not come from the inside of the can. Instead, they were formed by the condensation of water vapor in the atmosphere.

Water enters the atmosphere through the process of *evaporation*. Some molecules of water in the oceans, lakes, and ponds travel at sufficient speed so that they break through the surface film of the liquid water and enter the atmosphere as water vapor. These molecules may be said to be traveling at "escape velocity." If the water is heated, the average speed of the molecules is increased, more molecules achieve escape velocity, and water evaporates faster. This is the reason that water evaporates faster in warm regions than in cold. Actually, water can enter the atmosphere directly from ice. This process is called *sublimation*, and it is the process by which clothes dry when the temperatures are below feezing.

Water in its vapor form is invisible. The white cloud to be seen at the end of the spout of a teakettle is actually composed of very small droplets of liquid water. When the water in a teakettle has been boiling for some time, there is usually a small space between the end of the spout and the beginning of the cloud. This space is filled with invisible water vapor. Sometimes, usually in the morning or evening, rays are seen in the sky and the sun is said to "draw water." The rays are due to the illumination of water and dust particles by the sunlight. The dark areas between the rays are actually shadows of clouds. Water may be evaporating at this time, but it cannot be seen.

Strange as it may seem, water in its vapor phase is lighter than air. Water, H_2O, is made up of two molecules of hydrogen which has a comparative weight of 1 and one molecule of oxygen with a comparative weight of 16. The comparative weight of water, therefore, is 18 $(1 + 1 + 16 = 18)$. However, air, which is about 80 per cent nitrogen, has a comparative weight of about 29. From this it can be seen that if the atmosphere contains a great deal of water vapor, it will be comparatively light, and the atmospheric pressure will be reduced. A lowered barometric pressure can mean the arrival of an air mass that contains a great deal of water vapor.

The nature of the atmosphere and the changes that take place in it are due to the materials that make up air. Some of the changes are due to changes in the composition of air, particularly changes in the amount of water in the atmosphere. Other changes occur as the temperatures change. These various changes in the atmosphere are the weather that we observe and experience.

WEATHER

Weather is the state or condition of the atmosphere at a given time. The weather is always changing. It is affected by temperature, pressure, moisture content, winds, and amount of sunshine. All of these factors interact.

For example, the moisture content of a mass of air is likely to be higher when its temperature is relatively high; under these conditions, however, the pressure is likely to be lower. To forecast the weather, it is necessary to know the characteristics of a mass of air, where this mass of air can be expected to be after a given period of time, and what changes are likely to take place in the air mass. *Meteorology* is the scientific study of the atmosphere and the changes that take place in its weather.

Children can observe and study many weather phenomena. In these studies children can use, and in some cases make, thermometers, barometers, wind vanes, anemometers, and psychrometers. Often children set up weather stations to obtain and record data. Sometimes they use weather data to build respectable records of success in predicting future weather.

The following are some of the weather phenomena and characteristics of air masses that can be considered.

Clouds

When water vapor is cooled and small dust or smoke particles are present, the water vapor will condense into small droplets of water. These small droplets form clouds. As air rises, it is cooled. If there are sufficient water vapor and condensation nuclei present, clouds will form. In the mountains, clouds often form at the same altitude as the snow line. When air comes into contact with the snow-covered surface, it is cooled to the point where water vapor condenses into droplets.

There are four general cloud types, and these cloud types give some indications of atmospheric conditions. *Cirrus* clouds are very high, wispy clouds composed of small ice particles. If cirrus clouds are followed by other types of clouds, it is often an indication of approaching frontal conditions. *Cumulus* clouds are rolling, billowy clouds that indicate considerable convective activity in the atmosphere. Of special interest are the high, anvil-topped *cumulonimbus* or thunderclouds. The anvil tops are formed when rising air currents reach a level of stable air. *Stratus* clouds are sheet-like clouds that indicate that there is very little convective activity in the atmosphere. *Nimbus* clouds are low, dark, ragged rain or snow clouds.

Precipitation

The very small droplets that make up a cloud are falling toward the earth. But because they are very small, the resistance of the air causes them

Fig. 8-5 *Basic cloud types are shown at average altitude levels.*

to fall very slowly. Other motions in clouds, such as convective currents, have much greater velocities, and the small droplets never fall to the earth.

Under conditions that are still not completely understood, large raindrops and ice crystals are formed. It may be that most rain begins as snow. At the tops of clouds, the temperatures are probably low enough so that a few small ice crystals will be formed. These ice crystals will grow as the cold water droplets come into contact with them. As they become larger, the ice crystals will fall faster. But as they descend, they pass into warmer air and melt to form comparatively large drops. In cities where there are buildings four or more stories high, children can see part of this process in action. Even on a warm summer day, snowflakes can often be seen falling past the top floor of the building during a rain. The flakes melt, of course, as they come closer to the ground.

Knowledge of the raindrop-forming process, although inadequate, has been used in attempts to induce rain to fall. Ice crystals have been sprinkled on the tops of clouds in the hope that the water droplets in the cloud will adhere to them and thus form ice crystals large enough to fall out of the cloud. In another approach, silver iodide vapors are released into the air to provide nuclei around which particles of ice can form. Under the right conditions, it may be that artificial rainmaking can increase the amount of rainfall in an area by 10 or 20 per cent. However, it is difficult to determine whether rain is due to the rainmaking efforts or whether it would have fallen anyway.

Snow is formed by crystallization directly from water vapor. In order to have snow, the temperatures must be sufficiently low so that the crystals do not melt before striking the ground. Almost all snowflakes are six-sided, but they can be of a tremendous variety of intricate designs. Large flakes are formed by the combining of many smaller flakes.

Hailstones are pellets of ice. Usually, these pellets are quite small, although hailstones the size of marbles are quite common and some have been as large as baseballs. Hail is formed in cumulonimbus clouds where there are strong updrafts of air. According to one theory, the small crystals of ice fall through the cloud and then are carried upward again a number of times before they finally fall to the ground. Each time the crystal passes through the cloud, a little more water freezes to it. This theory is supported by the observation that many hailstones, when cut in half, have concentric rings somewhat like the growth rings in trees.

Dew and frost are forms of condensation, rather than precipitation. When grass and various objects are cooled to the dewpoint temperature or below, water vapor from the atmosphere condenses on the surface. When the temperature of the surface drops below freezing, the condensation is in the form of frost.

Winds

Winds are air currents moving with respect to the surface of the ground. Wind directions are designated in terms of the directions from which the wind is blowing. Wind direction can be used to determine the direction of a low pressure system and possible bad weather. When your back is to the wind, the area of low pressure is to the left. Wind speed indicates to a certain extent the differences in air pressure between a high-pressure region and a low-pressure region.

Table 8-1: BEAUFORT SCALE FOR ESTIMATING WIND

Wind	Speed	Number Symbol	Wind effects
Calm	0–1	0	Smoke rises straight up.
Light air	2–3	1	Smoke drifts slightly.
Light breeze	4–7	2	Leaves rustle. Vane moved by wind.
Gentle breeze	8–12	3	Light flag extended. Leaves and twigs in motion.
Moderate breeze	13–18	4	Dust and paper raised. Small branches move.
Fresh breeze	19–24	5	Small trees begin to sway.
Strong breeze	25–31	6	Large branches move. Umbrellas hard to use.
Moderate gale	32–38	7	Whole trees bend. Walking against wind difficult.
Fresh gale	39–46	8	Twigs break from trees.
Strong gale	47–54	9	Buildings damaged.
Whole gale	55–63	10	Trees uprooted. Buildings severely damaged.
Storm	64–75	11	Great damage.
Hurricane	above 75	12	Great violence and destruction.

Tornadoes, often called "twisters," are small storms having very high twisting winds. The tornado has a funnel in which there is very low air pressure. Motion-picture films of tornadoes show that some of the damage is caused by buildings exploding when the outside air pressure is suddenly reduced. Around the funnel, wind velocities may reach several hundred miles per hour. In the Northern Hemisphere the winds twirl around the funnel in a counterclockwise direction. Fortunately, the path of a tornado is usually less than a mile wide. However, within this path there is usually great destruction. The central region of the United States has a high tornado frequency.

Whirlwinds or "dust devils" are, in a sense, very small tornadoes. They are believed to be caused by upward movements of air over surfaces that are heated to fairly high temperatures by the sun. Whirlwinds are very common in desert regions.

Hurricanes are particularly destructive cyclones that originate in tropical regions. The barometric pressure within huricanes is very low. Readings of below twenty-seven inches have been reported. Therefore, there is a great deal of pressure forcing air into this region from areas of higher pressure. However, the air in the Northern Hemisphere moves in a counterclockwise direction. This movement of air can be compared to the flow of water out of a bathtub. At a distance from the drain, the water usually moves slowly. Near the drain, where the pressure is low, the water moves very fast in a very tight spiral. Similarly, in the regions around the low-pressure area, the winds are blowing at velocities of seventy-five miles per hour or more. At the center of the low-pressure area, the eye of the hurricane, the air, and often the sea, is calm and still. The very strong winds around the eye of the hurricane can do great damage.

The *jet stream* is a band of high-speed wind flowing at altitudes of twenty thousand to forty thousand feet and having a width of twenty-five to one hundred miles. Usually, the jet stream is located near the tropopause. In the Northern Hemisphere, the jet streams blow from west to east, and are found farther south over land than over water.

The jet streams are believed to be the result of contact between dry, cold polar air and warm, moist tropical air. The wind velocities are the greatest where the temperature contrasts between the two air masses are the greatest. It is believed that the jet streams have considerable effect upon surface weather. Eddies from the jet stream may be factors influencing the development of cyclonic conditions leading to storms, cold waves, blizzards, and even hurricanes.

The jet stream is a factor to be considered in high-flying planes. A plane flying from west to east may be able to fly as much as two hundred miles faster because of the jet stream. However, a plane flying west in the jet stream will be slowed up considerably. Slow-flying planes have been known to be actually carried backward by the fast jet stream.

Thunderstorms are storms in which the sound of thunder is heard. The thunder is set off by electrical discharges. The amount of electricity involved in these discharges is very great. When there is a sudden expansion of air due to heating the sound of thunder is heard.

The process whereby electrical charges are generated in thunderclouds is still not well understood. The violent air currents in a thundercloud may break up water droplets into fine particles of spray. The spray particles have an electrical charge, while the remaining drops have the opposite electrical charge, that is, different parts of a cloud may become negatively or positively charged. When the charge becomes large enough, sometimes as high as one hundred million volts, there will be an electrical discharge.

Electrical discharges also take place between clouds and between clouds and the earth.

Thunderstorms are most likely to occur when there is a large temperature difference between lower air and upper air. This often occurs on hot summer afternoons when the ground and the lower air have been heated by the summer sun. The warm air expands and rises rapidly through the cool air that surrounds it. When this rising warm, moist air is cooled to the point that water vapor condenses, a cumulus cloud forms. As the air continues to rise, raindrops form and start to fall. Many of the drops evaporate before they reach the ground. Evaporation, however, is a cooling process and the cooled air begins to descend down the center of the cloud. This simplified explanation suggests how there can be both violent up-currents and down-currents of air in the same cloud.

Over the oceans, thunderstorms are most likely to occur during the second half of the night. Here the upper air cools more at night than the air that is near the water. The cooling of the upper air causes the convective currents that are necessary for the beginning of a thunderstorm.

Violent vertical air currents create dangerous flying conditions, and most pilots try to avoid thunderclouds. Planes may be alternately lifted by up-currents or pulled down by downdrafts. There have been cases where men who have parachuted from planes in thunderclouds have been held in the air for quite a long time by the up-currents of air.

Relative Humidity

Relative humidity is the ratio of the amount of moisture in the air as compared with the amount of moisture the air could hold at that temperature if it were completely saturated. Relative humidity is expressed in percentages. When the relative humidity is high, precipitation is quite likely, and because the air is already almost completely saturated, very little water enters the air through evaporation. When the relative humidity is low, on the other hand, water will tend to enter the air through evaporation, but precipitation is unlikely.

"It isn't the temperature; it's the humidity" is a common refrain. If the relative humidity is low, perspiration on the surface of the skin can evaporate. This is a cooling process, and a person may feel quite comfortable even though the temperatures are high. When the relative humidity is high, however, perspiration will not evaporate readily, the atmosphere seems close and sticky, and a generally uncomfortable feeling is experienced.

During the summertime, comfort depends, to large extent, upon both temperature and humidity. The Temperature-Humidity Index (THI) combines these two factors. The THI can be obtained by adding the dry bulb and the wet bulb temperatures, multiplying the sum by 0.4 and adding 15. Many people become uncomfortable when the THI reaches 70. Almost all people will be uncomfortable at a THI of 80 or above.

Weather Analysis

The data that are obtained through the use of various instruments must be assembled, charted, and analyzed if they are to be of much value. This is part of the complex service that is provided by the Weather Bureau.

Storms and other weather conditions tend to move from one region to another. Often this movement is from west to east. After a passage of time, the East Coast may expect weather somewhat similar to that experienced in the Midwest. In fact, weather conditions often cross the Atlantic, for Europe has experienced stormy conditions a few days after it occurred along the East Coast of North America. The fact that weather conditions seem to move across the country was recognized by Benjamin Franklin. His correspondents in Boston could report experiencing weather in Boston similar to that which had passed through Philadelphia somewhat earlier. Utilization of modern weather analysis is made possible by the Teletype and other forms of rapid communication. In fact, one of the first uses of the telegraph was to report the weather.

The U.S. Weather Bureau maintains hundreds of weather stations. At each of these stations ground observations are made using the various weather instruments. In addition, many stations use radiosonde balloons and other devices to obtain data about the upper air. All of these data are transmitted by radio or Teletype to control offices where the daily weather maps are produced. The United States Weather Stations are part of a chain of more than fourteen thousand weather stations that are associated with the World Meteorological Organization. In addition, earth satellites such as the Nimbus are equipped to take pictures of the cloud cover around the world.

To be useful, this data must be assembled in a meaningful way and interpreted. The data are assembled on weather maps with the data from each station plotted throughout the nation. Figure 8-6 is an example of a weather map for the United States.[1]

The key to the symbols around each station is given in the station model. The lines drawn across the map connect points of equal barometric pressure and are called *isobars*. The shaded areas indicate precipitation.

[1] Daily weather maps may be purchased from the Superintendent of Documents, Government Printing Office, Washington, D.C. 20402.

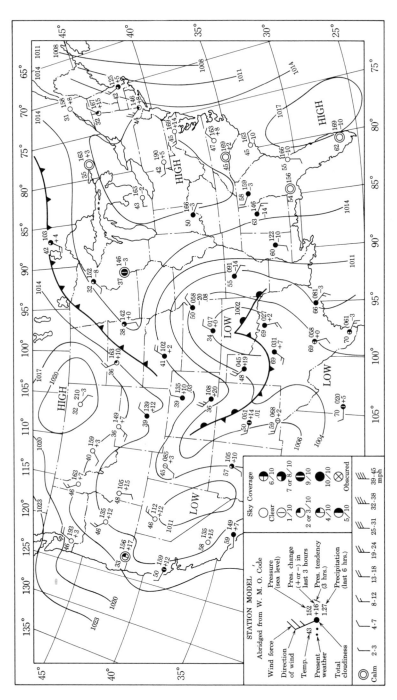

Fig. 8-6 *A Weather Map (Note the station model.)*

The professional weather forecaster uses many different approaches to analyzing the data. He usually locates areas of high and low barometric pressure. He recognizes that wind speed usually depends on differences in air pressure—the greater the difference, the greater the wind speed. In the United States, air masses usually move from west to east. Therefore, he can get some indication of future weather by looking at weather conditions at stations located west of his station. By looking at successive weather maps, he can get clues as to the speed at which these weather conditions are moving across the country. However, he must still predict what will happen to the air as it moves across the country and into his area.

Of growing importance in weather forecasting are the cloud pictures that are taken by cameras in earth satellites and relayed to the earth. Earth satellites make it possible to gain a view of cloud conditions around the globe. Earth satellite cloud pictures, when coupled with knowledge of general weather movement, are an important tool in the hands of the weather forecaster.

MODELS OF THE ATMOSPHERE

The changes that take place in the vast atmosphere are very complex. In an attempt to understand these changes, it is useful to have a conceptual model of the atmosphere to help to interpret various observations of changes in the atmosphere. Obviously, the atmosphere is not exactly like any model that may be used; the model is only useful as a means of interpretation.

The atmosphere can be compared to a heat engine such as the gasoline engines used in automobiles. Energy is supplied to the heat engine through the fuel. When the fuel is burned in the cylinder of the engine, hot gases are formed. These hot gases expand and push the pistons back and forth. In the process, the gases are cooled and forced out the exhaust pipe. Sometimes the gases are cooled to the point where the water vapor in the exhaust condenses to form small water droplets.

The sun is the fuel—the source of the energy—to drive the atmospheric engine. The atmosphere acts somewhat like a greenhouse to trap the solar energy. Some of the solar energy passes through the atmosphere and strikes the surface of the earth. The earth re-radiates much of this energy in longer wavelength heat radiation. This heat radiation is trapped largely by the water vapor and carbon dioxide in the atmosphere. The importance of water vapor in the air can been seen in that a ground frost is much less likely on a cloudy, moist night when the atmosphere traps heat from the earth than on a clear, dry night.

The atmosphere in the equatorial areas receives considerably more energy than that in the polar regions.[2] Therefore, the air in the tropics is heated, expands, and is pushed upward by air from the colder regions. The warm air is pushed toward the cooler regions. In the process of rising and moving toward the cooler regions, the air mass is cooled and sinks, to replace the cold air that has moved toward the equatorial regions. This generalized circulation, with many aberrations due to a variety of factors, permits an understanding of weather and climate on a global basis. As in the heat engine, warm air expands, does work, and, in the process, is cooled. The work that is done takes the form of moving tremendous quantities of water through the water cycle and moving huge amounts of air throughout the atmosphere. These movements of air are the winds, and these winds are extremely important in maintaining a "heat balance" on the earth.

The earth is continually receiving a tremendous amount of energy from the sun. On the average, a given area of the earth's surface receives enough solar energy to melt a sheet of ice one centimeter thick every hour. Although it might be expected that the earth eventually would become quite hot, it has not. Except for the glacial periods in recent geological history, it is believed that the earth has maintained a fairly constant average temperature.

The regions from the equator to about 40 degrees latitude receive more energy than they give off. For the regions from 40 degrees to the poles the outgoing radiation exceeds the incoming. The excess energy in the equatorial areas is transferred in the movements of warm air to the regions north and south of 40 degrees latitude. Here some of the energy is radiated out into space. The atmospheric engine helps to keep the average temperature fairly constant.

Air Mass Theory

It is useful to think of the atmosphere as being composed of masses of air that have certain characteristics. A large body of air that has essentially uniform characteristics throughout is called an air mass. The weather that occurs in any particular region depends upon the characteristics of the mass of air over that region.

The symbols used to designate air masses are: c for continental, m for maritime, P for polar, and T for tropical. There are several major air masses that affect weather in North America. The *Polar continental* (cP) air mass usually originates in Alaska or Canada and is a cold, dry air mass.

[2] For an explanation as to why the equatorial areas receive more energy, see pages 101–103, Chapter 6.

Polar maritime (mP) air comes from the North Pacific, or more rarely, from the Northwestern Atlantic and is humid and moderately cold. *Tropical maritime* (mT) air comes from the Gulf of Mexico, the Pacific, or the Atlantic and it is warm and humid. Usually these air masses are affected by the surfaces over which they flow. Both the temperatures and the moisture content can be affected.

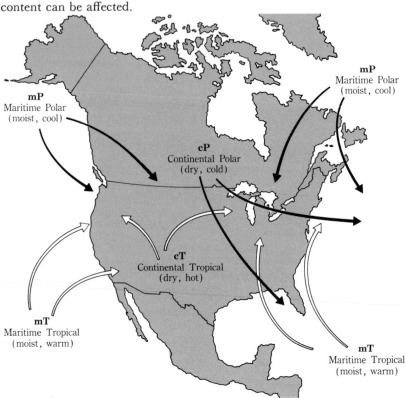

Fig. 8-7 *The origins of air masses.*

When two dissimilar air masses meet, there is usually a sloping boundary between them called a *front*. When cold air advances into warmer air, there is a *cold front*. Similarly, when a mass of warm air moves into a mass of cold air, there is a *warm front*. When one front overtakes another front so that there are three air masses in close proximity to each other, an *occluded front* is formed. Precipitation usually accompanies fronts.

At a cold front, cold air, which is comparatively dense, will force the warm air upward. As the warm air is pushed upward, it cools and water vapor condenses to form clouds, which usually result in rain or snow. Often there is thunder accompanying intense but relatively short storms. After the cold front passes and the cold air mass arrives there is usually a sharp drop in temperature, an increased pressure, a wind shift to the northwest, and a clearing of skies.

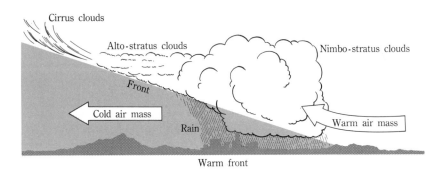

Warm front

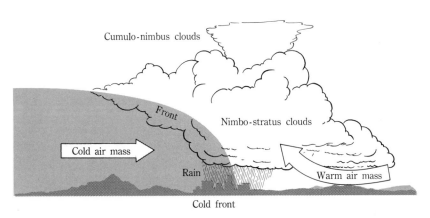

Cold front

Fig. 8-8 *In a warm front warm air moves up and over cold air. In a cold front cold air pushes the warmer air up.*

At a warm front, warm air, which is comparatively light, moves up over the cold air mass. If the warm air contains considerable moisture, as it usually does in North America, clouds will form. High clouds may form hundreds of miles ahead of the front. Gradually, the clouds become thicker and lower, and a slow, steady rain begins to fall. Warm fronts generally move more slowly than cold fronts. However, as the warm air mass moves in, there is a gradually rising temperature, a change in the wind direction, and gradual clearing.

Usually in the occluded front, one cold front overtakes another cold front, and the warm air mass is forced upward so that it is no longer in contact with the surface of the ground. When this occurs, a region may have the weather associated with both a cold and warm front.

Air mass theory can be used to interpret and predict weather phenomena. If an air mass is stationary, the same kind of weather can be expected for several days. However, these masses of air, with their characteristic weather, usually move across the country, being changed by contact with the ground surface and other air masses. In most of continental United States, these air masses tend to move from west to east. If an air mass is moving eastward at a known rate, it is possible to predict with some accuracy when the air mass, with its known characteristics, will arrive. From past experience, it may also be possible to predict what changes will take place in an air mass before it arrives.

Precipitation and other changes in the weather are likely to occur when one type of air mass meets another type. Many frontal weather conditions are caused by atmospheric changes, particularly temperatures, which affect the moisture content of air masses. A slight cooling may cause water vapor to condense to form clouds, and the small droplets in clouds will coalesce into ice crystals, resulting in large raindrops that fall as precipitation. When the cold, dry air from the polar regions meets the warm, moist air from the tropics, clouds will form, precipitation will fall, and sometimes violent storms will ensue.

On weather maps, the locations of various air masses are shown as areas of high pressure (HIGHS) or low pressure (LOWS). Areas of high pressure usually contain cold air with little water vapor. Areas of low pressure usually contain warm air with much water vapor. In the United States and Canada, as in most middle latitude regions, alternate highs and lows follow each other across the country. The pressure systems move from west to east at a rate of about five hundred miles per day in the summer and seven hundred miles per day in the winter. These movements cause many of the weather changes that are experienced.

In general, along the surface of the ground, air flows from a high pressure area to a low pressure area. At the top of the pressure systems, air flows up and out of the low, while air is being added at the top of the high, flowing down and out. These movements of air or winds are deflected by the spin of the earth so that they move around lows in a counterclockwise direction. This counterclockwise movement of air around a low-pressure area is called a *cyclone*. Clouds and precipitation are usually found in the region of the cyclone. The flow of air around a high-pressure area is in a clockwise direction. Such a high pressure area is called an *anticyclone*.

Wind direction can be used to locate the direction of the low- and high-pressure areas. In the Northern Hemisphere if you stand with your back to the wind, the low-pressure area is to your left and the high-pressure area to your right. This rule is known as Buys-Ballot's Law.

Perhaps the best explanation of the origin of cyclones and anticyclones is the *polar front wave theory*, first developed by the Norwegian meteorologist Jakob Bjerknes. According to this theory, large masses of cold air form over polar regions; similarly, large masses of warm air accumulate in tropical regions. These masses meet at the *polar front*. The warm air is moving as a westerly wind along the polar front and the cold air in the opposite direction as an easterly wind. There are always local disturbances in the air, and one of these causes the warm air to move to the north as a warm front. This warm air is replaced by cold air moving south as a cold front. Often, the spinning of the earth causes the air masses to swing into the counterclockwise motion associated with a cyclone.

Air Masses Move in a Small Model

The movement of small air masses when heat energy is supplied can be studied in a convection box. Place a candle under one of the chimneys of the convection box and use smoke to trace the pattern of air movements in and around the convection box. To make smoke, twist a piece of paper

Fig. 8-9 A convection box for the study of the movement of air when heated.

toweling into a tight roll. Ignite and allow it to burn for a while; then blow out the flame. Usually, considerable smoke ensues. Hold the source of smoke over the chimney above the candle. What happens? The air above the candle is heated and rises, causing the smoke to rise vertically.

Hold the source of smoke over the other lamp chimney. What happens to the smoke? The air in the lamp chimney and convection box is heavier than the warm air over the candle. The heavier cold air moves in to displace the warm air. This causes the smoke to pass down the chimney, through the box, and up the chimney above the candle.

There are several variations to this experiment. The candle can be placed under the second chimney to see if the flow of air is reversed. The candle can also be placed in the center of the convection box and the direction of air flow checked. In an interesting variation, candles are placed under both chimneys. Is there air flowing into the convection box under this condition? With the smoke source you can usually show that the air flows in through leaks in the box. Children should be asked to explain all results in terms of what they know happens to air when it is heated or cooled.

APPROACHES TO TEACHING

In this area of science there is no lack of opportunity for children to have firsthand, empirical experience. There is air all around us, and weather phenomena can be readily observed. Many of the preceding sections have been developed around suggestions for observation and activities in which children can become involved. The suggestions that follow may help children to make their observations more precise and to gain a better understanding of weather phenomena.

As these activities are developed, the central purpose of these studies should be kept in mind: To help children build a view of the world in which they live. Certainly, the atmosphere is an important aspect of this world. Participation in such science activities as those described can take on greater meaning if the teacher helps children extend the meanings of these observations and activities into a coherent world view.

How can the weather be forecast?

With thermometers, barometers, rain gauges, wind vanes, wind speed observations, wet and dry bulb thermometers, and cloud observations, children can obtain a fairly comprehensive description of existing weather. For a period of time, it may be of value to have the children forecast and "publish" a daily weather report.

In forecasting the weather the children can give special attention to the following:

1. The barometer. "Falling" barometer readings often indicate the arrival of moist, warm air. When this moist, warm air meets cold air, there are quite likely to be clouds and precipitation. A "rising" barometer, however, often presages fair weather.

193

2. Cloud formations. High cirrus clouds moving in from the west, for example, are often a harbinger of a cold front with its associated bad weather. Scattered cumulus clouds can mean continued fair weather. Murky nimbus clouds may indicate the arrival of a warm front. A line of cumulus or cumulonimbus clouds may be a squall line. These are usually accompanied by bad weather. In the Midwest tornadoes often occur along squall lines.

3. Weather reports. The Weather Bureau uses reports from stations around the world. Children do not have these facilities available to them, but they can use reports from neighboring radio and television stations and from daily newspapers. With these reports and a knowledge of the general movement of weather in their region, children can often achieve a surprisingly high rate of success in their predictions.

How does a thermometer work?

Fill a flask with colored water. Insert a one-hole rubber stopper with a long piece of glass tubing into the flask so that the colored water is forced

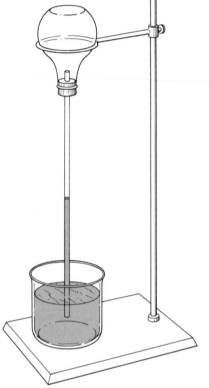

Fig. 8-10 The level of the liquid in an air thermometer indicates the relative temperature of the air. When the air in the flask is heated the level of the liquid in the tubing will be forced down. When it is cooled the level will rise.

up into the glass tubing. Mark the level of the water with a rubber band. Place the flask into some warm water. What happens to the level of the colored water in the tubing? Place the flask in ice cold water. What happens? This thermometer operates on the principle that liquids expand when heated and contract when cooled.

A more sensitive thermometer can be constructed on the principle that gases expand when heated and contract when cooled. Insert a one-hole rubber stopper with a long piece of glass tubing into a flask. Invert the flask so that the end of the glass tubing is immersed in a container of colored water. Heat the flask slightly, and watch the bubbles rise out of the liquid. When the flask cools, the pressure inside the flask will decrease, and the colored liquid will be forced up the tube. Such an air thermometer is usually sufficiently sensitive so that heat from the hand will cause a change in the level of the liquid.

How can precipitation be measured?

The simplest precipitation gauge is a straight-sided jar, such as a peanut butter jar with a ruler attached to the side, set in the ground. After a rain, the height of the water in the jar will indicate the amount of precipitation.

Usually, however, the amount of precipitation that falls is less than an inch and it is difficult to measure accurately this small amount of precipitation in this kind of gauge. For more accurate readings, obtain a narrow straight-sided jar, much as an olive bottle, and fasten a strip of tape lengthwise along its side. Now measure out exactly one inch of water in the wide-mouthed jar and pour it into the narrow bottle. Mark the height

Fig. 8-11 *After rain is collected in a wide-mouthed jar, it can be measured by pouring it into a narrow jar that has been calibrated.*

of the water in the bottle as "one inch." Divide the distance from the bottom of the bottle to the one-inch mark into ten equal spaces. Each one of these spaces will indicate a tenth of an inch of precipitation.

Place the wide-mouthed jar in a small hole in the ground so that it will not tip. It should be placed in a clearing away from trees and buildings. After a rain, the water in the jar can be poured into the narrow, calibrated bottle to determine the amount of precipitation.

Children can record the precipitation for storms and for longer periods of time such as a week or month. They may wish to place precipitation gauges in different places in the community to see if the same amount of precipitation falls throughout the community.

How can wind direction be determined?

Use a wind vane to indicate wind direction. Cut an arrow from a piece of cardboard, plastic, or plywood. The tail of the arrow should be considerably wider than the point. (A feather stuck into a cork that is free to turn on a pivot can also be used as a wind vane.)

Fig. 8-12   *A wind vane.*

Hold the tip of a medicine dropper or short piece of glass tubing in a flame to seal the end. Find the spot on the arrow on which it will balance on a knife blade. Fasten the sealed tube to the side of the arrow at this point.

For a pivot, drive a narrow nail into a wooden board and file the head of the nail to a sharp point. Place the glass tubing and the arrow down onto the sharp nail. The arrow should be free to turn and point in the direction from which the wind is blowing.

Children may be asked, "Why does the arrow turn to point in the direction from which the wind is blowing?" Actually, the arrow serves as a lever, and the wind exerts a greater force on the tail section of the arrow than on the head.

How can wind speed be determined?

At a weather station, wind speed is determined with an *anemometer.* An anemometer consists of several round cups fastened on the ends of crossbars. The cups catch the wind and the anemometer spins around. The faster the wind blows the faster the cups turn. Usually, the anemometer is connected to an indicator that resembles a speedometer and shows the wind speed.

For most purposes a satisfactory indication of wind speed can be obtained by using the Beaufort Scale shown on page 181. Children can use this scale to get the wind speed indication for their weather station.

How can relative humidity be determined?

To determine the relative humidity, obtain one thermometer to determine the temperature of the air (dry bulb thermometer) and another to determine the temperature of a surface from which water is evaporating

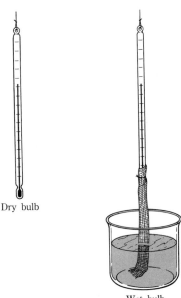

Fig. 8-13 *Unlike the dry bulb thermometer, the wet bulb thermometer has a piece of cloth tied around its bulb. One end of the cloth is immersed in water.*

Dry bulb

Wet bulb

(wet bulb thermometer). A wet bulb thermometer is made by wrapping a wick or cloth around the bulb of a thermometer and immersing the other end of the cloth in a bowl of water. Water moves up through the cloth or wick in the same way that kerosene moves up the wick in a lamp.

Table 8–2: CHART OF RELATIVE HUMIDITY

Wet-Bulb Depression	Air Temperature Reading of Dry-Bulb Thermometer, °F														
	25	28	32	36	40	44	48	52	56	60	64	68	72	76	80
1	87	88	89	91	92	93	93	94	94	94	95	95	95	96	96
2	74	76	79	82	83	85	86	87	88	89	90	90	91	91	92
3	62	65	69	73	75	78	79	81	82	83	84	85	86	87	87
4	49	54	59	64	68	71	73	75	77	78	79	80	82	83	83
5	37	43	49	55	60	63	66	69	71	73	75	76	78	79	79
6	25	32	39	46	52	56	60	63	65	68	70	71	73	74	76
7	13	21	30	38	45	49	54	57	60	63	65	67	69	70	72
8	1	10	20	29	37	43	47	51	55	58	60	63	65	66	68
9		3	11	21	29	36	41	46	50	53	56	58	61	63	64
10			2	13	22	30	35	40	44	48	51	54	57	59	61
11				5	15	23	29	35	39	43	47	50	53	55	57
12					7	16	23	29	34	39	43	46	49	52	54
13						10	18	24	29	34	38	42	45	48	51
14							12	19	25	30	34	38	42	45	47
15								12	20	25	30	34	38	41	44
16								6	15	21	26	31	34	38	41
17									11	17	22	27	31	35	38
18									6	13	18	23	28	31	35
19									2	9	15	20	24	28	32
20										5	11	16	21	25	29

The water around the bulb of the thermometer evaporates and cools the thermometer. The wet bulb thermometer should be fanned to get the lowest possible temperature.

Read the dry and wet bulb thermometer readings. Subtract the wet bulb reading from the dry bulb reading. Find this difference in the left-hand column of the chart below. Read straight across the chart to the column underneath the dry bulb temperature reading. The number in this column is the relative humidity.

How are clouds formed?

Swish a little warm water around in a gallon jug so that the air becomes saturated with moisture. Light a match and toss it into the jug to provide smoke particles as condensation nuclei. Fit a one-hole rubber stopper with a piece of glass tubing into the jug. With rubber tubing connect the glass tubing to a bicycle pump. Now pump air into the jug. Notice what happens as the pressure inside the jug is increased. Then release the stopper and note the formation of a cloud in the jug.

Have the children use their knowledge of cloud formation to explain their observations. When a gas is compressed it is heated. This causes some of the small water droplets to evaporate as the air in the jug seems to become clear. When the stopper was released, there was rapid expansion, and the air was cooled. Water vapor condensed around condensation nuclei to form a cloud.

Try the experiment without the smoke. Usually there are sufficient condensation nuclei in the air for water droplets to form.

What are the shapes of snowflakes?

Snowflakes have many different and beautiful shapes. To see them, however, they must be caught and kept in such a way that they do not melt.

A black cloth may be chilled in a refrigerator or left in the cold outside. Spread the cloth across a cold board and catch a few snowflakes. With care the flakes can be kept for some time for study.

How can heat energy be trapped?

Heat energy can be trapped by glass, as it is in the greenhouse, in much the same way as it is trapped by the atmosphere.

Place one thermometer in a test tube or narrow glass jar and another in the open air alongside the test tube. Put them in the direct sunlight or shine a projection light on them. Have the children note the temperatures shown by the thermometers over a span of time.

Usually, the temperature of the open thermometer will rise first, but soon the thermometer in the test tube will become warmer. The test tube,

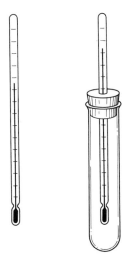

Fig. 8-14 *What happens when these two thermometers are placed in sunlight—one in the open air, one in a glass tube?*

like the atmosphere, keeps some of the radiant energy out. This is why the temperature in the test tube rises a little more slowly than that outside.

Eventually, however, the test tube traps sufficient heat radiation that is re-radiated by the thermometer and the air in the test tube, thus raising the temperature inside the test tube considerably higher than that outside.

INVESTIGATION

What are some of the differences between local microclimates?

A microclimate is the climate of a small area. Often there is considerable variation between microclimates in and around a school. The characteristics of a microclimate that can be studied by children are: temperature, barometric pressure, wind direction (a sensitive feather wind vane can be used for this), relative humidity, and other special features.

One of the microclimates that can be studied is that of the classroom. In fact, there may be microclimates near the ceiling and near the floor that differ in temperature.

Other microclimates that can be studied are: above a sidewalk or road surface on a hot sunny day, underneath a thick shade tree, in a greenhouse, within a closed automobile, and near the surface of a pool or pond.

Selected References

Blair, Thomas A., and Fite, Robert C., *Weather Elements*. Englewood Cliffs, N.J.: Prentice-Hall, Inc., 1957.

Forrester, Frank H., *1001 Questions Answered About the Weather*. New York: Dodd, Mead & Co., Inc., 1957.

Jacobson, Willard J., Kleinman, Gladys S., Sugarbaker, John, Hiack, Paul, and Carr, Albert, *Weather and Climate*. New York: American Book Co., 1968.

Koeppe, Clarence E., and De Long, George C., *Weather and Climate*. New York: McGraw-Hill Book Co., Inc., 1958.

Sutton, O. G., *Understanding Weather*. Baltimore, Md.: Penguin Books, Inc., 1960.

READINGS FOR THE PRIMARY GRADES

Branley, Franklyn M., *Air Is All Around You*. New York: Thomas Y. Crowell Co., 1962.

Jacobson, Willard, Lauby, Cecilia J., and Konicek, Richard D., *The Air Around You*. New York: American Book Co., 1968.

Jacobson, Willard J., Lauby, Cecilia J., and Konicek, Richard D., *The Sun, Seasons, and Climate*. New York: American Book Co., 1968.

Jacobson, Willard J., Lauby, Cecilia J., and Konicek, Richard D., *Weather*. New York: American Book Co., 1968.

Rukeyser, Muriel, *Bubbles*. New York: Harcourt, Brace & World, Inc., 1967.

Wolfe, Louis, *Let's Go to a Weather Station*. New York: G. P. Putnam's Sons, 1959.

WYLER, ROSE, *The First Book of Weather*. New York: Franklin Watts, Inc., 1956.

READINGS FOR THE INTERMEDIATE GRADES

ADLER, IRVING, *Weather in Your Life*. New York: The John Day Co., 1959.
GALLANT, ROY, *Exploring the Weather*. New York: Doubleday, 1957.
HITTE, KATHRYN, *Hurricanes, Tornadoes, and Blizzards*. New York: Random House, Inc., 1960.
SCHNEIDER, HERMAN, *Everyday Weather and How It Works*. New York: Whittlesey House, 1961.
SLOANE, ERIC, *Eric Sloane's Weather Book*. Des Moines, Iowa: Meredith, 1952.

SELECTED FILM

The Unchained Goddess. Bell System. A film on different kinds of weather. The section on tornadoes is especially interesting.

9 Water and the Hydrosphere

If a child spins a globe, he can observe how much of the surface is covered with the blue or green that usually is used to indicate bodies of water. If he were out in space and could observe the earth as it spins beneath him, he might very well call the earth the "water planet." Almost three-fourths of the earth's surface is covered with water. If the observer from space were to view only the Southern Hemisphere, he would see that this half of the earth is largely covered with water. The part of the earth that is water is called the *hydrosphere*.

What is this water that covers so much of the earth? It can be observed that water in a drinking glass has no color. Unless other materials have been added to it, it is also tasteless and odorless. Some bubbles in the water may be observed. These are usually bubbles of air and are extremely important for the life that lives in the water. Even though one child has observed that "water looks like ordinary stuff," it is actually a very remarkable substance.

There is a great deal of life in water. In fact, the oceans as a whole are more than twice as productive as most fertile soils. There are probably many more living things in the oceans than there are on land. Life also probably started in the water, and many land animals still have to go back to the water for part of their life cycle. Interestingly, the blood in the human body is surprisingly similar to sea water, an indication of man's evolutionary background.

It is not surprising that recently there has been a renewed interest in the science of the oceans, and it is becoming increasingly important that water and the oceans be considered in the elementary school.

There is an interchange of water between the hydrosphere, atmosphere, and lithosphere. Water evaporates to become water vapor in the atmosphere. The water vapor condenses to form the small water droplets that make up the clouds. From these clouds come snow, rain, and other forms of precipitation. Some of this water seeps beneath the surface of the land to become ground water. All of this water, eventually, again becomes a part of the hydrosphere. This interchange of water is called the water cycle, and all surface water is in some stage of the water cycle.

WATER AND ITS CHARACTERISTICS

Water is composed of two atoms of hydrogen and one of oxygen; the familiar formula is H_2O. If a wooden match is lighted, a drop of water will form on the match stick at the edge of the flame. There is hydrogen in the wood, and it combines with oxygen in the air to form water.

To understand water better, the atoms of hydrogen and oxygen and how they combine must be understood.

Hydrogen is the lightest chemical element. In its most common form it has a nucleus consisting of one proton with a positive (+) electrical charge, and circling around the nucleus, one electron with a negative (−) electrical charge.

The most common form of oxygen has 8 protons and 8 neutrons in the nucleus and 8 electrons in shells around the nucleus.

The oxygen atom has 6 electrons in its outer shell. It has been found that atoms that have 2 or 8 or 18 electrons in the outer shell are most stable. Oxygen needs two electrons to become stable. Each hydrogen atom has an electron in its outer shell which it can share with an oxygen atom in what is called a *covalent bond*. Therefore, each oxygen atom can enter into a covalent bond with two hydrogen atoms to form the water molecule H_2O.

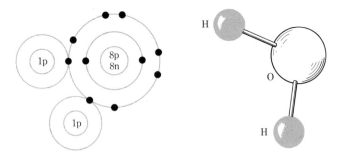

Fig. 9-1 *A model of the water molecule can be constructed if we know that oxygen needs two electrons in its outer shell to be stable and that it shares electrons with two hydrogen atoms.*

Water as a Solvent

Water is an excellent solvent for minerals, gases, and organic material. When these materials are dissolved in water, they become available to plants and animals. Water is also an important solvent in the bodies of animals. Human blood, for example, is largely water. It circulates the digested food substances to various parts of the body. The body wastes are carried away from cells by the blood and excreted as perspiration or urine, both of which are almost entirely water. Water has been called "the universal solvent," and life would be impossible without it and this property.

The most important reason for the solvent properties of water is the nature of the electrical field around a water molecule. Both of the hydrogen atoms are bonded to the same side of the oxygen atom. Actually, they are separated by an angle of 105 degrees. This means that on one side of the water molecule there is a positive electrical charge because of the exposed hydrogen nuclei. On the other side of the molecule there is a negative electrical charge from the electrons of the oxygen.

When a substance such as table salt, $NaCl$, dissolves, it breaks up into *ions* or charged particles. These ions have positive (Na^+) and negative (Cl^-) charges. Since unlike electrical charges attract, these ions should be expected to come together. In water, however, there is a tendency for them to stay apart because of the strong electrical charges of the water molecule.

Water Changes Form

Water changes from solid to liquid to gas at temperatures that can be fairly easily produced. When a piece of ice is heated, the molecules will reach a speed, at about 0°C., when the ice will change into a liquid form. If the liquid reaches a higher temperature, some of the water molecules will escape through the surface of the liquid water. At about 100°C., bubbles of gaseous water will break through the surface, and we say that the water *boils*. Since considerable energy is needed to change water from one phase to another, regions near large lakes, such as the Great Lakes, which are frozen over in winter, remain cool for a long time in the spring as the ice is melting.

Energy is given off as water changes from a gas to a liquid and to a solid. This means that energy in the form of heat will be given off to the surrounding region as water freezes, giving these areas a moderate climate. The energy given off as gaseous water changes to liquid can be harnessed by steam engines and turbines.

Water Absorbs Heat

Water has a high *specific heat*. Specific heat is the amount of heat in calories that will raise the temperature of one gram of a substance one degree Celsius. The specific heat of water is 1, which is a higher specific heat than of most other substances. As water is being heated, it absorbs a great deal of heat. On the other hand, as it cools, it gives off a great deal of heat. Because of the high specific heat of water, a large body of water such as a lake or an ocean can have a tremendous moderating effect upon the climate of an area.

Water Is a Heavy Liquid

Water is one of the heaviest liquids. One of the effects of this is that relatively heavy substances can be transported on its surface. More materials are transported over water in ships than by any other single mode of transportation.

Because water is a heavy substance, it has considerable energy as it falls. This energy may result in splash erosion, as when a raindrop strikes a cultivated field. Or energy of falling water can be harnessed at a waterfall or dam.

THE STUDY OF THE OCEANS

The study of the oceans is the science called *oceanography*. In the study of the ocean, basic principles from such sciences as physics, chemistry, biology, geology, and meteorology are used. Scientists from a wide range of specialties are involved in oceanographic studies, and a number of ingenious devices and instruments have been developed.

Measuring the Depth of the Ocean

Magellan measured the depth at various places in the Pacific by a method known as *sounding*. Sounding is done by simply fastening a weight to a line and dropping the weight into the water. The length of line that must be let out until the weight strikes the bottom can be measured. However, this method is slow. Several hours may be required to let a line and weight drop a length of several miles.

The modern way of measuring ocean depths is by *sonic sounding*. Sound waves are directed from the bottom of a ship downward to the bottom of the ocean. The ocean bottom reflects the sound waves back to the ship.

The time required for the sound waves to travel to the ocean bottom and back will depend upon the depth of the ocean. Since the speed of sound in ocean water is known, the depth of the ocean can be calculated:

$$\text{depth of ocean} = \frac{\text{speed of sound in ocean water} \times \text{time}}{2}$$

Actually, oceanographic ships equipped with sonic sounding devices can make continuous soundings of ocean depths. Through sonic soundings the depths of the oceans and the contours of the ocean bottom in many regions have been charted.

Studying the Ocean Bottom

An important aspect of oceanography is the study of the ocean bottom. Bottom samplers are large scoops that pick up samples of the ocean floor for examination and study.

It is especially important to get samples of the layers of sediment at the ocean bottom. By studying the layers of sediment, scientists can learn something about the conditions that existed when the sediment was washed off the land. The cores of sediment, for example, have provided clues for a new theory of the ice ages. Cross-sectional cores of the ocean bottoms are obtained through the use of *corers*. Essentially, these are hollow tubes that are driven into the ocean bottom by an explosive charge. The hollow tube is filled with sediment and hauled to the surface where the core can be analyzed.

Samples of water at different depths are obtained by using specially designed bottles. The opening and closing of the bottles can be controlled so that the depth at which the samples were obtained can be determined.

Studying Life in the Ocean Depths

One of the most interesting phases of oceanography is the study of life under water, especially in the ocean deeps. The most effective way to do this is to send divers down to make observations.

Divers equipped with *aqualungs*, or *SCUBA* (self-contained underwater breathing apparatus), can study life at shallow depths. The wide range of life over coral reefs has been studied with the help of such breathing devices. However, the greatest challenge is the ocean deeps thousands of feet beneath the surface of the sea. To probe the ocean deeps specially designed *bathyscaphes* are used.

Bathyscaphes are spheres, usually made of steel, designed to withstand the tremendous pressure found deep in the oceans. In the deepest parts of the oceans, the pressure may be as much as nine hundred times as great as they are at the surface. If the human body were exposed to this kind of pressure, it would be crushed. The bathyscaphe is able to withstand these tremendous pressures from the outside and maintain sea level pressures for the occupants on the inside. Specially constructed portholes of glass make it possible to view life in the ocean deeps. Below a thousand feet there is total darkness in the oceans, and floodlights have to be used in order to see. A bathyscaphe has been used to explore one of the deepest places in the oceans, more than 35,000 feet down to the bottom of the Pacific. Strange as it may seem, animals were found even at these great depths.

Observatories such as Sealab have been built under the sea so that scientists can remain at the bottom of the sea for extended periods. Methods are being explored by which to capture and maintain for further study in special pressurized aquariums certain animals found at these depths.

The Ocean Currents

An important task in oceanography is the study of ocean currents. One of the simplest ways of studying surface currents is to put empty bottles or other floating objects into the water and chart their paths. They will be carried along by the currents.

The propeller type *current meter* is a sophisticated way of measuring the speed of ocean currents. The current meter works very much like the anemometer which measures wind speeds. The rate at which the propeller turns depends upon the speed of the ocean current.

It is more difficult to study deep currents in the ocean. One of the devices used is the *neutral buoyancy float*. This instrument is essentially a tube that will withstand compression. Water is slightly compressed by the weight of the water above it. By carefully controlling the over-all density of the tube, it can be made to float at a desired level in the ocean. The tube can carry a small sound emitter that can be detected with instruments in a nearby oceanographic vessel. The movement of the neutral buoyancy float can be checked, thus indicating the speed and direction of the underwater current. This device has made possible the discovery of the great deep currents that so often flow in a direction opposite to surface current.

Ocean Temperatures

The temperatures at different depths of the ocean are taken with specially designed recording thermometers called *bathythermographs*. One of the special problems in constructing such thermometers is preventing the great pressures from influencing the temperature readings. The great pressure can squeeze a thermometer and make it read too high. For a number of years the waters near the bottom of the Antarctic were unexplainably thought to be seven degrees higher than they should be. Later it was discovered that this high reading was caused by the great pressure on the thermometer sent deep into the ocean.

THE OCEAN CURRENTS

When Ponce de Leon, in his quest for the fountain of youth, tried to sail south around the tip of Florida, he encountered a powerful ocean current. Even though there was a strong wind filling his sails, he was unable to make progress against the current. One of his ships, which was unable to anchor, was carried to the north by the current. Ponce de Leon had encountered the Florida current that flows northward along the coast of Florida.

Perhaps the most famous of the ocean currents is the Gulf Stream. This great stream of water flows out of the Caribbean Sea and the Gulf of Mexico, along the southeastern coast of the United States, and is deflected across the Atlantic Ocean. Some of it circles to the south, but a large part of it flows past the British Isles and Northwestern Europe. In places, the Gulf Stream is ninety-five miles wide. It travels at speeds of up to six miles an hour and transports more than a thousand times as much water as the Mississippi River. The water in the Gulf Stream is warm, and although it is about the same latitude as Labrador, Northwestern Europe has a comparatively mild climate because of the Gulf Stream.

There are other important currents. The Labrador current that moves down from the north along the eastern coast of North America chills the venturesome bather along the New England coast. The life-giving Humboldt current is a large ocean stream of cold water flowing along the west coast of South America that probably contains more life than any other section of the ocean. Along the equator there are the Equatorial currents in both the Atlantic and Pacific that flow from east to west. The Pacific Equatorial current carried Thor Heyerdahl and his men in the *Kon-Tiki* from South America to an island in Polynesia.

Forces Behind the Ocean Currents

One of the major forces behind some ocean currents is the wind. The wind blowing across the surface of the ocean causes the water to move in the same direction. For example, just north of the equator the Trade Winds blow regularly from the northeast. In the Atlantic, they are undoubtedly a factor in setting up the Gulf Stream by blowing surface water into and out of the Caribbean Sea and the Gulf of Mexico. Farther north there are the Westerlies. These are factors in setting up ocean currents that flow from west to east in the northern latitudes.

Other ocean currents are essentially convection currents set up by the heating and cooling of water. Warm water is less dense than cold water. Therefore, the denser cold water will tend to push the warmer water upward and outward. This is another factor contributing to the Gulf Stream. Water in the tropical areas such as the Caribbean and the Gulf of Mexico receive comparatively large amounts of energy from the sun. The water in these regions is heated and pushed upward and outward by the deep cold water coming down from the north.

The rotation of the earth also affects the ocean currents. This is called the *Coriolis effect*. Looking down upon the earth from a point above the North Pole, an observer would see the earth spinning from west to east. The regions near the equator are moving faster than those near the poles. At the equator the earth is turning at about one thousand miles per hour while at the latitude of Oslo, Norway, the speed is only about five hundred miles per hour. An ocean current flowing from the equator northward retains some of this speed and veers to the east. A current flowing toward the equator from the north will veer to the west because the earth underneath it is spinning faster than it is. In the Northern Hemisphere currents tend to veer to the right. In the Southern Hemisphere the currents will veer to the left.

Ocean currents are also set up by differences in the saltiness of water. Salty water is denser than fresh water; therefore, it tends to sink to the bottom. Because of the high rate of evaporation, water in the Mediterranean flows out along the bottom of the Straits of Gibraltar into the Atlantic. The speed of this bottom current is so great that some instruments sent down to measure it have been smashed against the rocks at the bottom. The relatively fresh water from the Atlantic flows into the Mediterranean near the surface. During World War II, German submarines used the surface and bottom currents to pass through the Straits of Gibraltar without having to use their engines.

The Heat Balance of the Earth

The earth receives almost all of its energy from the sun. Since the flow of this energy from the sun to the earth is continuous year after year, it might be expected that the earth gradually would become hotter and hotter. However, there is little or no evidence that this is taking place. Therefore, the earth must be radiating energy at about the same rate as it receives it to make the average temperatures remain fairly constant. This balance between the energy received and the energy re-radiated is called the *heat balance* of the earth.

Solar energy is not received equally over the surface of the earth. The tropical areas near the equator receive a great deal more radiation than the polar regions. In fact, the tropical areas receive more radiant energy than is radiated back into space. However, some of the energy received in the tropics is transferred to the temperate and polar regions of the earth where more energy is re-radiated out into space than is received.

The energy is transferred from the tropics in the direction of the poles largely by the convective movement of masses of air and water. Because water has such a large heat capacity, the ocean currents are a major mechanism of transfer of heat energy. The water is heated by solar energy. As it expands and becomes less dense, it is forced outward by the colder water that wells up from underneath. When the warm ocean currents reach the colder temperature regions, some of the heat energy is transferred to the nearby land surfaces and the atmosphere, and some of the energy is re-radiated into space.

The ocean currents, as well as the atmospheric winds, are actually driven by energy received by the earth. Since any mechanism that utilizes heat energy to produce motion is called a heat engine, the ocean currents and the atmospheric currents may both be considered heat engines.

Some Effects of Ocean Currents

Ocean currents have very profound effects upon nearby land surfaces. The Gulf Stream, for example, makes Northwestern Europe and the British Isles habitable. Labrador, which is at about the same latitude as Northwestern Europe, has a very cold climate and supports a relatively small population. Northwestern Europe is one of the most densely populated areas on the earth, and tropical palm trees survive in the south of Britain.

The cold Humboldt current of Antarctic water that surfaces off the coast of South America and flows along its western shore affects all phases of life in Western South America. Since cold waters can hold in solution large amounts of the oxygen and carbon dioxide that are needed by living things, the Humboldt current supports a tremendous amount of life. One of the forms of life supported by the tremendous numbers of fish in the Humboldt current are the Guano birds. The Guano birds feed on the multitudinous small fish that have, in turn, found nurture in the rich crops of plankton that thrive on the minerals and life-giving gases dissolved in the Humboldt current. The droppings from the Guano bird form guano deposits that are one of the world's richest sources of nitrates.

Infrequently, the Humboldt current is deflected away from the South American coast. These years of *El Niño* are years of disaster. The small fish and other animals in the coastal waters starve. As they are the food supply for the Guano birds, many of the birds also die. More of the warm water than usual enters the atmosphere and torrential rains may fall in areas where there usually are few rains at all, with destructive effects on adobe homes and the loosely held soil on steep mountainsides.

The ocean currents determine the location of important fishing grounds. Most fish are found in the cold currents that support the myriad forms of smaller life that provide the sustenance for fish. The great fishing banks in the North Atlantic are in areas of cold water as are those in the Pacific. In fact, the economies of nations such as Iceland and Norway, that depend heavily upon fishing, can be greatly affected by slight fluctuations in the temperatures of the ocean waters in their traditional fishing grounds.

The Over-all Circulation in the Oceans

The great ocean currents are driven by the sun and the spin of the earth. In the Northern Hemisphere the surface currents make a clockwise pattern, while in the Southern Hemisphere the pattern is counterclockwise. These surface currents are largely due to the action of the winds on the surface and the expansion of the warmer water as it is heated in the tropics.

Beneath the surface there are gigantic currents that flow in the opposite direction to the surface currents. The Cromwell current, for example, is a huge ocean river, perhaps 250 miles wide and 700 feet deep, that flows eastward at a speed of about three miles per hour beneath the westward flowing Pacific Equatorial current. There apparently is a similar reverse flow beneath the Gulf Stream and other ocean currents. These deeper currents are probably composed of the surface waters that have cooled and descended.

Near the bottom of the oceans there is a slow deep current. Much of this water probably comes from the Antarctic, where it becomes very cold and hence quite dense and settles to the bottom. This deep, near-freezing water moves slowly northward at a very slow rate and fills most of the ocean deeps.

THE OCEAN BOTTOMS

At one time the bottoms of the oceans were thought to be like smooth, gently, sloping plains. Now it is known that there are more rugged, higher mountains and deeper canyons on the ocean floor than on the continents of the earth. Most studies of the ocean bottom are recent, and the new findings have upset previously held theories. Indeed, finding satisfactory explanations for many of the new discoveries is an exciting challenge to oceanographers.

The Ocean Deeps

The areas of great depth in the ocean are called the *ocean deeps*. In the western Pacific, there is at least one place where the bottom of the ocean is more than 36,000 feet below the surface. The highest mountain on any continent, Mount Everest (29,028 feet), could be put into this ocean deep and still be covered by several thousand feet of water.

Many of the ocean deeps are at the edges of the oceans. The Philippine Trench lies just to the east of the Philippine Islands. In fact, the Pacific Ocean seems to be almost ringed by deep, awesome trenches and, on land, young mountain chains such as the Rockies and the Andes. Along the edges of the Atlantic there are such trenches as the Puerto Rico Trench and a trench off Cape Horn.

The ocean deeps are the most forbidding parts of the oceans. There is no light; consequently, there is no plant growth. The pressure of the thousands of feet of water overhead is tremendous. Still there is life in these deeps. Bathyscaphe exploration of the Marianas Trench revealed animal life at its bottom, where animals must live on plant and animal debris that slowly falls from near the surface of the ocean. The pressure on the bodies of these organisms is balanced by pressure on the inside. When animals from deep in the ocean are brought to the surface, the pressure on the outside becomes less than that on the inside, and the animals literally explode.

The origin of the ocean deeps is not known. However, there probably is some connection between the ocean deeps and the nearby mountain chains. Some of the mountains are, or have been, active volcanoes. It may be that the pushing up of the vast quantities of materials that make up mountains results in a settling of material into cavities that are formed. Some of the settling and slipping may lead to the formation of the ocean deeps.

Mountains Under the Sea

Strange as it may seem, some of the world's highest and largest mountains rise up from the ocean bottoms. Many of these mountains, although they may be many thousand feet high, are completely covered with water. The peaks of some of these mountains rise out of the water to form islands.

Mauna Kea on the island of Hawaii is the world's highest and largest mountain with its top more than thirty thousand feet above the floor of the Pacific. With this height, it rises much higher above its surroundings than Mount Everest.

The greatest mountain chain on the surface of the earth is the Atlantic Ridge which stretches from the south of Iceland underneath the Atlantic to the far South Atlantic, curving eastward into the Indian Ocean. The Atlantic Ridge is more than ten thousand miles long and in some places more than five hundred miles wide. Such Atlantic islands as the Azores and Ascension Island are really high mountain peaks in the Atlantic Ridge.

During World War II, some interesting submerged mountains were found in the Pacific. These mountains are flat-topped, and it appears that their flat tops have been worn smooth by wave action. It may be that these mountains once rose above the sea, and then sank as the ocean bottom was depressed under their weight.

Many of the ocean mountains are either active or extinct volcanoes; almost all of them may be volcanic in origin. Sometimes the tops of these volcanoes can be seen as the lava they spew out forms new islands in the Atlantic or Pacific. The Indian Ocean is the only ocean that apparently does not have a rugged ocean bottom with mountains and deeps. Much of it seems to be underlain by a thick sheet of cooled lava much like the thick sheets of igneous rocks that cover large areas of the Pacific Northwest and the Deccan Plateau in India.

Continental Shelves

The continental shelves are really extensions of the continents where the land gently slopes under the sea. The continental shelf off the east coast of North America may be as much as 150 miles wide. Along the Pacific coast, on the other hand, the continental shelf is much narrower. This seems to be characteristic of places where there are young mountain chains, such as the Rockies, near the edge of the ocean.

The waters over the continental shelves are usually only a few hundred feet deep. These waters are often rich with plant and animal life. In the shallow areas light may reach the bottom so that plants can live at the bottom and manufacture food. Most of the world's fisheries are found over the continental shelves; the schemes to use the ocean to grow food usually envisage the utilization of the waters over the continental shelves.

Some of the interesting features of the continental shelves are the long, deep canyons that cut into the shelves off the mouths of some of the large rivers. One of the most famous of these is the Hudson Canyon which is a large gash in the continental shelf more than 150 miles long off the mouth of the Hudson River. These canyons are V-shaped with steep walls often much deeper than the Grand Canyon of the Colorado. Although it is not known how these canyons were formed, it has been suggested that they are the results of currents or avalanches of mud sliding out of the continental shelves near the mouths of rivers. An observation that supports this view is that at the mouths of these canyons there are smooth "plains" that may have been formed by the mud flow.

Minerals at the Ocean Bottom

The ocean bottoms are, and can be, sources of great wealth. Great pools of petroleum lie underneath some of the continental shelves. Some of the richest oil fields in the world are found in the shallow waters of the Persian Gulf and the Gulf of Mexico.

Apparently, in many places on the ocean bottom there are large numbers of potato-shaped nodules that are as much as 10 inches across. These nodules are especially rich in manganese and also contain such valuable substances as nickel, cobalt, and copper.

The manganese in these nodules may have been leached out of the soil and carried by rivers to the ocean, or it may have come from volcanic action at the ocean bottom. Some of it may have been leached from undersea rocks. As the manganese settled out of solution, it carried with it small amounts of nickel, cobalt, and copper. The minerals probably settle out around small objects such as lumps of clay or teeth from dead animals, and eventually fairly large nodules of minerals are formed. Someday these nodules will probably be mined for their mineral content.

The Ocean Bottoms and a Record of the Past

Year upon year, sediment is deposited at the bottom of the sea. These layers of sediment are something like the growth rings of a tree. From them some indication of conditions in the past can be obtained. A study of ocean sediments reveals something about climate on the continents where the sediments originated. Encased in the sediments may be fossils of living things that populated the oceans in the past. If a hole could be drilled through all of these sediments, the drill core would be a rich source of information about the history of the earth and its inhabitants. To date, few fossils have been found that are older than 500 million years. By 500 million years ago, however, most of the large groups of plants and animals, except the vertebrates, had already appeared on the earth. The ocean bottoms may provide even further information about the development of living things on the earth.

In some places under the oceans, the earth's crust is only 11,000 to 15,000 feet thick. A hole drilled through the earth's crust in such a place, a *Mohole*, down to the Mohorovicic discontinuity which is the boundary between the crust and the mantle, promises to provide more information about the history of the earth as well as about the structure of the earth's interior.

THE OCEANS AND LIFE

Life on earth undoubtedly began in the ocean. There, all the things that are necessary for life are readily available; conditions remain very much the same season upon season, year after year, and the early organisms would not have had to adapt themselves to rapidly changing conditions of temperature and moisture, such as those on the land. Many animals, such as the amphibians, return to the water for part of their life cycle. The bodies of many living things, including man, are made up largely of water. Water is one of the prime essentials for life on this planet.

The plants and animals of the sea have no need for special structures to support their bodies, for the water environment provides the support. Animals the size of the whale probably could not exist on the land. A whale that is washed up onto the shore will die as it is crushed by the weight of its own body.

Plant life in the oceans is limited to the upper part of the ocean where light can penetrate. This is because light is required for the food-producing process of photosynthesis. All plants and animals are dependent upon this process for their food. Therefore, all organisms in the ocean are dependent upon the food that is produced by plants near the surface. The animal dwellers of the deep are dependent upon the animal and plant remains that float down to them from above.

Most of the living things in the ocean are very small, often single-celled. These are the plankton that float helplessly with each swirl and current of their ocean home. At the other extreme are the huge whales, the largest animals on earth. Since they are mammals, they belong to the same group of animals as man. The octopus with its eight tentacles, the dolphin with its speed and seeming intelligence, the squid that can becloud the water around it, the sea stars that can crush the hardest clam, and the creatures of the deep with their odd luminescence are a few of the many examples of the wide variety among the animals that make the sea their home. The plants also exhibit a wide variety, ranging from the one-celled diatoms that are the food for so many to the giant kelp that may be stretched to a length of tens of feet. This variety of plants and animals lives and thrives in the oceans of the world.

Obtaining the Requirements for Life in the Oceans

In the oceans, as on land, living things need water, food, oxygen, heat, and a means of protection if they are to survive and live.

Water, of course, is everywhere, but the ocean water surrounding a plant or an animal also has to contain all of the other requirements for life. Water and all other requirements pass through membranes either at the surface of the organism or within specialized organs such as intestines or gills. There is a tendency for solutions to flow through a permeable membrane until there is an equal concentration of solution on each side of the membrane. This process is called *diffusion*. The diffusion pressure in organisms that live in the water is relatively small, because the internal composition of sea organisms is quite similar to that of sea water.

Most of the organisms that live in the sea are small, and in many ways this is an advantage. Small organisms have comparatively more surface area through which nutrients can pass. As a spherical object increases in size, its volume increases as the cube of the radius according to the formula

$$V = \frac{4}{3} \pi r^3$$

However, the surface area through which nutrients can be absorbed increases only as the square of the radius according to the formula

$$A = 4\pi r^2$$

All larger organisms have developed specialized surfaces, such as flat leaves in plants and gills in fish, through which the necessities of life can be absorbed.

All living things need oxygen, and plants need carbon dioxide to manufacture food. Both oxygen and carbon dioxide become available to plants and animals as these gases dissolve in water. Organisms of the sea do not get oxygen by splitting H_2O. The hydrogen and oxygen in water are bound together much too tightly to be decomposed in this way. Cold water can hold more oxygen and carbon dioxide in solution than can warm water. As cold tap water that has been placed in a tumbler warms, bubbles form along the sides of the tumbler. These are bubbles of air that have been forced out of solution. Because cold water can hold in solution more of these gases needed by living things, the colder areas of the ocean are richer in life than the warm. Places where cold currents well up from the bottom bringing with them rich supplies of mineral matter are especially productive of life.

Sunlight is necessary in the process of making food through photosynthesis. However, light does not travel as readily through water as does sound. Usually, sunlight cannot penetrate more than two hundred feet into ocean water. This means that almost all the food needed by living things in the ocean is manufactured within about two hundred feet of the surface.

But how about life in the ocean deeps? As has already been noted, life in the deepest waters of the oceans is sustained by the food that drifts down from above. They, too, then, are dependent upon the zone of light near the surface of the ocean for the manufacture of their food, the remains of both plants and animals that slowly drift downward to the bottom. Apparently, there is sufficient oxygen dissolved in the cold waters at the bottoms to sustain the animals that live there.

Organisms are able to live under the great pressure within the oceans because the pressures on the inside balance the pressures on the outside. Many organisms, however, cannot change levels within the sea. A fish brought to the surface from the ocean deep is likely to explode because the great internal pressure is not matched by an equal pressure on the outside. Nitrogen in the blood of a deep sea diver will begin to bubble and he will suffer from the "bends" if he tries to come to the surface too fast. The whale is one animal that can make remarkable adjustments to changing pressure. It has been known to dive to depths of more than three thousand feet and then rise quickly again to the surface to get air. It is not known how whales make the adjustments to the great changes of pressure.

Animals in the oceans have many kinds of devices for protecting themselves. Many employ camouflage. The plaice, for example, can quickly change itself to the color of the ocean bottom. Oysters, crabs, clams, and sea turtles have hard outer shells that serve as armor plate. The squid and sea hare eject ink-like substances in which they can hide. There are other animals that eject stinging poisons and give off electric shock, and some small animals attach themselves to larger animals, such as the whale, for protection. Some small fish protect themselves from their predators by hiding among the stinging tentacles of such animals as the sea anemone. There are fewer places to hide in the oceans than on land, and the organisms of the sea have developed a wide variety of means of protecting themselves.

Food Chains in the Oceans

A food chain is a diagram or record of who eats whom. All food chains on land and in the water start with green plants. They alone have the ability to combine the raw materials carbon dioxide, minerals, and water into food.

The basic food supply in the ocean is the *plankton*. An oceanographer once defined plankton as "those living things caught in a plankton net."

He used the unsatisfactory definition to illustrate the difficulty of defining exactly what is and what is not plankton. Actually, plankton are those small forms of plant and animal life that drift with the currents of the sea. The basic food producers among the plankton are the *diatoms*. Diatoms are small one-celled green plants that can carry on the process of photosynthesis.

Many animals, ranging from the minute copepods to the huge whales, eat plankton directly. Small fish will feed on the copepods, while larger fish will feed on the smaller fish. The large fish may eventually die and begin to sink. At the bottom and on the way to the bottom, the dead fish will provide food for a host of scavengers. Some of the minerals trapped in the dead remains are eventually released, and upward currents of water may bring the minerals to the surface again to take part in the process of photosynthesis.

The food cycle continues to repeat itself. If some part of the cycle is broken, such as happens during an *El Niño* off the coast of South America, there are usually catastrophic results throughout the food chain.

APPROACHES TO TEACHING

Many of the processes that take place in the oceans can be shown and investigated in the classroom. Children who live near the seashore should be encouraged to make various observations of the sea as it rolls in upon the land. In inland areas, many of the same observations can be made on the shores of lakes and reservoirs. Fortunately, a growing number of films are also available to bring the ocean to the classroom.

What is water like?

Although water is a common substance, many children will never have had the experience of examining it carefully.

Fill a clean glass container with water. Ask the children such questions as:
"What is the color of the water?"
"Can you see through it?"
"What is its taste?"
"What does it smell like?"

If samples of ocean water and river water can be obtained, have the children examine them in the same way.

What happens when warm and cold bodies of water meet?

Obtain two milk bottles that have the same size openings. Fill one bottle with warm water and the other with cold. Put a few drops of food coloring or ink in the bottle of warm water. Place a 3 × 5 card over the top of the bottle of cold water. Invert this bottle and place it on top of the bottle of warm water. (The card will be held on the opening by air pressure. The first time you do it you may wish to hold the card on the bottle with your fingers.) Slip the card out from between the two bottles.

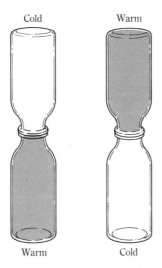

Fig. 9-2 *What happens when warm water meets cold? The dark bottles have colored warm water in them.*

Have the children watch the movement of the warm and cold water. Call their attention to what happens at the point where the two bodies of water meet. Have them explain what happens and relate to processes that take place in the oceans.

Repeat the experiment, but this time place the colored warm water on top of the cold. Why do we get a different reaction in this case?

By pressing the two bottles together, the bottles can be placed on their sides. Children can watch the warm water move up over the cold. Usually, a fairly definite front is formed between the warm water and the cold.

What happens when salt water meets fresh water?

Repeat the activities described above, but now fill one bottle with fresh water and the other with salt water made by dissolving some table salt in fresh water. Relate the results to the salinity currents to be found in such places as the Straits of Gibraltar.

What currents are there in a nearby lake or pond?

A simple way to study the surface currents in a lake or pond is to place some light object, such as an empty bottle, on its surface and chart the direction it floats. This is an excellent research project for children. They may wish to start bottles at various places on the lake or pond and prepare a chart of the currents. They should be encouraged to propose an explanation for the currents they find.

Why do ocean currents tend to turn to the right in the Northern Hemisphere?

The Coriolis effect is one of the more difficult concepts to explain in elementary science. The Coriolis effect is due to the fact that masses of water tend to retain the rotational motion of the region from which they have come. The following demonstration may help.

Spin a globe in a counterclockwise direction (as viewed from the top), and as the globe is spinning, make a chalkmark straight down from the North Pole of the globe. The mark on the globe will be seen to curve to the right. Similarly, an ocean current coming from the North Pole would have little or no rotational velocity. It would tend to veer to the right as the earth spins underneath.

To show what happens when a mass of water moves north or south from the equator, paint a ball bearing with aluminum paint. While the paint is still wet, roll it into a rotating turntable. The ball bearing will acquire some of the rotational velocity of the outer rim of the turntable and veer to the right or left as it moves toward the center, depending on the direction the

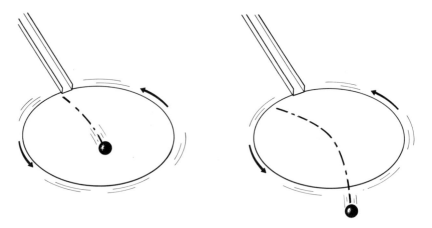

Fig. 9-3 *Because of the spin of the earth, ocean currents tend to veer to the right in the Northern Hemisphere.*

turntable is turning. Similarly, a mass of water near the equator has the rotational velocity of the earth's surface near the equator. As this mass of water moves north it veers to the right because it has a greater rotational velocity than the earth underneath it.

Have the children spin a merry-go-round as fast as they can in a counter-clockwise direction as viewed from above. Have one of the children try to throw a volleyball or basketball at a target on the opposite side of the merry-go-round. Since the ball will have the rotational velocity of the outside of the merry-go-round, the ball will veer to the right. Similarly, an ocean current moving north from the equator will veer to the right.

How much salt is there in different kinds of water?

Put equal amounts of water from a well, a nearby lake or river, rain and, if possible, the ocean into dishes or beakers. Allow the water to evaporate. The process can be speeded up by heating on a hot plate.

The materials left on the bottom after the water evaporates are mineral compounds of various kinds and often are referred to collectively as "salt." In which samples of water was there the greatest amount of salt?

What happens to the air dissolved in water when the water is warmed?

Gases as well as mineral matter are often dissolved in water. Fill a large glass container with cold water from the tap. Warm the water slowly on a hot plate. Do bubbles form at various places along the sides of the container? It might be well to point out that the water is not boiling. Instead, the bubbles are formed by air that has been dissolved in the water.

Since water plants and minerals need air, would more life be expected in cold ocean water or warm?

Do large or small organisms have the most surface area per volume?

When possible, it is highly desirable to relate science and mathematics. Older children who have had elementary work with equations can calculate the relationships between surface area and volume in spherical objects.

$$\text{Surface area} = 4\pi r^2 = 12.57r^2$$
$$\text{Volume} = 4/3\pi r^3 = 4.189r^3$$

How much greater is the surface area of a sphere of 2 millimeter radius than of a sphere 1 millimeter radius? How much greater is its volume?

What happens when water is heated?

Fill a bottle with water. Into the mouth of the bottle insert a one-holed rubber stopper with a piece of glass tubing in it. Note the level of water in the glass tubing. Warm the bottle. What happens to the water as it is warmed? Now cool the water. What happens?

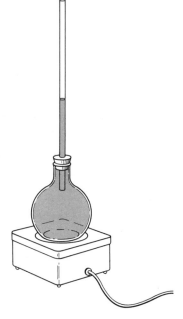

Fig. 9-4 What happens when the water in the flask is heated? Cooled?

What happens when water freezes?

Fill a small bottle with water. Screw the cap on tight and place the bottle in a tin can. Place the tin can in the freezing compartment of a refrigerator. What happens when the water in the bottle freezes?

How does the weight of water compare with that of other liquids?

Measure out and weigh equal quantities of water, kerosene, rubbing alcohol, and any other liquids that can be obtained. Which is the heaviest? What is the significance of this?

Will an object such as a boat float higher in water or in kerosene?

Fill one tall, thin glass container, such as a graduate, three-fourths full of water and fill another to the same height with kerosene. Float identical pencils in each container. In which container does the pencil float the highest? How would the sailing of ships be affected if the world's oceans were filled with a substance such as kerosene rather than water?

How do water and other common liquids compare as solvents?

One of the important characteristics of water is that foods, minerals, and other materials necessary for living things readily dissolve in it. To compare the solvency of common materials in water and another liquid such as kerosene, put equal amounts of water and kerosene into separate beakers. Add a tablespoon of sugar to each and stir. Does the sugar dissolve equally well in both liquids? Repeat with salt.

How do materials pass from the ocean waters into living organisms?

Many small organisms in the oceans are covered by semipermeable membranes through which substances can diffuse. To demonstrate how these work, fill a plastic bag full of water. Add a few drops of phenolphthalein to the water. (Phenolphthalein can be obtained from most scientific supply houses and is an excellent indicator of changes in the acidity of a solution.) Put the bag in a large glass container and clamp it so that the opening is outside the container. Fill the glass container with water to which a small amount of ammonia water is added.

If the ammonia diffuses through the plastic membrane, the solution inside the bag will become pink in color. (You may wish to demonstrate what happens by adding a small amount of ammonia water to some water and phenolphthalein in a separate beaker.) The only way that ammonia can enter the bag is to diffuse through the plastic.

Some plastics are not permeable to ammonia. However, the bags commonly sold in grocery stores usually are permeable.

The children may wish to reverse the demonstration and put the ammonia in the bag and the phenolphthalein on the outside to see if ammonia will diffuse in both directions.

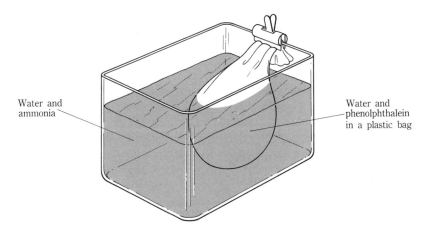

Water and ammonia

Water and phenolphthalein in a plastic bag

Fig. 9-5 *If the liquid in the bag changes color, it is probably due to the ammonia diffusing through the membrane and into the bag.*

How does water change from one phase to another?

One of the remarkable and important characteristics of water is that it can exist in solid, liquid, or gaseous phases within a fairly narrow range of temperatures. To demonstrate how water changes from one phase to another, place some ice cubes in a container and heat the container. The ice cubes will, of course, melt, and water will enter its liquid phase. Continue to heat the water until it boils. In boiling, the water changes to its vapor or gaseous phase.

It might be well to point out that water vapor is invisible. The small clouds that we see when water boils are composed of small water droplets that have condensed from vapor. The small clear space between the spout of a teakettle and the cloud of water droplets is filled with invisible water vapor.

Change of phase in the opposite direction can also be demonstrated. Water vapor will condense into liquid water on a cool surface such as a pan filled with water. The liquid water that is collected can, of course, be frozen again in the freezing compartment of a refrigerator.

How can salt water be distilled?

Children can set up a simple distilling apparatus to distill salt water. Make some salt water by adding table salt to tap water or obtain some ocean water. Have the children dip a finger in the salt water and then taste the water that adheres to their fingers.

Boil the salt water. Above the boiling water, place some object that

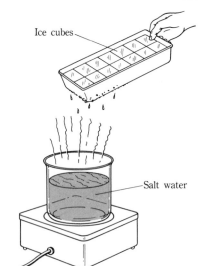

Ice cubes

Salt water

Fig. 9-6 *How do the drops of water that drip off the cold container taste?*

will maintain a cold surface. A pan or dish filled with ice cubes or cold water will work nicely. Have the children taste the drops of water that form on the bottom of the pan. Does it taste the same as the salt water?

INVESTIGATION

At what rate does water travel upward and downward in different soils?

Groundwater travels both upward and downward in soils. However, the rate at which it moves depends upon the nature of the soil.

Obtain four glass lamp chimneys or pieces of wide diameter glass tubing. Fasten pieces of cloth across the bottom ends of the lamp chimneys. Fill two of the chimneys two-thirds full of clayey soil and the other two with sandy soil. Suspend all chimneys from ringstands or tripods and place pans underneath them.

Pour equal amounts of water into a chimney containing sand and one containing clay. Through which soil does the water percolate fastest? Measure the amount of water that percolates through each soil sample. Which soil holds the most water?

Fill two similar glass containers with equal amounts of water. Lower the chimney with dry sandy soil and the one with dry clayey soil into the water. Watch the water rise in the soil. In which does it rise the fastest? Does there seem to be a relationship between the rate at which water travels upward and downward in different soils?

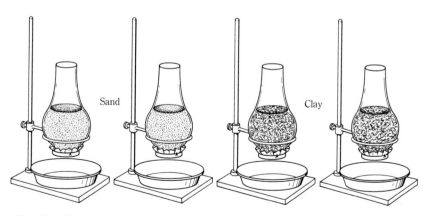

Fig. 9-7 *Pour equal amounts of water into each chimney and measure the amount that percolates through.*

Selected References

CARSON, RACHAEL, *The Sea Around Us*. New York: New American Library, 1951.

DAVIS, KENNETH S., AND DAY, JOHN ARTHUR, *Water: The Mirror of Science*. Garden City, N.Y.: Doubleday & Co., Inc., 1961.

UNITED STATES DEPARTMENT OF AGRICULTURE, *Water*. U.S. Department of Agriculture Yearbook 1955. Washington, D.C.: U.S. Government Printing Office, 1955.

YASSO, WARREN E., *Oceanography*. New York: Holt, Rinehart & Winston, 1965.

ZIM, HERBERT S., AND INGLE, LESTER, *Seashores: A Guide to Animals and Plants Along the Beaches*. New York: Simon & Schuster, Inc., 1955.

READINGS FOR THE PRIMARY GRADES

ELTING, MARY, *Water Come—Water Go*. Irvington-on-Hudson, N.Y.: Harvey House, Inc., Publishers, 1964.

EVANS, EVA KNOX, *The Snow Book*. Boston: Little, Brown & Co., 1965.

KINNEY, JEAN, *What Does the Tide Do*. New York: Young Scott Books, 1966.

READINGS FOR THE INTERMEDIATE GRADES

BRINDZE, RUTH, *The Rise and Fall of the Seas*. New York: Harcourt, Brace & World, Inc., 1964.

CARLISLE, NORMAN, *Riches of the Sea: the New Science of Oceanology*. New York: Sterling Publishing Co., Inc., 1967.

CARSON, RACHAEL, AND WHITE, ANNE TERRY, *The Sea Around Us*. A Special Edition for Young Readers. New York: Simon and Schuster, Inc., 1958.

GASKELL, T. F., *World Beneath the Oceans*. Garden City, N.Y.: Natural History Press, 1964.

GEORGE, JEAN CRAIGHEAD, *Spring Comes to the Ocean*. New York: Thomas Y. Crowell Co., 1965.

JACOBSON, WILLARD J., LAUBY, CECILIA J., AND KONICEK, RICHARD D., *The Ocean*. New York: American Book Co., 1968.

SHANNON, TERRY, AND PAYZANT, CHARLES, *Project Sealab*. San Carlos, Calif.: Golden Gate Junior Books, 1966.

WATERS, BARBARA AND JOHN, *Salt-Water Aquariums*. New York: Holiday House, Inc., 1967.

SELECTED FILMS

Ocean Currents. McGraw-Hill. Shows the ocean currents and how they are affected by various forces.

Water and Life. McGraw-Hill. Shows many of the ways in which water is critical for life.

10 The World of Living Organisms

If a visitor from outside the solar system were to circle the planet earth and report his findings, the most interesting and important feature of his report probably would be, "There is life on this planet."

Life on the earth exists in a myriad of forms. There are three great kingdoms of living organisms: the *plant kingdom*, the *animal kingdom*, and the *protists* (some kinds of microorganisms). Within these kingdoms there is great variety. For example, there are more than 650,000 kinds of insects. In addition to the millions of kinds of organisms that exist today, the fossil record contains evidence of many kinds of organisms that once existed but have now become extinct. Great variety is one of the key factors in the evolution of the species.

Another important feature of life on the planet earth is that it exists almost everywhere. Life is found at the equator and at the poles. It is found at the top of the highest mountains and at the bottom of the ocean deeps. Living organisms exist in the boiling water of hot springs, and others can survive being frozen in ice. Perhaps the only places on the earth where there is no life is in the caldrons of molten lava in the craters of volcanoes. Here, apparently, the temperatures are too high for the existence of life. The ability of some life to exist under extreme conditions is one of the factors supporting the view that life probably exists in many other places in the universe.

Many living organisms are able to make responses to changes in the environment. The leaves of corn will curl during a drought, and the leaves of many plants will slowly turn in the direction of sunlight. Moths and other insects will be attracted to light, and many animals will shy away from a hot flame. Higher animals are not only able to respond to stimuli, they are also able to remember their responses. The acme of the development of intelligence is found in man. Man is not only able to remember but can symbolize his experiences and use these symbols to think and plan for his future actions.

THE LIVING AND THE NON-LIVING

What is living and what is non-living? This may seem like an easy question, and in most cases it can be answered with considerable assurance. Certainly, the children in the classroom are alive while their desks and chairs are not; the birds that fly through the air are alive, while the telephone wires on which they perch are not. These are obvious and easy differentiations to make. As in the case of a candle flame, however, there are objects in the environment which may be quickly classified as living or non-living but when subjected to a more thorough examination cause the investigator to think second thoughts.

Characteristics of Living Organisms

Movement

Many living organisms, especially animals, are able to move. Many plants are also able to turn their leaves in the direction of a light source, and plants such as the mimosa and the Venus flytrap may respond quickly to touch. However, a seed or spore may lie dormant for a long period of time without moving, yet it would be classified as living. While all animals can move during some stage of their life cycle, many animals such as the oyster do not move during much of their life history. However, "self-propelled" movement is a characteristic of many living things.

Response to stimuli

Most living organisms can make some kind of a response to changes in the environment. The leaves of the corn plant will curl when there is a lack of water, and the microscopic ameba will react to chemicals dropped into the water. Higher animals have well-developed nervous systems that are sensitive to stimuli and can direct complicated responses. But again, many plants and animals in the egg stage of development do not respond in obvious ways to stimuli from the environment.

Use of food

All living organisms use food of some kind as a source of energy and raw materials for growth and repair. All of this food is manufactured by green plants through the process of photosynthesis, and it is used by both plants and animals. However, a number of non-living objects such as internal combustion engines use fuel in a way similar to the use of food by living organisms.

Respiration

Living organisms obtain energy through the oxidation of food in the living cell. Oxygen is taken into the organism, and carbon dioxide is discharged as a waste product. Again, however, internal combustion engines also use oxygen and discharge carbon dioxide.

Growth and repair

Living organisms are able to use food for growth and repair. In twenty years a six-pound baby can become a two-hundred-pound fullback. Also, when a finger is cut, the cut will eventually be repaired. Of course, almost all organisms reach a point when there is no more growth, and, if the injury to the organism is serious enough, it will not be repaired. Also, a snowball that rolls down a hillside will grow, and some machines can automatically replace a part when it is worn out.

Reproduction

Many living organisms are able to reproduce their kind, and many students believe that this is the key characteristic of living organisms. But, of course, many individual organisms do not reproduce. Among humans, for example, young children and old people do not reproduce, and yet they certainly are very much alive. A seed crystal dropped into a saturated solution may cause many other crystals to form. Is this reproduction?

Distinguishing Living and Non-living Matter

There is no clear, unequivocal test which will differentiate between the living and the non-living. The differentiation has to be made in terms of a number of characteristics such as those that have been listed.

The question of living or non-living is further complicated if organisms that were once alive but are now dead are considered. While dead organisms do not have many of the characteristics of the living, the material is composed of cells and the "stuff of life"—protoplasm. Also, there is the difficult question of when an organism is dead. Human hair, for example, will continue to grow even after the body has been legally declared dead. Is it "really" dead?

Some forms of matter, such as some viruses, are especially difficult to classify as living or non-living. At times, the viruses have the characteristics of living organisms, including the ability to reproduce. But at other times, they appear to be more like crystals. The viruses apparently are on the borderline between the living and the non-living and at times are living and at other times are not.

Many living organisms contain materials that are non-living. The cork in trees is non-living. In fact, much of the material in human bones is not living. However, even though organisms may contain considerable non-living material, the entire organism is considered to be alive.

To demonstrate how difficult it may be to differentiate between the living and the non-living, it may be useful to consider a candle flame—an object that most children would consider to be non-living.

Fig. 10-1 In what ways is a candle flame like and unlike a living organism?

Look at the flame of a candle. Is it alive? Let's look at some of the characteristics of living organisms:

1. The candle flame *moves*. If there are air currents in the room it may flicker a great deal.
2. It *responds* to a number of stimuli. Clap hands near it. It will probably react to the sudden gust of wind passing by.
3. The candle flame uses *food*. In fact it will burn many of the same kinds of materials that are taken into the human body as food.
4. *Oxygen* is used by the candle flame and *carbon dioxide* given off.
5. A flame can *grow*. A lighted candle near a window curtain may set a house on fire.
6. There is *reproduction* in the sense that, if a lighted candle is brought brought near the wick of an unlighted candle, the second candle will be lighted.

Is a candle flame alive? Children, after considering the candle, may not be as certain as they usually are initially as to what is living and non-living.

The Cell

When Anton van Leeuwenhoek constructed the first crude microscope and examined drops of water, he was amazed at the variety of small creatures that he saw. Although he did not realize it, Leeuwenhoek had opened up for study the world of the microorganisms, and his invention made it possible to make much more detailed studies of the nature of living matter.

The scientist and inventor Robert Hooke, using a compound microscope that he had invented, investigated very thin slices of cork. He was amazed to see that the slices of cork seemed to contain neat rows of holes. To Hooke, these holes looked like the cells in honeycombs where bees store honey, and he called them cells.

The cells that Hooke observed were, of course, dead. However, cells were found in almost all living matter. Cells have often been called the "building blocks of life," and unless the matter being examined contains cells it can be seriously questioned as to whether it has ever been alive. Actually, this is one criterion that the candle flame does not meet and on the basis of this it can be said to be non-living.

In these building blocks some of the most important life processes take place. It is in the cell that digested and assimilated food combines with oxygen to release energy. While a similar reaction takes place in the candle flame at temperatures of several hundred degrees, it is remarkable that special chemicals called *enzymes* make it possible for the oxidation of food to take place at the body temperature of 37.5°C. (98.6°F.). The cells discharge the wastes from this oxidation. The organism grows as the cells reproduce by dividing to form two cells where there was one before. New cells are formed to replace cells that may have been killed when an organism is injured, and there is also a continuous replacement of old cells by new in living organisms.

Cell structures

While most living matter contains cells, there are both great similarities and differences between the cells of different organisms. (There is a serious question as to whether the viruses and some fungi actually have cells.) However, there are certain generalized structures in most cells that can be seen by children through a microscope. Around the cell there is a boundary. In plant cells this boundary, called the *cell wall*, is thicker than the *cell membrane* that surrounds animal cells. In fact, one of the ways to determine whether an organism is a plant or animal is to determine whether its cells have walls or membranes. If a cell is stained with a solution, such as dilute iodine, part of the cell will become darker than the rest. This is

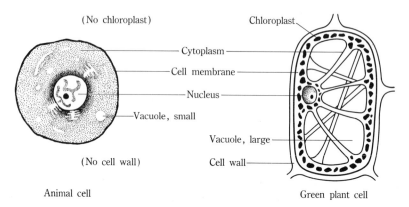

Fig. 10-2 *Compare these generalized structures of an animal cell and a plant cell.*

the *nucleus*. Among other matter, the nucleus contains the genetic material by which physical characteristics are transmitted from one generation to the next. The rest of the cell is filled with *cytoplasm*. It is in the cytoplasm that many cellular functions such as oxidation take place.

Cell processes

Materials, usually dissolved in water, enter and leave the cell through the cell wall or cell membrane by the process of *diffusion*. (The diffusion of water through a membrane is called *osmosis*.) The membrane surrounding the cell is a *semipermeable membrane*, that is, some substances will pass through the membrane while others will not. In general, substances will move through semipermeable membranes from the side of higher concentration to the side of lower concentration. For example, if the concentration of a food material is higher outside the cell than inside, there will be a tendency for the food material to diffuse into the cell. Similarly, as waste products become concentrated within the cell, they will diffuse outward through the cell membrane to areas of lower concentration. While diffusion is the general process of material transfer into and out of cells, there are processes called *active transport* by which some substances can move through membranes from low concentrations to high. The materials that enter the cell take part in the chemical processes that are essential to life.

One of the essential cellular processes is that of energy release. This is the energy that is used by organisms for movement and to carry on all vital processes. To understand this process, compare it to the burning candle which is also a energy-release process.

1. Similar sources of energy. The energy is released as chemical bonds in complex molecules are broken. In the living cell, carbon compounds are common sources of energy and one of the compounds that is broken down is the simple sugar glucose $C_6H_{12}O_6$.
2. Smaller simpler compounds are formed. In both the cell and the candle the two major products of the energy release are carbon dioxide and water. Both carbon dioxide and water are waste products and have to be removed.
3. Additional oxygen is needed. In both the cell and the candle the process of energy release involves the oxidation of the complex compound such as glucose. In the candle the oxygen comes from the air, and in the living cell oxygen from the air is obtained through respiration.
4. In the living cell the oxidation goes on at much lower temperatures than in the candle. Enzymes produced by cells serve as catalysts that make it possible for the energy-release reactions to go on at the temperature of the living organism.
5. Energy in the cell is stored in a chemical form so that it can be used gradually as needed. Energy is given off by a candle as long as it is burning, but in the cell the energy is stored in another large molecule. Energy is then released gradually by the breaking down of this large molecule.

Chemical processes that lead to energy release are carried on in the cells, the basic building blocks of life. It is remarkable that the fuels are molecules containing carbon somewhat like the molecules that make up the cell. This process has been compared to burning wood in a wooden house. But, as in the wood stove, the process is controlled, and it is an efficient source of energy.

THE ORIGINS OF LIFE

How did life begin? This is a question that has long perplexed man, and certainly it is asked by many children. In a sense, this is a historical question, but since no observer was there to record the event, it is only in laboratories that the beginnings may possibly be reconstructed.

The first living matter may have originated two and a half billion to three billion years ago when the earth was already at least two billion years old. This allows time for certain events to have occurred that were precursors of life and time for the evolution of the forms of life existing today. Living matter may have originated in the following way.

The Primeval Earth

The atmosphere of the early earth was probably different from that of today. The early atmosphere probably had much more hydrogen, and this hydrogen combined with many other elements to form such compounds as methane (CH_4), ammonia (NH_3), and water (H_2O). There was much less oxygen in the air, and this permitted much more ultraviolet light from the sun to penetrate to the earth surface. Now the earth is largely protected from this ultraviolet light by the ozone (O_3) that is formed in large quantities in the upper reaches of the atmosphere. The ultraviolet light was an important source of energy needed for the eventual origination of living matter. The Russian authority on the origins of life A. I. Oparin has suggested that an atmosphere with little oxygen was also essential for the formation of the building blocks of life.

There was a great deal of water on the earth. Then, as now, more than two-thirds of the earth's surface was covered by ocean. Various minerals had already been washed off the solid part of the earth and dissolved in the waters of the oceans. Also in solution in the oceans were hydrogen, methane, and ammonia. Thus, the ingredients for living matter were to be found in the waters of the oceans, and it has been suggested that living matter may first have been formed in tidal pools near the edge of the sea.

How It May Have Happened

A basic characteristic of living matter is that the molecules are complex. In order to build complex molecules, energy is needed and this energy probably came from the ultraviolet light. Through the action of ultraviolet light, some molecules of ammonia, methane, and carbon dioxide in the primeval pool may have become joined together to form more complex molecules. In the millions and hundreds of millions of years that followed, these complex molecules may have joined together to form more complex molecules, and then joined again and again and again.

Some of these more complex molecules contained the element carbon, which has the property of being able to link up with other atoms in more ways than any other element. Life on the earth is based on the element carbon. In fact, organic (meaning related to life) substances are defined as containing complex molecules based on carbon. Many authorities believe that carbon is necessary for living matter to exist.

Under the conditions that existed in these primeval pools, some of the hydrogen, ammonia, methane, and water were eventually rearranged into amino acids. Amino acids are the building blocks from which proteins are formed, and proteins are an important part of living organisms. The nucleic acids that are so important in the living cell are made up of these amino acids.

As these large molecules continued to be exposed to light and to be mixed with other molecules in these tidal pools, nucleic acids may have joined with other nucleic acids. Some nucleic acids could be formed that would only join with other similar nucleic acids and were held together as pairs. When the pairs were split, however, they would join with similar nucleic acids to form new pairs. Note that pairs of nucleic acids have now been formed that can, in a sense, reproduce themselves.

Suppose a nucleic-acid molecule paired with another protein molecule so that the nucleic acid was surrounded by protein. The protein might protect the nucleic-acid nucleus from forces that tend to break down large molecules. These new molecules would then be better able to survive under these primeval conditions. These were, perhaps, the precursors of the nucleus and cytoplasm of the living cell.

These large molecules containing nucleic acids surrounded by proteins are less likely to break down than other molecules. Also, these molecules tend to split and join with similar molecules to increase the number of such molecules. Perhaps, these protein-nucleic acid molecules would join similar molecules to form larger aggregates of molecules.

The large molecules that may have been formed in these pools near the ancient oceans already had two essential characteristics of life: they were able to reproduce like molecules, and they were able to transmit changes that may have taken place in the molecule to the molecules that were reproduced. To a certain extent, the formation of living matter was due to the chance linking of molecules formed under the conditions prevailing in the atmosphere and oceans of the primeval earth. But two billion years probably elapsed between the formation of the planet earth and the origins of living matter. Given two billion years, chance encounters become probable. Some scientists who have studied the problem of origins have concluded that given the conditions that existed on primeval earth and sufficient time, the formation of living matter was almost inevitable. Once formed, its ability to replicate itself led to multiplication of numbers and eventually new and bigger molecules and organisms.

Did It Really Happen This Way?

No one knows, of course, but this is a plausible explanation. It has the advantage that no materials or processes are needed that are not available for study and investigation.

The American scientist Stanley Miller, while he was a graduate student, enclosed the gases believed to have been in the primeval atmosphere (ammonia, methane, hydrogen, and water vapor) in a glass container and subjected the gases to an electric spark. Upon analysis, he found that amino acids were formed, and these are the building blocks for proteins. Variations of this experiment have been carried out many times always with similar results. Thus, laboratory investigations suggest that this is a possible explanation.

THE EVOLUTION OF LIFE

Evolution is the most important and central idea of the life sciences. There are a great variety of living organisms. These organisms live under many kinds of environmental conditions, and different organisms seem to be adapted to live under different conditions. An examination of living organisms leads to the discovery of interesting similarities. An examination of the bodily structures of fish and apes, for example, reveals that both have backbones and four appendages. In some way these similarities have to be explained.

As fossil records are studied, evidences of organisms that no longer exist are revealed. On the other hand, some kinds of organisms that exist at the present time undoubtedly did not exist in past millennia. All of these observations, and many more, can be explained and take on greater significance in terms of the broad and encompassing theory of evolution.

The theory of evolution is an extremely useful one. It makes possible the fitting together of many seemingly disparate facts and provides an effective framework for the continuing study of the world of life. The theory of evolution is basic in the life sciences and is accepted by almost all biological scientists.

Evolution from Single Cells

The first organisms were probably single cell organisms. Several kinds of bacteria, the ameba, and the paramecia are examples of unicellular organisms that exist at the present time. These single-celled organisms were probably formed by the joining together of large numbers of nucleic-acid molecules and the protein molecules that formed the cytoplasm. These single cells had the capability of dividing to form additional cells.

All living material must have energy. As has been noted, the source of the energy to build the complex molecules that were joined together to form living matter was probably ultraviolet light from the sun. The earliest cells also probably obtained their energy directly from the sun. Over a long period of time, a complex molecule called *chlorophyll* evolved in some cells. Chlorophyll, in the presence of light, can cause water and carbon dioxide to unite to form carbohydrates. This provided the cell with a source of energy other than ultraviolet light. It made it possible for energy to be stored in the cell. Some single-celled bacteria contain chlorophyll, and the first cells to manufacture their own food may have been somewhat like these bacteria. Organisms that contain chlorophyll are usually greenish in color. The process whereby light is used to manufacture food is called *photosynthesis*.

Oxygen is an important by-product of the process of photosynthesis. This oxygen is usually released into the atmosphere. The release of this oxygen made possible the evolution of the organisms that use oxygen to oxidize food for energy. In this group are most of the organisms, both plants and animals, that exist today.

There are many more possibilities for life with increase in size. New environments open up, and there are new possibilities for locomotion. One way to enlarge is to merely expand the membrane that surrounds the cytoplasm in the cell. The slime molds, which can often be found on fallen trees, and leaf molds are examples of organisms that enlarged in this way. While some microorganisms, such as the paramecia, have the nucleus in one part of the cell, in the slime molds the nucleate material moves about in the cytoplasm. This makes possible the interaction between the nucleus and the surrounding cytoplasm. But the slime molds are usually spread very thinly over a surface. These kinds of organisms, although they have some advantages over the much smaller microorganisms, lack internal support and can only spread in a thin film over a surface.

Multicellular organization has opened up many evolutionary possibilities. In many cases multicellular organisms develop by having the daughter cells remaining attached to the related cells. In these multicellular organisms there is a little more internal support. In some of these organisms, energy is obtained by keeping the green chlorophyll exposed to the sun. The plant kingdom probably evolved from organisms that obtained energy in this way. The evolution of animals, however, presented more difficulties.

Animal cells must have some external source of food. In general, this food comes from green plants. Also, there must be some system of processing food that enters the organism. The small hydra has the beginnings of a digestive system. The hydra is really a hollow tube. Unlike the digestive systems of higher organisms which are open at both ends, the hydra's tube is open at only one end. It ingests food and egests wastes through the same opening. With this tube it is able to process food for all of its cells. In a similar but much more highly developed digestive system, food is processed for the billions of cells that make up the human body. Food materials still diffuse through membranes into the body. In unicellular organisms this diffusion takes place through the outer membrane covering the cell. But there is a limit to how large organisms can evolve and still depend on diffusion through the outer membranes for all the materials needed for life. By evolving a hollow tube, which in many organisms, including man, is twisted and coiled so that it is many feet long, the surface area is greatly increased.

With the evolution of size, came specialization among cells and structures of cells. Some cells and structures perform digestive functions. Other structures process the oxygen from the atmosphere, distribute food and oxygen to all the cells, remove waste materials, and carry on the many functions necessary to sustain life. But this specialization made possible greater variety among living organisms from the giant whale and enormous kelp to the tiny diatoms and microscopic hydra. This great variety has led to organisms that inhabit almost all of the available environments on the planet earth.

From Water to Land

Life originated in an aquatic medium. Some forms of life are almost entirely water; in fact, about 70 per cent of the weight of the human body is water. The gases and minerals needed by the primeval organisms were dissolved in the water and could diffuse through membranes into the organism to be used for food and growth. And the water medium provided external support for the jelly-like microorganisms.

But another environment was available—the terrestrial environment, the dry land of the continents. The first organisms to invade the terrestrial environment may have been such plants as the primitive mosses that remained very small and could only live in places like the shores of seas and rivers that remained moist all of the time. Since there were advantages such as increased sunlight and absence of competition, plants may have evolved that could live in environments where there was less moisture, although all organisms need access to water in some way or other. The organisms that successfully invaded the terrestrial environment needed such developments as the following:

1. Outer coverings to reduce the loss of water to the atmosphere. The waxy coatings of plants and the outer shells of turtles are examples of such coverings.
2. A source of water and minerals. Many organisms get the water and minerals they need from the soil.

3. A transportation system for water, food, and minerals. The vascular systems in plants and circulatory systems in animals carry these necessities throughout the organism.
4. A system of support for the organism. Fibers in plants and skeletons and exoskeletons in animals provide the support that prevents terrestrial organisms from collapsing.

The invasion of the terrestrial environment led to the evolution of a great diversity of forms among land plants and animals. Among the plants, the mosses were followed by varieties of ferns, evergreens, and flowering plants. The evolution of sexual reproduction among both plants and animals was a mechanism for increasing variety. Among the animals there were amphibians, reptiles, arthropods, birds, and mammals. During successive periods in evolutionary history, different kinds of plants and animals became dominant. Although certain kinds of organisms ceased to be dominant, many of them remained on the scene. Some kinds of organisms such as the giant ferns and the dinosaurs have become extinct; yet other kinds of ferns and reptiles are still with us. It is noteworthy that probably no major basic type of animal became extinct, and most types of plants also remain with us. New kinds of organisms have evolved while the older types continue to exist. All of this leads to great variety among living organisms.

Variety Among Living Organisms

One of the most profound observations that children can make on a trip to the zoo is of the variety among living organisms. They may see the giant rhinoceros and the tiny ant, the black panther and the white polar bear. A visit to a botanical gardens or even a walk through a forest can reveal great diversity among the plant kingdom. There are almost one and a half million species of living organisms that have been discovered and described.

This variety among living organisms can be examined and considered in many ways. With children it may be advantageous to view it from the following standpoints. Although examples could be given from either the plant or animal kingdom, variety among animals may be of more interest to many youngsters.

1. *Size*. Animals range in size from unicellular organisms, such as ameba that can be seen only with the aid of a microscope, to the gigantic whale, which can grow into the largest animal on earth.
2. *Color*. Animals can be of almost any color with a great variety of color patterns. Children can be led to consider how the color patterns of animals may be related to the environments in which they live.

3. *Movement.* Probably all animals move during some period of their life cycle. They may run, crawl, twist, fly, or swim. There is also great variety among the various structures and appendages that animals use for locomotion.

4. *Coverings.* Animals have coverings for protection, warmth, and to prevent the body from drying out. These coverings may range from the chitinous exoskeletons of insects to the feathers of birds and the thick fur on some mammals.

5. *Body form.* What is the shape and structure of animals? Which have legs? How many? Which have wings? What other structures do certain organisms have? The variety ranges from the earthworm to the long necked giraffe.

6. *Food-getting.* Many animals have specialized structures for food-getting. Examples are the long darting tongue of the frog and the thin tube with which the hummingbird sips the nectar of flowers.

7. *Life cycles.* Individual animals pass through life cycles. Among the more striking life cycles are those of some insects that metamorphose through egg, larval, pupal, and adult stages.

There are marked similarities between offspring and parents, that is, baby elephants are like mature elephants and young robins resemble adult robins. However, there are important variations within species. As most children will know, human babies are much more like other babies than like the offspring of any other species, but there are many differences between babies. These variations among individuals of a species are very important in terms of evolutionary theory.

The evolution of sexual reproduction led to greater variety within species. Among organisms that reproduce by simple division, such as the ameba, the offspring have to be very much like the parent organism because they are made up of material that has been divided off the parent. But among organisms that multiply by sexual reproduction, the offspring develop from material from two parents, and these materials can combine in an almost infinite number of combinations. "No two human beings are alike" can also be applied to other organisms that reproduce sexually. The great variety among these organisms is the major reason that the plants and animals that reproduce sexually have been so successful from an evolutionary standpoint.

Adaptations Among Living Organisms

Living organisms are adapted to live in their environment. However, there are great differences between environments. Contrast, for example, the humid and sweltering tropical rain forest with the arid and windblown desert. There are living organisms in both of these environments, but these organisms will have different adaptations. Most organisms that thrive in the rain forest would die in the desert, and desert organisms would not survive in the rain forest.

The chameleon—the animal noted for its ability to change color—can live in the rain forest. In addition to its ability to blend with the color of its environment, the chameleon is adapted for life on the swaying branches and twigs of trees. It has a tail with which it can grasp a twig or branch; in fact, it can hang suspended only by the tail. Also, it can place its four legs in line on a branch and grasp it firmly with its toes. Apparently, it can maintain a grasp on a branch even when it is asleep. The chameleon can swivel its eyes so that one is looking back while the other peers ahead. Since the chameleon is rather slow moving, these independent eyes make it possible for it to observe a delectable fly in front while watching a potential enemy to the rear. Since most animals are most sensitive to the sight of motion, the chameleon can wait to make its move to capture the fly until the enemy is no longer to be seen by its rearward looking eye. Then it shoots out its remarkable tongue—a tongue that can be as long as its body and tail combined. The fly adheres to the tip of the tongue and in a split second is pulled back into the mouth to be devoured. The chameleon, like other organisms, has adaptations that help it to survive and live in its environment.

Plants also have adaptations that enable them to live in their environment. A desert plant, for example, such as a cactus, often has deep roots that prevent the plant from being blown away and also make it possible for it to tap the groundwater that exists even in the desert. Usually it has thick leaves covered with a waxy substance that tends to minimize water loss. Sharp barbs on trunk and leaves help prevent depredations by animals. The seeds of many desert plants can lie dormant for long periods of time and then germinate and grow quickly when there is a little rain. In many respects, the desert is a very harsh environment, but a considerable number of organisms have adaptations that make it possible for them to live there.

Organisms have a variety of adaptations for protection. With *protective coloration* animals such as the plaice and the grasshopper blend in with the background colors. In *mimicry*, harmless organisms look like other more dangerous or inedible organisms. Some snakes mimic the deadly cobra; the viceroy butterfly appears to birds to be just like the ill-tasting monarch butterfly. The opossum and certain snakes play dead until their enemies leave. The skunk can eject an odorous liquid at its attackers. Hard outer coverings protect animals such as the turtle and crab. The zebra and the deer, on the other hand, protect themselves with their speed which enables them to escape most pursuers.

There are many adaptations for food-getting. The hawk has the equivalent of an eight-power magnifier with which to see mice and other small animals from high in the sky. The hummingbird has a long tube through which it extracts nectar from the flower. The Venus flytrap is adapted to life on soil low in nitrogen by trapping small insects and devouring them for their nitrogen. Since animals do not manufacture their own food, almost all animals have some kind of adaptation for food-getting.

Reproduction is an essential for all kinds of organisms, and most plants and animals have adaptations that increase the likelihood of reproduction. Flowering plants often have colorful petals and pleasant odors to attract the insects that carry the pollen to the pistil. When the seed is ripe it may be dispersed by hooking onto the fur of animals as with the sandbur, or it may float on the wind as with the dandelion and thistle. The seeds of some maples are spread by a turning, helicopter-like action, and still others float for long distances in the sea as can the coconut. Elaborate behavior patterns are a part of the reproductive process of some animals. The male stickleback, for example, lures females to his tunnel where he causes them to leave their eggs. After the eggs are fertilized, the male guards them and "fans" the water around them to make certain that there is an ample supply of air in the water. All these adaptations for reproduction make it more likely that the various kinds of organisms will continue to exist.

Organisms with these various kinds of adaptations did not always exist. Instead, organisms with certain kinds of characteristics were more likely to survive in a particular environment. Their offspring tended to have these same characteristics. Over long periods of time, organisms with adaptations that would help them to survive to the time of reproduction evolved by the process of natural selection.

Natural Selection

How did the great variety of form and structure among living organisms come about? How did organisms acquire the adaptations that have made it possible for different kinds of organisms to survive and live in various environments? These are perplexing questions to which two contrasting answers have been given. One answer has been that organisms have always existed very much as they are today. But the fossil record gives evidence of organisms that have become extinct, and, animals such as the passenger pigeon and the dodo have become extinct within recent historic times. This certainly indicates that there have been changes in the kinds of organisms that inhabit planet earth. Then, as a prominent zoologist has remarked, "It is really hard to believe that something like the rhinoceros came into being all at once." A second answer, more complicated but also more intellectually satisfying, is that the adaptations and great variety among organisms have evolved over a long period of time and organisms are still in the process of evolving. Natural selection is the process largely responsible for this evolution.

The enunciation and description of the principle of natural selection was the most important contribution made by Charles Darwin. It remains central to evolutionary theory and is a basic principle in the biological sciences. The principle of natural selection is that *those individuals in a population most fitted to survive and reproduce will survive and leave the most offspring.* As an example, consider a population of deer. If some deer are born with less powerful legs than others, they will be less likely to escape such natural predators of deer as the mountain lion. They may be killed before they reach the age of reproduction. The fleetest deer, however, are more likely to escape and have offspring. There may be slight, but important, genetic differences between the slow and the fleet deer. Since the fleet are more likely to survive and reproduce, these genetic characteristics will be transmitted to the offspring. Over a long period of time, there will tend to be a natural selection of those kinds of deer that are best able to escape their enemies.

Very often in science, and in other fields, an idea seems obvious after it has once been stated, but it takes an unusual man to crystallize and state the idea. So it was with natural selection, and the man who stated the idea and buttressed it with observations was Charles Darwin—one of the great men in the history of science.

From early in life, Darwin was a curious and observant naturalist. Fortunately for the development of the biological sciences, Darwin took a position as a naturalist on H.M.S. *Beagle* which was to embark on the famous voyage that enabled Darwin to make the observation of natural history that led him to conclude that species of organisms could change and that new species could and had evolved. His consideration of the geological evidence and his observations, notably in the Galápagos Islands, led him to conclude that these transmutations of species had taken place.

How could new species have originated? Apparently Darwin was greatly influenced by Malthus' *An Essay on the Principles of Population.* The central thesis of this essay is that human populations tend to reproduce at such a rate that they outstrip their food supply. Perhaps a similar principle holds for all organisms. Then those organisms that are best adapted to compete for the essentials of life will tend to survive and reproduce. This could be a natural process of selection, and over a large number of generations new species could evolve.

A little over twenty years after the return of the *Beagle*, after a great deal of thought and procrastination, Darwin published his *Origin of Species*. From a scientific and cultural standpoint, the time was ripe for such an idea. In fact, Alfred Russell Wallace expressed the idea of natural selection at about the same time, and the views of Darwin and Wallace were announced jointly. However, Darwin had built a much firmer base of observation and theory to support his statement.

Origin of Species challenged deeply held popular views, and it was the subject of great controversy. To a limited extent, the controversy still continues, but natural selection and the theory of evolution are almost universally accepted by biologists. The theory of evolution is probably the most important generalization in the life sciences, and natural selection is the principal mechanism by which evolution takes place.

Examples of Natural Selection

Scientists have studied the evolution of species through the fossil record. In many cases, however, the fossil record is incomplete and difficult to interpret. The evolution of the horse family has been carefully studied. The progenitor of the horse was a small, fox-like animal called *Eohippus* that had four complete toes with a splint of a fifth on its forefeet, and three complete toes with a splint of a fourth on its hind feet. The Eohippus evolved in many different directions. One of these directions went through several stages

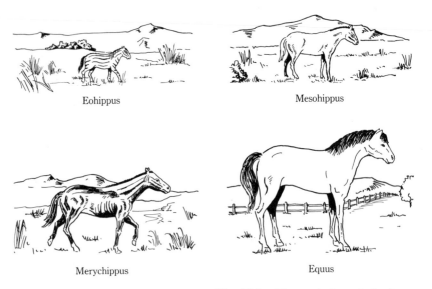

Eohippus   Mesohippus

Merychippus   Equus

Fig. 10-3 *The evolution of the horse.*

and led to the evolution of the present-day horse. In contrast to the Eohippus, the modern horse has a well-developed hoof, long mane and tail, and teeth adapted to grazing. Interestingly, although fossil evidences of the early horse are found on the North American continent, the horse disappeared from the Americas sometime during its evolution, and now all horses living in the Americas are descendants of horses brought from Europe or Asia. The evolution of the horse was complicated, involving at least 14 distinct stages, and taking place over a period of at least 50 million years.

A clearer example of natural selection is believed to have taken place recently and involves moths in Britain. It has been noticed that there has been a marked increase in the proportion of dark-colored moths in areas that are subjected to the darker colored industrial smoke and fumes. It has been hypothesized that the dark-colored moths have more effective protective coloration against darkened bark of trees and are less likely to be found and devoured by the many kinds of birds that feed on insects. To check this hypothesis, an investigator placed a large number of light and dark moths in a wooded area near some factories and in another area far away from any cities. In the rural area the light-colored moths blended with the environment, and more of the dark-colored moths were eaten by birds. In the industrial area, however, the trunks and branches of trees were dark colored, and fewer of the dark moths were detected and eaten by birds. In industrial areas, a dark color was an adaptation that made it more likely that a moth would survive and reproduce. The tendency toward a dark color was a genetic factor, and the dark-colored moths would tend to have dark-colored offspring.

The example of the dark-colored moths also shows how changes in the environment are a factor in natural selection. In the case of the dark-colored moths, industrialization led to a darkening of the bark of trees and made more likely the survival of dark-colored moths. Natural selection led to a predominance of dark-colored forms in a relatively short period of time. A similar process of selection has led to the evolution of DDT-resistant insects in areas where there has been a great deal of spraying with DDT. Some individual insects have had a higher resistance to DDT than others. They have had a greater likelihood of survival and reproduction. Since their offspring also tend to have similar resistance, populations of insects that are less susceptible to control by insecticides such as DDT have evolved. These examples of relatively minor changes in populations of organisms as result of environmental changes can help clarify the mechanism of natural selection.

How might some of the other evolutionary changes have taken place? Certainly, the invasion of dry land by living organisms was one of the great events in evolution. Organisms had to survive in a much different environment. Possibly, the individual organisms that had adaptations that would keep them from drying out would be better able to survive in a terrestrial environment. The lungfish of Africa and Australia can burrow into the mud, secrete a capsule of slime around themselves, and survive the drying up of rivers. Animals that could get some of their oxygen directly from the air would be able to survive for longer periods of time out on land. The evolution of organisms that could live completely on land took place over great periods of time and involved natural selection on the basis of many different adaptations. However, the general process was probably the same as that which has led to predominantly dark-colored moths in industrialized regions and DDT-resistant insects.

Genetics and Inheritance

Although Darwin described and provided observational evidence for his theory of natural selection, he did not know the mechanism by which physical traits are passed on from one generation to the next. What traits are transmitted from parent to offspring was obvious to anyone who had noticed similarities between generations. "Jane looks just like her mother." Similar kinds of comments might be made from observations of parents and offspring among other kinds of living organisms. But what kinds of traits are passed on from one generation to the next? How are these traits transmitted?

Unknown to Darwin, an Austrian monk named Gregor Mendel reported on his studies of the inheritance of physical traits among peas seven years after the publication of *Origin of Species*. From his study of the transmission of physical traits in peas, Mendel propounded his three laws of heredity:

Law of Dominance. Some traits are dominant over others. When an individual with a dominant trait is crossed with an individual with a recessive trait, all the offspring will show the dominant trait. Among Mendel's peas, tallness was dominant over shortness; when a tall plant and a short plant were crossed the offspring were tall.

Law of Segregation. When *hybrids* (the offspring of parents having contrasting traits, such as tall and short) are crossed, the ratio of the dominant trait to the recessive trait will tend to be three to one. If a large number of the offspring of tall peas crossed with short peas are in turn crossed, there will tend to be three times as many tall peas as short.

Law of Unit Characters. Each trait is inherited independently of other traits. The tallness of the pea plant, for example, will have no effect on the inheritance of color.

Law of dominance

Parent plants   Offspring

Tall (pure)   Short (pure)   All tall hybrids

Fig. 10-4   *Tallness is dominant over shortness.*

Unlike the reception of Darwin's theory of evolution little notice was taken of Mendel's laws of inheritance. It was as if the intellectual climate was not yet ready for them; it was not until the early 1900's that they were "rediscovered" and further intensive work was undertaken to build the science of genetics.

Traits are transmitted from parent to offspring by *genes* within the cell. In the case of sexual reproduction, the genes are carried by the male sperm and the female egg. When a sperm and egg unite, there is a pairing of the genes. As a result of this pairing, the offspring will have some traits like the male parent and some like the female parent. But because such a great variety of combinations is possible, the offspring will be somewhat different from either of the parents.

It is the genetic transmission of traits that is involved in evolution. Consider again the dark-colored moths. These moths transmit genes that control color to their offspring. Since the individuals that do not have these genes are more likely to be found and eaten by birds before they can reproduce, natural selection tends to enlarge the pool of genes for dark color among the population of moths. Over a long period of time the genes for light color might be almost completely removed from the gene pool among these moths. However, if environmental conditions should change, natural selection might again begin to change the nature of the gene pool.

It is important to remember that it is hereditary traits that are transmitted—not acquired characteristics. At one time, it was suggested that evolutionary changes could take place as a result of use and disuse. It was suggested, for example, that the giraffe's long neck may have come about from the stretching of the neck to reach leaves in trees. The suggestion that acquired characteristics could be inherited has been associated with the name of Jean Lamarck. Although Lamarck, an important figure in the development of evolutionary theory, was among the first to suggest that transmutations of species had occurred, his theory that acquired characteristics are inherited has been quite thoroughly discredited. Although a man may work hard and become a great scholar, his offspring will not inherit this scholarliness, although they may inherit genes that influence intelligence and live in a cultural environment that encourages scholarliness.

Mutations

Infrequently, there are changes in the chemical structure in a gene. These changes, called *mutations*, produce changes in the gene pool and result in traits that would previously not have been possible. In most cases, mutations are harmful to the individual organism, and it does not survive to reproduce. A few mutations, however, are helpful and bring about changes that make the organism better able to survive and reproduce. Since mutations involve actual changes in the genes, these changes are transmitted to the offspring.

It is known that radiation such as X rays and cosmic rays and emanations from radioactive materials can increase the mutation rate. It has been estimated that under ordinary circumstances one cell in every two hundred thousand undergoes mutation. Since the earth is continually being bombarded by cosmic rays, these usual mutations may be due to this source of energy. However, if there is bombardment with intense X rays, the mutation rate may be increased by a factor of 150. This has proved to be a boon to those scientists who study evolution in such rapidly reproducing organisms as bacteria and fruit flies.

However, no way has been found to control the directions that mutations will take. Since most mutations tend to be harmful to the organism, exposure to heavy doses of radiation can have unpredictable and often harmful genetic effects.

Plant and animal breeders have used unusual mutations to develop new kinds of plants and animals. For example, in Massachusetts in 1791, a very short-legged sheep was born of two sheep that had normal legs. This short-legged sheep was a mutation. It was used to develop a new breed of sheep called the Ancon sheep. This short-legged sheep had several advantages including an inability to jump over fences.

Mutations, of course, are of great importance in evolution. While most mutations are harmful to the organism, occasionally a trait appears that makes that individual better adapted to its environment. For example, sometime in the distant past an ancestor of man may have had a mutation that produced a thumb that opposed the other fingers of the hand. The opposable thumb was very helpful in grasping and manipulating objects.

Another ancestor may have had a mutation which resulted in a somewhat larger cerebrum. The enlarged cerebrum made its possessors better able to use the highly effective opposable thumb. Mutations such as these may have been steps in the evolution of an organism that can read a book and learn about evolution.

THE EVOLUTION OF CULTURE

One of the very distinctive features of man is culture. Culture may be thought of as the sum total of behavior patterns and the products of that behavior. In the culture of the scientifically literate man, for example, there is the predisposition to keep an open mind to new ideas and to weigh the evidence against as well as for an idea. Among the products of this behavior are countless books, inventions, and various kinds of artifacts. Both the *behavior* and the *material artifacts* are part of the culture.

Culture is transmitted from generation to generation. Among other organisms it is probably only genetic traits that are transmitted from one generation to the next. In man, genetic traits are transmitted biologically, but, in addition to this, there is the cultural transmission made possible by the intellectual communication between generations. Hopefully, those behavior patterns that are associated with scientific literacy can be transmitted to human offspring. Almost certainly a wide range of books, inventions, and many other kinds of artifacts will also be transmitted.

Culture is cumulative; that is, each generation can add to culture. Somewhere in the distant past, an ancestor learned how to use fire. Since then man has learned to use it in many different ways from broiling steaks to smelting ore, and in future generations additional ways of using fire may be invented. Science is also a cumulative undertaking, and it is a way that culture develops. The cumulative nature of culture can lead to significant changes in patterns of behavior. Although there are many similarities, there are also significant differences in the ways that modern man lives with his family and community, obtains and eats his food, provides for shelter and protection, and uses the materials and energy in his environment as compared to the early man who fashioned the first tools out of wood and stone.

It can be hypothesized that culture has evolved. How did this evolution, which led to one of the most distinctive characteristics of man, take place?

Cultural Evolution

Although it is difficult to differentiate precisely between early man and his immediate predecessors, man probably evolved in Africa, Asia, and possibly Europe. The diggings in Olduvai Gorge and other sites in Africa suggest that an organism that could be called man evolved more than two million years ago. From a geological standpoint, the arrival of man was a very recent occurrence. Still, man was on the scene during the very extensive glaciation that profoundly affected the American, European, and Asian continents.

Perhaps the most distinctive feature of man is his brain—particularly the cerebrum—which is large in proportion to his body size. It is the cerebrum that makes abstract thought and conceptualization possible. This large cerebrum is believed to have evolved. Early man probably left the forest and made his home in the savannahs and plains. Here he was able to operate in an upright posture, moving about with his legs and leaving his forelimbs free for other tasks. He also developed an opposable thumb which could be used to grasp and manipulate objects. It has been theorized that these structural developments opened up a wide variety of possibilities for early man and that the cerebrum developed as man used his rather unique features to cope with and exploit his environment.

Man was also social and lived in families and communal groups. In these groups it was important to have some means of communication. To be able to express and understand signs of danger could be an important survival factor. Probably the process of natural selection became a factor, and those early men who could best communicate tended to survive and reproduce. This natural selection probably was a factor in the evolution of men with language.

Communication

Among many social animals there are systems of communication. We know, for example, that bees can communicate the locations of food by an intricate system of dances, sounds, and smells. Although we suspect that porpoises, gibbons, and other animals may have some form of language, the bee language is the only one that we have been able to translate in any detail.

Many animals communicate by *signs*. Signs are indicators of things or events. A crow can warn other crows by calling when a hunter approaches. A cow will call for her calf, and some birds will warn other birds to stay out of their territory. Signs are largely limited to use for communications related to the "here" and "now." There is no way in which a crow can communicate about the hunter that may have passed last week or communicate to others the ways that the approach of hunters can be predicted or detected.

Man can use *symbols* in communication. The symbol "science," although it may be difficult to define and much of Chapter 2 in this book is devoted to this, represents a kind of activity and the products of that activity. The meanings of this symbol are not limited to the here and now. If you mention to the children in your class the nature of some of the science studies planned for next year, this will have some meaning to them. If you write on the chalkboard "11–11:45, Science," this will convey to children some notion of the kinds of activities in which they will engage.

Symbols also represent abstract ideas. The symbol "science" represents an abstract idea. Since they are abstractions, it is possible to use the symbols in thought. For example, it is possible to contemplate the similarities and differences between "science" and "art," to analyze systematically the processes involved in science and to examine the interrelationships between the process of science, the broad scientific generalizations that are among the products of science, and the technological innovations that develop out of scientific endeavors. The ability to manipulate symbols has enabled man to see new relationships, to carry out mental experiments, and to invent new ways of doing things.

Symbols make it possible for man to learn from experience and to transmit this learning to future generations. Apparently, certain behavior patterns are transmitted from generation to generation among many kinds of animals as instincts. The bee language and the patterns of web spinning among spiders are transmitted in this way. However, it would be impossible, apparently, for bees to analyze and improve upon their language or for some enterprising spider to perfect its web by spinning it a little differently. This kind of behavior is possible only when symbols can be used to represent experiences and ideas. In an obvious example, it is no longer necessary for each human generation to learn at firsthand that certain compounds and plants are poisonous. The symbol ☠ indicates to almost everyone that a substance should not be ingested. This symbol and its meaning can be conveyed from generation to generation. To the best of current knowledge, man is the only organism that can use symbols. This ability gives man a distinct and all-important advantage.

The Distinctiveness of Culture

Culture may be the most distinctive attribute of man. It probably evolved from man's ability to use sounds to communicate. Many other organisms can use sounds as signs to communicate. The parrot and mynah bird can even learn to pronounce the words of human language. But sounds have greater utility among men. Even in cultures where there is no written language, ideas and experiences are transmitted from generation to generation by the storyteller.

The complete story of how written language developed is not known. But pictures painted by ancient cave dwellers that have been found in France, India, and Mexico can be considered a form of language. Certainly they communicate ideas and preserve these ideas for future generations. Probably some written languages have developed out of picture writing. The very complicated Chinese written languages have characters that are similar to the objects and ideas they represent. A step in a somewhat different direction of cultural evolution was to develop graphic symbols that would represent different sounds of the spoken language. Most written languages, including English, evolved in this direction.

Languages will continue to evolve. Attempts have been made to develop languages such as Esperanto that could be used and understood by all peoples. It has been suggested that the development of television and other new communications media may lead to a diminishing of the importance of written language. It may be significant that these proposals and most discussion of them are carried out through the written language.

To a certain extent, human culture has an independent existence. It has been suggested that if human kind should suffer a catastrophic disaster, the survivors would be able to build a civilization anew if some libraries and other depositories of culture were not destroyed. Ingenious man learned to decipher the hieroglyphics of the Rosetta stone. Similarly, the countless symbols stored in libraries probably would also be deciphered. In culture, man has created an entity that is used, evolves, and survives.

ORGANISMS IN THEIR ENVIRONMENT

Individual organisms do not live alone. There are interrelationships between the organism and its environment, other organisms of the same kind, and other organisms of different kinds. Consider the woodchuck that browses beside the asphalt thruway. It has its burrow in the soil where it hibernates in the cold winter. It has interrelations with other woodchucks for reproduction and as it suckles and cares for its young. But it also has interrelationships with other organisms not the least of which is the fellow mammal who has cleverly contrived a steel and aluminum vehicle that can travel at great speeds and kill thousands of unwary woodchucks each year

There is often a delicate balance maintained in these interrelationships. Charles Darwin suggested an interesting interrelationship between cats in a village and clover in a nearby field. On a sunny summer day a field of blossoming clover will be alive with buzzing bumblebees. The bumblebees are harvesting nectar and, in the process, are providing an essential service to the clover by carrying pollen from one plant to another. But the number of bumblebees in a field are controlled, to a certain extent, by the field mice that raid their nests. But what controls the field-mouse population? The cats in the neighboring village, of course. So there is a delicate balance between the cats in the village and the clover in the field. Darwin's example illustrates the nature of some of the interrelationships between living organisms and living organisms and their environment.

Systems of Living Organisms

Living organisms can be studied in terms of their relationships with other organisms and their environment. In fact, a strong case can be made that an organism cannot be understood until some comprehension of these interrelationships is understood. However, these interrelations can be studied in terms of several different kinds of systems.

Populations include the individuals of a particular kind or species. For example, the size of the human population and its relationship to the available food supply is a critical matter and a subject for study. In a somewhat similar manner, game biologists will study and be concerned about the deer population in a region, and fish and wildlife specialists will monitor the population of a certain kind of fish in a stream or lake. A population consists only of the individuals of a particular kind.

A *community*, on the other hand, consists of the various populations that live together in a region. On the grasslands of the plains, for example, the grass may be the dominant population. But there are the cattle and other animals that graze on the grass, the insects that pollinate the flowers, the worms and microorganisms in the soil, and the man who raises the beef cattle for the big city markets. The community is made up of all of the living organisms in a region that interact with each other.

The *ecosystem* includes such physical elements of the environment as air, water, and soil as well as the living organisms. A city may be considered as an ecosystem in which the human population is dominant. But, there also are grass, trees, birds, mice, rats, insects, and many other organisms. However, the soil is covered with concrete; the water is polluted with wastes, and the air is contaminated with the outpourings of smokestacks and exhaust pipes. These physical conditions affect living organisms, and only certain kinds of organisms can survive the harsh environment of the city ecosystem.

In studying the world of living organisms choices must be made of what units and systems should be considered. The cytologist, for example, focuses his attention on the cell, and this has been a very fruitful approach to the study of living matter. In the science of ecology, however, the focus is on the interrelationships between living organisms and between living organisms and their environments. The development of the science of ecology has led to a greater appreciation and understanding of the intricate interrelationships that exist in ecosystems. Sometimes, however, it is important to shift from system to system. It may be important, for example, to study the effect of various air pollutants on living tissue, but it will also be important to investigate the impact of atmospheric pollution upon various ecosystems.

Limiting Factors

Plants and animals have certain requirements for life. They need water, food, temperatures within a certain range, and most plants also need light. On the other hand, the presence of too much of certain substances can limit life and growth. Often, for example, there are too many toxic substances in the atmopshere in a large city for some plants to grow. All of the factors that control or regulate the growth of organisms in an environment are called limiting factors. The nature and extent of the limiting factors will help to determine what kinds of organisms will grow in a region.

Water can often be a limiting factor. On the western plains, trees grow naturally only along the water courses. Most trees require twenty-five to thirty inches of annual rainfall. Since there is not this much rainfall on the plains, trees do not grow, and the grasses that can subsist on less water are the dominant form of vegetation. In the desert, of course, water is even more of a limiting factor and only plants with adaptations that allow them to live under arid conditions can survive.

Temperatures can be critical. While some forms of life can exist within a temperature range of three hundred degrees most organisms can survive only within a much narrower range of temperatures. Warm-blooded animals have mechanisms such as perspiration and shivering which help to keep the body temperature almost constant. Some animals burrow into the ground or find refuge in the shade of rocks to escape the high temperatures of the midday sun in the desert. The length of the *growing season* is of special importance in agriculture. The growing season is defined as the period between the last frost in the spring and the first frost in the autumn. The length of the growing season is the factor that limits how far north corn can be grown.

For some plants, light is the limiting factor. Little sunlight penetrates to the floor of a dense forest. Plants such as the evergreens that need considerable sunlight will not grow there, while the seedlings of such deciduous trees as maple and beech can survive. This is the essential reason why many forests in North America, where there is sufficient rainfall, eventually become deciduous forests. A very striking example of light being a limiting factor is in caves where the introduction of light from an electric light bulb makes it possible for mosses to grow.

Nutrients are needed by both plants and animals, and some organisms have very specific needs. Strawberries and blueberries need the nutrients released in acid soils. The fungi are dependent upon organic matter produced by other plants. All animals are ultimately dependent upon green plants for food, and if there is a short supply of certain kinds of food the animal population may be limited. A severe drought which limits rice production, for example, may be a limiting factor for the human population in regions where rice is the staple food.

Cover can also be a limiting factor. Rabbits, field mice, and many kinds of birds depend upon bushes, brambles, and grass for protection from hawks, owls, and other animals of prey. If fire or the farmer's plow removes too much of this cover, the population of these animals will be threatened.

All around us we see factors limiting the growth and multiplication of plants and animals. A path on the school grounds becomes barren of grass as it is trod by young feet. The grass under a board left carelessly on the lawn becomes yellow and ceases to grow. The bluebird population diminishes as starlings move into their former nesting places. An apple crop is ruined by a late frost.

A worthwhile endeavor for children is to analyze ecosystems in their neighborhoods to try to determine the factors that are limiting the growth of various organisms.

A Succession of Life

A gradual change in a living community is called succession. In many cases, succession takes place through recognizable stages, and sometimes the stage which a community is in can be determined. Two common kinds of succession are from barren rock and open water.

A barren rock is a harsh and forbidding environment. In the hot summer sun the temperatures may rise very high, but on a cold winter's night the temperatures plummet. The winds blow hard; organisms that are not securely fastened will be blown away. The hot sun dessicates the surface of the rock; organisms that are to survive conditions on the rock must be able to go for long periods without moisture.

Often it is the lichens that begin the succession from barren rock. Actually, the lichens are made up of two kinds of plants: a green alga that carries on photosynthesis, and a fungus that feeds on the alga and absorbs and holds the water that keeps the alga from drying out. The lichens, like most living things, give off carbon dioxide, and in water this forms the

(a) Lichens   (b) Moss

(c) Grasses   (d) Shrubs and trees

Fig. 10-5 *Succession can begin on barren rock.*

weak carbonic acid that can attack some parts of the rock. Particles of rock
with the decomposed remains of dead lichens begin to form the soil in
which the mosses can grow. The mosses also help to form and hold soil,
and, when enough soil has been formed, grasses begin to grow. As more
soil is formed, and if there is sufficient rainfall, various shrubs will grow,
followed by forest trees.

A somewhat similar kind of succession can take place in the open water
of a pond or lake. The first plants to grow are the algae that need have no
connection with the bottom. As the pond or lake fills in, water lilies and
other plants that are rooted in the bottom can grow. Their broad leaves
that float on the surface reduce the amount of light available to the algae.
As the lake continues to fill in, cattails and other rushes that can live with
roots under water while the rest of the plant is above the surface begin to
grow. They are followed in turn by sedges that grow at the water's edge,
grasses, shrubs, and trees.

If succession is allowed to proceed without interruption, a balanced condition called the *climax* condition is reached. Unless there are serious
climatological or geological changes, the climax conditions will persist

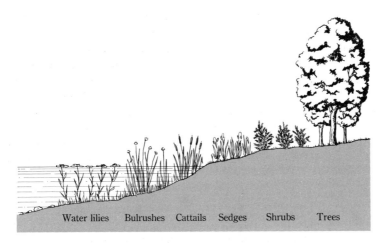

Water lilies   Bulrushes   Cattails   Sedges   Shrubs   Trees

Fig. 10-6   Succession can also occur from a pond.

indefinitely. In Eastern North America where there is considerable rainfall, the climax condition is a deciduous forest with trees such as maple and beech. Farther north the conifers are the climax condition. On the Central Plains, limited rainfall leads to a climax condition of grass, and in the tundra of the Far North mosses may be the climax.

The length of time required for climax to be reached will vary greatly with the nature of the conditions and the climax. On the island of Hawaii, for example, it is known that several hundred years are required before a climax forest will again grow on a lava flow. Where grass is the climax condition, less time may be needed to attain climax.

Succession may be arrested by such natural catastrophes as forest fires and hurricanes. The farmer who plows his fields is trying to control succession. Sometimes succession is also arrested by controlled burning.

All environments are in some stage of succession. Children can be led to study the succession that is taking place around them. Have them examine a barren rock, abandoned road, and a small pond or lake. What kinds of plants grow there? If there is an area of virgin vegetation that has never been touched by plow, fire, or ax they may see one of the climax conditions for their region.

Energy and Matter in Ecosystems

The basic source of almost all energy in ecosystems is the sun. Green plants, through the process of photosynthesis, are able to convert solar energy into chemical energy that can be used by plants and animals. The chemical energy is stored in food. Organisms use this energy for movement, warmth, and to carry on essential life functions. As the energy is used it is eventually converted into forms that cannot be used by living organisms. However, the energy supply is continuously replenished by the sun.

Much of the matter involved in ecosystems is recycled through ecosystems over and over again, Almost all water used by living organisms is involved in the *water cycle*. Most plants, for example, use a great deal of water, and much of this water is exuded as water vapor in the transpiration process. The water vapor will eventually condense into small droplets to form clouds and from the clouds will come rain. When the rainwater enters the ground, it is again available for use by plants. Oxygen and carbon dioxide are involved in the *oxygen-carbon dioxide cycle*. Green plants use carbon dioxide in photosynthesis to manufacture food, and in this process oxygen is released. Both plants and animals use oxygen to oxidize food to release energy, and in this process carbon dioxide is released again. Nitrogen is another essential element, and it is involved in the *nitrogen cycle*. While the atmosphere is 78 per cent nitrogen, most living organisms cannot use this nitrogen directly. Plants obtain nitrogen from nitrates in the soil and use it to manufacture food for both plants and animals. When organisms die, decay organisms convert the material in the bodies of the dead organisms into a form that can be used again. Nitrogen-fixing bacteria, such as those that live on the roots of leguminous plants, are able to take nitrogen directly from the air and form nitrates that can be used by plants. Below bodies of water where there is practically no air, there are microorganisms that decompose organic matter and release nitrogen into the atmosphere. This helps to maintain the nitrogen supply in the atmosphere. As a result of these cycles, the bulk of the matter that is used in living organisms is available for use over and over again.

Organisms in ecosystems can be classified in terms of their functions relative to matter and energy. The *producers*, green plants, use energy from the sun and such raw materials as carbon dioxide, water, and minerals to build up more complicated compounds that can be used as food and fuel. The *consumers*, both plants and animals, use the foods and fuels. Usually, the foods and fuels are combined with oxygen to release energy, and, in the process, the complicated compounds are broken down into such simpler compounds as water and carbon dioxide. The *decomposers*, such organisms as bacteria and fungi, convert the bodies of dead plants and animals into compounds that can be used again by plants. Each of these types of organisms have an essential function, and they are found in almost all ecosystems.

Among the consumers there are interesting and critical interrelationships called *food webs*. In a sense, the food webs start with green plants for

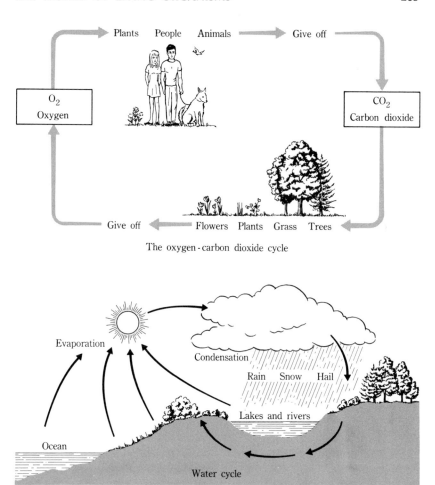

Plants   People   Animals ⟶ Give off

O_2
Oxygen

CO_2
Carbon dioxide

Give off ⟵ Flowers   Plants   Grass   Trees

The oxygen-carbon dioxide cycle

Evaporation

Condensation

Rain   Snow   Hail

Lakes and rivers

Ocean

Water cycle

Fig. 10-7 *Cycles are found in nature.*

they are the key producers. Many animals live directly off the green plants. Although there are many notable exceptions, such as cows and horses, many of the animals that live off green plants, such as insects, are small and numerous. Other animals prey upon these smaller animals. Such large carnivorous animals as hawks, eagles, tigers, and lions live almost entirely off other animals. When plants and animals die, they are decomposed and again become food for green plants. Food webs are intricate interrelationships, and a disturbance in some segment of the web may affect many other organisms. For example, in Darwin's illustration of the bumblebees, an increase in the number of cats might lead to more bumblebees and clover, but, at the same time the increased stands of clover would provide more food and cover for field mice.

The Forest as an Ecosystem

A forest is an excellent example of an ecosystem. Plants, of course, are the producers in this ecosystem. In thick forests, trees are the dominant plants. When the leaf canopy is thick, so little sunlight will penetrate to the floor of the forest that few green plants will grow there. The plants in the forest produce fruits and nuts that are food for many animals.

A variety of consumers inhabit the forest. In the original deciduous forest found in North America there were squirrels, birds, deer, bear, fox, bobcat, and a wide variety of insects. Most of the insects ate the leaves and other parts of the trees. It is not uncommon to see whole forests denuded of leaves as a result of the depredations of insects. But the birds feed on insects. When the rat-a-tat-tat-tat of the woodpecker is heard, the bird is probably seeking insects within the trunk of a tree. Most birds capture insects "on the fly." The fox and the bobcat live almost entirely off other animals.

On the floor of the forest are the decomposers. A stroll through the forest will reveal decaying leaves, branches, and trunks of trees. A few inches under the duff on the forest floor, the organic matter that has fallen some time ago has been completely decomposed and returned to the soil. The nitrates and other minerals that were incorporated in the organisms are again available for use by the living organisms of the forest.

There are many ways to analyze and classify the organisms that live in an ecosystem, whether it be a forest or a grassland, a lake or a stream, but one approach to use with children is to identify the organisms as producers, consumers, or decomposers. In most ecosystems a fluctuating balance is maintained between these types of organisms. If this balance is upset by the introduction of new species, fire, or severe drought, many of the interrelationships within the ecosystem may be changed. When changes occur, the effects on some of these interrelationships can be studied. There may be, for example, the start of succession toward a climax community,

APPROACHES TO TEACHING

In the study of the world of living organisms, the science process of observation can be stressed. Ecosystems can be observed, and if observed with care, some of the intricate interrelationships between organisms can be discussed. In the field and forest the careful observer tries to remain as motionless as possible because many organisms are alerted and frightened away by sudden movements. Although children often are tempted to prod and to scare and "to do things to" organisms, the observer of living organisms is usually more effective if he influences the organisms as little as possible.

Through observation children can learn a great deal more about the nature of various living organisms—what they need to live and their characteristics during various periods of their life cycles. Plant and animal behavior can also be observed. From all of these activities, children should learn how to become more perceptive and effective observers.[1]

How do organisms live in a terrestrial environment?

The terrarium is an important tool that children can use to study how organisms live in a terrestrial environment. The terrarium is a land habitat for living things, and terrariums can be used to simulate such environments as desert, bog, grassland, and woodlands. If a terrarium is well planned and carefully set up, organisms will thrive in it for long periods of time. For example, terrariums were used to transport plants from continent to continent in the days of sailing vessels when weeks or months were required for the long sea voyage.

[1] For further discussion of the process of observing, see Chapter 13.

To set up a terrarium, obtain a container with glass sides. An aquarium, a commercially made terrarium, or a large glass jar can be used. Put a layer of small rocks or pebbles on the bottom and then cover with a little wood charcoal. The charcoal will tend to absorb any noxious gases that may form. Cover the pebbles and charcoal with soil.

Place plants that would grow in the environment to be simulated in the soil. Small cacti are excellent for a desert terrarium, small ferns and tree seedlings for the woodland terrarium (put in, also, some pieces of decaying

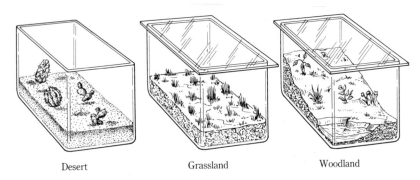

Desert   Grassland   Woodland

Fig. 10-8 *Three types of terrariums can illustrate ways in which organisms live on land.*

wood), and grass seed can be planted in the soil for the grassland terrarium. Water the plants in the terrarium. For all but the desert environment, cover the terrarium with a piece of glass to reduce loss of water.

As children observe organisms growing in the terrarium, ask them such questions as the following:

1. Do plants grow about the same amount on each side (symmetrical growth), or does there tend to be more growth on one side?
2. Do plants grow in the direction of the source of light?
3. What happens when the amount of light changes? The amount of water?
4. Do roots grow in the direction of a source of water? Do they tend to grow downward?
5. What happens when roots encounter a pebble or some other obstacle?

Terrariums can be used to study various interrelationships between organisms and organisms and their environments. These simple experiments, difficult to duplicate in the natural environment, can be carried out in terrariums:

1. What is the effect of temperature changes on plants and small animals such as insects? Usually, a terrarium should be kept at a comfortable room temperature of 68°-72° F. A desert terrarium will do better at a higher temperature. Keep a record of the temperatures. Then place a small source of heat near the terrarium. Watch for changes. Try not to permanently damage the plants in the terrarium. Remove the source of heat. What happens?
2. What is the effect of changes in the amount of light on plants? First expose the terrarium to light for twenty-four hours a day. What happens? Then cover the terrarium so that it receives no light. What happens when the terrarium is returned to normal light conditions? Again, as in the study of the effect of changes in temperature, try not to permanently damage the plants.
3. What is the effect of changes in humidity on plants and animals? Except for the desert terrarium, a glass plate should be kept over the terrarium to prevent the loss of water vapor. Do drops of water form on this glass plate? If so, where do these drops come from?
   Remove the glass plate from the terrarium for a few days. Do any changes take place? Replace the glass top. (It may be necessary to add a little water after having removed the glass top to replace water that has been lost.)
4. Are there organisms in the terrarium that are harmful to other plants and animals? Such organisms would be considered to be consumers. Are there any signs of damaged organisms? In some cases you may wish to spray with insecticides or other chemicals. What are the effects of the use of these chemicals?
5. What happens when plants grow so that the leaves touch the sides or top of the terrarium?

How do organisms live in a water environment?

The aquarium is an important tool for the study of plants and animals that live in the water, interrelationships between them, life cycles, and some of the behavioral characteristics of fish and other animals.

To set up an aquarium, obtain a glass container such as a commercially available aquarium or a large glass jar. At the bottom of the aquarium place one or two inches of clean sand. (Sand can be washed by pouring it into a pail of water and then pouring off the water. Continue until the water is clear.) Pour in clean water to a height of three or four inches. Now set a few aquarium plants such as Vallisneria, Sagittaria, Cabomba, and Elodea in the sand. They can be anchored by placing a few stones over their roots. Fill the aquarium to within two or three inches of the top with clean water. Allow the water to stand for two or three days so that any chlorine that may be dissolved in the water will escape. Dissolved chlorine will be harmful to fish and other animals. Place fish, snails, and other water animals into the aquarium. Because of their hardiness and ability to withstand changes in temperatures goldfish are excellent for the aquarium.

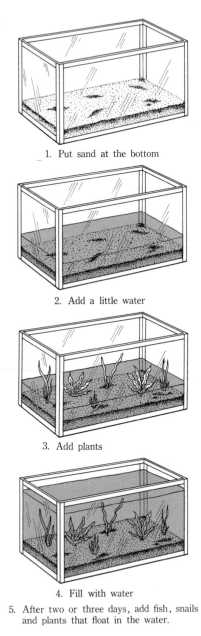

1. Put sand at the bottom

2. Add a little water

3. Add plants

4. Fill with water

5. After two or three days, add fish, snails
and plants that float in the water.

Fig. 10-9 *Setting up an Aquarium helps illustrate ways in which organisms
live in water.*

Most aquariums require relatively little care. The aquarium should receive some, but not too much, light. Usually it is best to place the aquarium along the wall opposite the windows. If an aquarium turns a greenish color (the green is due to the growth of algae), it is probably receiving too much light. Fish food can be obtained from pet shops and department stores and should be given to the fish two or three times a week. Children often have a tendency to overfeed fish. The temperature of the aquarium should be kept fairly constant. If the classroom temperature goes down too low at night, a special aquarium heater may be needed. Usually, the aquarium should be covered with a glass pane to reduce the loss of water and prevent dust and dirt from contaminating the aquarium.

After having had some experience in maintaining an aquarium, it may be desirable to have the children set up and maintain a more sophisticated aquarium. A pump will help insure that sufficient air will be dissolved in the water. A thermostatically controlled aquarium heater will make it possible to introduce tropical fish and other organisms that are sensitive to changes in temperature. A salt-water aquarium can be set up to maintain fish and snails that live in the oceans.[2]

As a tool for learning, the aquarium can provide the opportunity for observations:

1. How do plants grow? Do plants without roots in the sand grow as well as those rooted in the sand? Do some plants seem to lose their leaves? What may be destroying some of the leaves of the water plants?

2. Where do air bubbles appear in the aquarium? By what processes might these bubbles have been formed? Do the fish come to the surface to gulp air? What could be the reason for this? What should happen if the number of animals in the aquarium were changed?

4. Does the number of animals in the aquarium change? Periodically, the children should take a census of the various kinds of animals in the aquarium. They may be able to see eggs and the very small fish and snails.

5. How do animals move in water? The movement of snails across the glass sides of an aquarium is especially interesting. The way that the fish uses its tail to move about can also be observed.

6. Can fish learn? Children can try tapping the sides of the aquarium before feeding. Do the fish eventually learn to come to the top in search of food whenever the aquarium is tapped?

7. Do any kinds of materials form on the bottom of the aquarium? If so, what might be the source?

[2] The salts needed to set up a marine aquarium can be obtained from: Wards Natural Science Establishment, P.O. Box 1712, Rochester, New York.

What changes take place during the life cycle of an insect?

Many insects undergo a metamorphosis in which there are radical changes in body structure. This change can be observed in a variety of insects.

Find a caterpillar on a leaf and place it with some of the leaves in a glass jar with a screen over the opening. Have the children watch the caterpillar spin its cocoon. Later they may be able to see the adult insect emerge from the cocoon. If the adult can be maintained for a sufficient period of time in a screened cage, the children may be able to see the eggs that are laid and then the larva emerge from the eggs to begin the cycle all over again.

The mealworm is an excellent organism for the study of life cycles as well as insect behavior. A mealworm colony and its adult beetle form can be maintained for a long time in a jar of oatmeal.

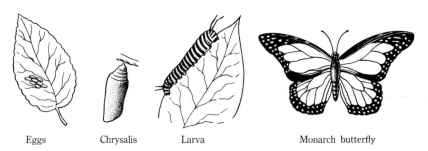

Eggs   Chrysalis   Larva   Monarch butterfly

Fig. 10-10   *We can point to four stages in the life cycle of the butterfly.*

What are some different kinds of insects that live in the locality?

In the spring, summer, and fall a wide variety of insects live in almost any community. They can be found in basements, in the grass, on trees, flying through the air, and in other places.

A simple insect net for catching insects on the fly can be made by fastening a piece of a nylon stocking to a wire loop. The wire loop can be fastened to the end of a stick and the other end of the nylon stocking tied.

Insects can be killed painlessly in a "killing bottle" made by soaking some cotton in carbon tetrachloride and placing the cotton in the bottom of a glass jar with a screw-on top.

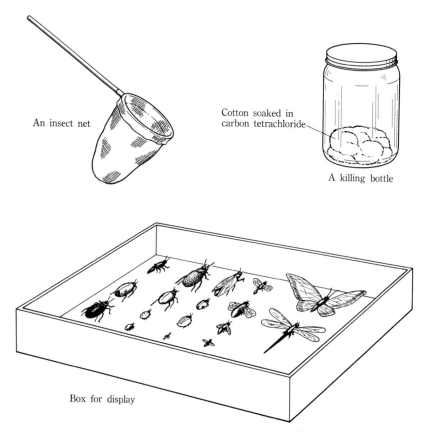

Fig. 10-11 *Tools are necessary for the study of insects.*

The insects can be mounted by inserting a pin through their bodies into a soft piece of wood or laying them in small boxes filled with cotton. On the label for each specimen there should be the name[3] and place caught.

What adaptations do various organisms have?

Examine a plant and an animal that are living in a particular environment. How are these organisms adapted to live in this particular environment?

---

[3] Keys to help identify most common insects may be found in: Willard J. Jacobson, Cecilia J. Lauby, and Richard D. Konicek, *Investigating in Science* (New York: American Book Co., 1968), pp. 139–147. See also: Herbert S. Zim and Clarence Cottam, *Insects: A Guide to Familiar American Insects* (New York: Simon and Schuster, 1951).

Try to find quite different environments and describe the adaptations of a plant and an animal in these environments.

What are some methods of seed dispersal?

Different plants have a wide variety of adaptations for the dispersal of seeds. Have the children try to find seeds that are dispersed by such methods as the following: wind, attachment to animals, spring-like action to catapult seeds away from plants, helicopter effect as seeds fall, and carried by birds and other animals.

How much water can lichens absorb?

The ability of lichens to absorb a great deal of water can be demonstrated by adding water to a small amount of lichens with a medicine dropper. Continue adding water until the lichens can no longer absorb the water.

Older children may be able to determine the ratio of the amount of water that can be absorbed to the weight of the lichens. Have them weigh their sample of lichens and their sample of water, and record the weights in grams. Add water until the lichens can no longer absorb water and weigh the water remaining. Subtract this weight from the original weight of water to find the weight of the water absorbed.

$$\frac{W_O \text{ (grams)} - W_R \text{ (grams)}}{W_L \text{ (grams)}} = W_A/W_L$$

where W_O is the weight of the original water, W_R the weight of the remaining water, W_L the weight of the sample of lichens, and W_A the weight of the absorbed water. Since the weight units, grams, cancel out in the equation, the final answer W_A/W_L is a ratio of the amount of water absorbed per unit weight of lichens.

What are cells like?

A microscope is needed to examine plant and animal cells. Peel off a thin inner layer from an onion and put a small piece of it in a small drop of water on a slide. Cover with a cover slip. Mix one part of a 2 per cent iodine solution (from the drugstore) with two parts water; place a drop of this iodine solution at the edge of the cover slip. Touch the water at the opposite side of the cover slip with a piece of toweling, drawing the iodine solution underneath the cover slip to stain the cells.

Place the slide on the stage of the microscope and examine the onion skin with both high and low power. Can you see the cell wall? The nucleus?

To obtain animal cells for examination, gently scrape the inside of your

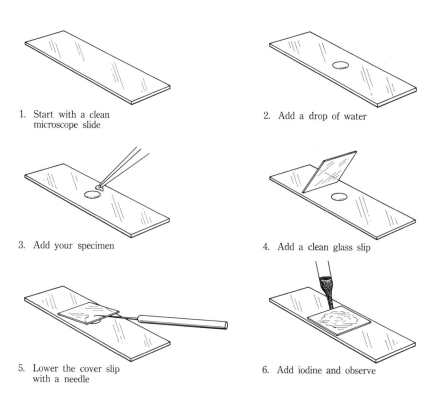

1. Start with a clean
   microscope slide

2. Add a drop of water

3. Add your specimen

4. Add a clean glass slip

5. Lower the cover slip
   with a needle

6. Add iodine and observe

Fig. 10-12   *Preparing a slide for observation involves six stages.*

mouth with a spoon. Dip the scrapings into a drop of water on a slide and cover with a cover slip. Stain with dilute iodine.

Examine these epithelium cells from the mouth under both low and high power. Can you find the nucleus? The cell membrane? Compare these cells with the onion-skin cells.

How does diffusion take place?

The diffusion of a liquid through a material can be demonstrated using a large carrot. Hollow the carrot with a knife or apple corer. Pour some molasses or syrup into the cavity. Into the top of the hole fit a one-hole rubber stopper with a long glass tube. If the rubber stopper does not fit tightly, seal with melted wax. Clamp the tube and carrot to a stand and immerse the carrot in a jar of water. Wrap a rubber band around the glass tubing to indicate the height of the liquid in the tube.

After a few hours, again note the height of the liquid in the tube. What is an explanation for the change?

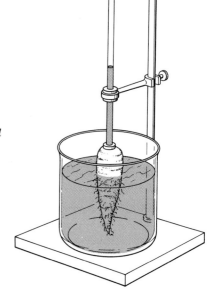

Fig. 10-13   Diffusion can be illustrated
with a carrot.

How can plants be cared for and studied in the classroom?[4]

It is important that children have the opportunity to observe and study living organisms as they grow. For many youngsters it is also important that they begin to take responsibility for the care of living organisms. It is possible to grow plants in almost any classroom, and in most cases it is possible for every youngster to have his own plants for which he can take responsibility.

Few materials and little equipment are needed to grow plants. Plants can be grown in flowerpots, window boxes, and such containers as the bottoms of paper milk cartons. Seeds, a little fertile soil, and water are the other necessities.

Some plants can be grown by partial immersion in water. Stick some toothpicks in the sides of a sweet potato or white potato and stick them into a jar of water so that the lower part is in the water. Occasionally, replenish the water. Have the children observe the growth of the roots, leaves, and stem. The source of the energy and material for this growth is the food material stored in the tubers. If possible, the children may wish to observe how long the plant will continue to grow.

Children should have the experience of growing some plants from seeds. One way to do this is to provide each child with a container made

4 For a description of how to care for and study animals, such as the rat, see Chapter 17, pages 446–447, 459–461.

Fig. 10-14 Some plants can be grown by immersing in water.

by cutting off the bottom 3 or 4 inches of a paper milk carton. Have them almost fill this with soil. Have them place a few seeds in the soil and then sprinkle the soil with water. How many of the seeds grow? How do the plants emerge from the ground? By periodically measuring the plants with a ruler the children can determine how fast they grow.

Some plants, such as geraniums and begonias, can be grown from cuttings. The stem of the plant should be cut with a slanting cut just below a leaf and several inches below the growing tip. Remove all but two or three of the leaves and place in a jar of water until roots begin to grow. The plant can then be planted in a flowerpot or a box that has had holes punched in the bottom.

Plants can also be propagated from bulbs. Begonias and African violets can be propagated by placing the leaves in moist sand.

INVESTIGATION

On what kinds of substances can bread molds be grown?
On what kinds of substances do they grow best?

Molds will eventually grow on a loaf of bread that is exposed for a period of time. This will occur even though most modern breads contain a mold growth inhibitor, calcium propionate. But on what other substances will mold grow?

Moisten pieces of paper, cloth, leather, plastic, orange peel, apple peel, wood, aluminum foil, and other materials and put each of them in a shallow jar. All of the materials should be kept moist during the period of the investigation. Place approximately equal amounts of mold from bread onto each of the substances, and store the jars in a dark place.

Periodically examine the substances. On which of them does the mold appear to be growing? On which is the mold growing best? How long does the mold continue to grow on various substances?

Selected References

BEADLE, GEORGE, AND BEADLE, MURIEL, *The Language of Life.* Garden City, N.Y.: Doubleday & Co., Inc., 1966.

BONNER, JOHN T., *The Ideas of Biology.* New York: Harper & Row, 1962.

DALE, ALAN, *Observations and Experiments in Natural History.* Garden City, N.Y.: Doubleday & Co., Inc., 1962.

PALMER, E. LAURENCE, *Fieldbook of Natural History.* New York: McGraw-Hill Book Co., 1949

SIMPSON, GEORGE G., *The Meaning of Evolution.* New Haven, Conn.: Yale University Press, 1950.

STORER, J. H., *The Web of Life.* New York: The Devin-Adair Co., 1953.

VESSEL, M. F., AND HARRINGTON, E. J., *Common Native Animals.* San Francisco, Calif.: Chandler Publishing Co., 1961.

READINGS FOR THE PRIMARY GRADES

ADRIAN, MARY, *The North American Wolf.* New York: Hastings House, Publishers, Inc., 1965.

BAKER, JEFFREY J. W., *Patterns of Nature.* Garden City, N.Y.: Doubleday & Co., Inc., 1967.

CHENERY, JANET, *The Toad Hunt.* New York: Harper & Row, Publishers, 1967.

CONKLIN, GLADYS, *I Caught a Lizard.* New York: Holiday House, Inc., 1967.

COSGROVE, MARGARET, *Eggs—and What Happens Inside Them.* New York: Dodd, Mead & Co., 1966.

DeSyn, Donna E., *Termite Works for His Colony*. New York: Holiday House, Inc., 1967.

Earle, Olive L., *Birds and Their Beaks*. New York: William Morrow & Co., Inc., 1965.

Freeman, Mae Blacker, *Finding Out About the Past*. New York: Random House, Inc., 1967.

Gibson, Gertrude Hevener, *About Insects That Help Plants*. Chicago: Melmont Publishers, Inc., 1963.

Goldin, Augusta, *Ducks Don't Get Wet*. New York: Thomas Y. Crowell Co., 1965.

Goldin, Augusta, *Spider Silk*. New York: Thomas Y. Crowell Co., 1964.

Goudey, Alice E., *Butterfly Time*. New York: Charles Scribner's Sons, 1964.

Goudey, Alice E., *Red Legs*. New York: Charles Scribner's Sons, 1966.

Harris, Louise Dyer, and Harris, Norman Dyer, *Flash, the Life Story of a Firefly*. Boston: Little, Brown & Co., 1966.

Hawes, Judy, *Fireflies in the Night*. New York: Thomas Y. Crowell Co., 1963.

Hawkinson, John, *Our Wonderful Wayside*. Chicago: Albert Whitman & Co., 1966.

Hess, Lilo, *Sea Horses*. New York: Charles Scribner's Sons, 1966.

Hogan, Inez, *Dinosaur Twins*. New York: E. P. Dutton & Co., Inc., 1963.

Hornblow, Leonora and Arthur, *Birds Do the Strangest Things*. New York: Random House, Inc., 1965.

Jacobson, Willard J., Lauby, Cecilia J., and Konicek, Richard D., *Animals*. New York: American Book Co., 1968.

Jacobson, Willard J., Lauby, Cecilia J., and Konicek, Richard D., *Living Things on the Earth*. New York: American Book Co., 1968.

Jacobson, Willard J., Lauby, Cecilia J., and Konicek, Richard D., *Plants*. New York: American Book Co., 1968.

Jacobson, Willard J., Lauby, Cecilia J., and Konicek, Richard D., *Prehistoric Plants and Animals*. New York: American Book Co., 1968.

Johnston, Johanna, *Whale's Way*. Garden City, N.Y.: Doubleday & Co., Inc., 1965.

Lauber, Patricia, *The Friendly Dolphins*. New York: Random House, Inc., 1963.

Lauber, Patricia, *The Story of Dogs*. New York: Random House, Inc., 1966.

May, Julian, *They Turned to Stone*. New York: Holiday House, Inc., 1965.

McClung, Robert M., *Ladybug*. New York: William Morrow & Co., Inc., 1966.

MITCHELL, ARTHUR A., *First Aid for Insects.* Irvington-on-Hudson, N.Y.: Harvey House, Inc., Publishers, 1964.

POSELL, ELLA, *The True Book of Whales.* Chicago: Childrens Press, Inc., 1963.

RAVIELLI, ANTHONY, *Elephants, the Last of the Land Giants.* New York: Parents' Magazine Press, 1965.

RUSSELL, SOLVEIG PAULSON, *About Nuts.* Chicago: Melmont Publishers, Inc., 1963.

SELSAM, MILLICENT E., *When an Animal Grows.* New York: Harper & Row, Publishers, 1966.

STERLING, DOROTHY, *Spring Is Here!* New York: Doubleday & Co., Inc., 1964.

STEURT, MARJORIE RANKIN, AND CRAMPTON, BERNIE AND CYNTHIA, *Rocky and Sandy.* Los Angeles, Calif.: The Ward Ritchie Press, 1967.

WRIGHT, DARE, *Look at a Gull.* New York: Random House, Inc., 1967.

ZIM, HERBERT S., *Sharks.* New York: William Morrow & Co., Inc., 1966.

READINGS FOR THE INTERMEDIATE GRADES

ADRIAN, MARY, *The American Alligator.* New York: Hastings House, Publishers, Inc., 1967.

BAKER, SAMM SINCLAIR, *The Indoor and Outdoor Grow-it Book.* New York: Random House, Inc., 1965.

BARLOWE, SY, *The Child's Book of Insects.* New York: Maxton Publishers, 1952.

BURGER, CARL, *All About Cats.* New York: Random House, Inc., 1966.

COE, GEOFFREY, *The How and Why Wonder Book of Fish.* New York: Grosset & Dunlap, 1963.

CONKLIN, GLADYS, *The Bug Club Book: A Handbook for Young Bug Collectors.* New York: Holiday House, Inc., 1966.

COOPER, ELIZABETH K., *Insects and Plants.* New York: Harcourt, Brace & World, Inc., 1963.

DARLING, LOUIS, *The Gull's Way.* New York: William Morrow & Co., Inc., 1965.

DUGDALE, VERA, *Album of North American Animals.* Chicago: Rand McNally & Co., 1966.

FOGEL, BARBARA R., *What's the Biggest?* New York: Random House, Inc., 1966.

GILBERT, BIL, *How Animals Communicate.* New York: Pantheon Books, Inc., 1966.

HUTCHINS, ROSS E., *This Is a Tree*. New York: Dodd, Mead & Co., 1964.

JACOBSON, WILLARD J., LAUBY, CECILIA J., AND KONICEK, RICHARD D., *Living Things in Their Environment*. New York: American Book Co., 1968.

KURTZ, EDWIN B., JR., AND ALLEN, CHRIS, *Adventures in Living Plants*. Tucson, Ariz.: University of Arizona Press, 1965.

McCLUNG, ROBERT, *Mammals and How They Live*. New York: Random House, Inc., 1963.

McCLUNG, ROBERT, *The Mighty Bears*. New York: Random House, Inc., 1967.

OMMANNEY, FRANCIS D., *The Fishes*. New York: Life Nature Library, Time, Inc., 1963.

PETERSON, ROGER T., *The Birds*. New York: Life Nature Library, Time, Inc., 1963.

SELSAM, MILLICENT E., *Animals as Parents*. New York: William Morrow & Co., Inc., 1965.

SELSAM, MILLICENT E., *The Courtship of Animals*. New York: William Morrow & Co., Inc., 1964.

SHUTTLESWORTH, DOROTHY E., *The Story of Horses*. Garden City, N.Y.: Garden City Books, 1960.

SNYDER, DICK, *Talk to Me Tiger*. San Carlos, Calif.: Golden Gate Junior Books, 1965.

STERLING, DOROTHY, *Fall Is Here!* Garden City, N.Y.: Natural History Press, 1966.

TEE-VAN, HELEN DAMROSCH, *Small Mammals Are Where You Find Them*. New York: Alfred A. Knopf, Inc., 1966.

WHEELER, RUTH L., *The Story of Birds of North America*. Irvington-on-Hudson, N.Y.: Harvey House, Inc., Publishers, 1965.

SELECTED FILMS

Adaptations in Animals. McGraw-Hill. Explores the relationships between adaptations and survival of species.

Darwin's Finches. Film Associates of California. A portrayal of Darwin's view of natural selection among finches and iguanas in the Galapagos Islands.

III

Building a
Conceptual Structure
of Science

Science is the investigation and interpretation of events that occur in the natural, physical environment and within the human body. These investigations usually deal with problems that the scientist judges to be of some importance in those areas of science in which he has special interest and to which he believes he can find some solution. Some scientists, for example, have devoted their efforts to the study of the relationships between the algae and the fungi in lichens. This is their special area of interest, and the results of their work fill scientific journals and contribute to the development of the conceptual structure of science. Other scientists have developed conceptual structures in many other areas of science.

Based on the work of many scientists, broad generalizations are formulated that codify, simplify, and make more useful the results of scientific work. Prior to Darwin, a great deal of work had been done in such fields as comparative anatomy, taxonomy, comparative embryology, palentology, and plant and animal breeding. However, the theory of evolution and the principle of natural selection helped to give additional meaning to the results of many of these investigations. The theory of evolution is a broad generalization[1] that can be used to link together the results of a great deal of scientific investigation. One of the great goals in science is to formulate ever-broader generalizations that can be used to link together a wider range of studies. Albert Einstein, who early in his career succeeded in

[1] Some writers use the term "paradigm" to mean essentially the same as "broad generalization."

formulating the general and special theories of relativity that certainly qualify as broad generalizations, devoted the latter part of his career to an attempt to develop a broad generalization that would link together the magnetic, electrical, and gravitational fields. He did not succeed. However, a great deal of effort is going into the linking of the biological and physical sciences, and in this effort there has been considerable success.

The development of broad generalizations leads to economy of effort in the pursuit of science. The student of science, unless he has a concern for the history of science, need not study all of the investigations that led to the formulation of such generalizations as the theory of evolution. Instead, he can devote himself to the key generalizations of science, their meanings, and the applications of these generalizations in different situations. Most scientists devote themselves to extending the use of these generalizations to new situations and, in some cases, formulating new sub-generalizations. Occasionally, a Newton, a Darwin, or an Einstein formulates a grand new generalization.

There is no "final truth" in science. New generalizations may be broader and more useful, but they are not "the truth" that will end investigations in an area. It is a widely held misconception that the aim in science is to find the truth, or a close approximation of it, concerning the natural, physical environment. Instead, science evolves and a more consistent and useful conceptual structure is built. But there is no final end; science has an endless frontier.

The generalizations of science are judged by the community of scientists who have some competence in that area of science. Although a wide variety of people debated the validity of Darwin's theory of evolution, the key judgments were made by Darwin's peers in the biological and related sciences. The judgments are usually made in terms of consistency with empirical observation and experimentation. No popular appeal for support is made; in science the majority does not rule and is often wrong. Similarly, appeals to kings and heads of state are not germane. The judgments that count are those of the qualified and the informed.

There is a useful distinction between *generalizations* and *concepts*. Generalizations are crystallizations from the experiences of mankind. They are developed by scientists and recorded in articles, monographs, textbooks, and the general literature of the field. Concepts are the individual's view or mental picture. One of the aims in education in science is to help students develop concepts that are consistent with the generalizations of science. As a result of their study of the world of living organisms, for example, students should develop a view of the biotic world that is consistent with the theory of evolution.

There are interesting parallels between the intellectual development of children and the development of the sciences. The child initially becomes aware of his environment and later begins to discern objects, to see inter-relationships between systems of objects, and to observe various kinds of interactions in his environment. Later he is able to formulate hypotheses, make deductions from these hypotheses, and carry out observations and experimentation to check his deductions. In a somewhat similar way, the broad generalizations of science have been developed on a base of concrete experience, and much of the effort in science is devoted to testing logical deductions made from these generalizations.

The parallel between the intellectual development of children and the development of science is used to organize the parts of the science program that are devoted to the conceptual structure of science and the processes of science. As children have experience in investigating objects and systems and interactions of various kinds, they gain some proficiency in various processes that will lead them to carry out the operations characteristic of the formal stage of intellectual development with its logical deductions and empirical testing.

11 The Study of Objects and Systems

The newborn child probably first becomes aware of the environment as "something out there." It is a dim other world. However, as he grows, the environment is delineated into objects and materials and systems of objects. However, he can view and deal with the objects in his environment in different ways, and how he interacts with the materials and objects of the environment is important in the study of science.

THE STUDY OF OBJECTS

Objects are composed of matter and occupy space. Objects may be living or non-living. The chairs, desks, and chalkboard are non-living objects children can see in the classroom; plants, pets, and other children are living objects.

It is important that children begin to describe objects in terms of their physical properties. Too often, descriptions are in terms of functions rather than properties. The statement "A chair is something to sit on" is a description in terms of function, and it has limited usefulness. In some cases the statement may not be true because there are many chairs that have never been "sat on." Also, chairs are used in many other ways—chairs have been used to stand on and as supports in science experiments. Under careful scrutiny, descriptions in terms of function tend to break down and are not as useful in science as descriptions in terms of physical properties.[1]

Such physical properties as color, shape, texture, magnetic properties,

[1] For children's science activities that emphasize the physical properties of objects, see Willard J. Jacobson and Eileen Cowe, *Beginning Science* (New York: American Book Co., 1966).

287

luster, freezing point, boiling point, melting point, specific gravity, hardness, viscosity, and thermal conductivity can be used to describe objects and materials. Children will first observe properties such as color, shape, and texture that they can obtain directly. Later in the elementary school they will begin to use thermometers and other instruments to determine other properties of objects and materials.

Sorting is an important operation that is carried out in science and in everyday life. While objects can be sorted on almost any basis, one of the most useful systems of sorting is on the basis of physical properties. Objects can be sorted on the basis of color, shape, and texture. Sorting is a basic operation in the more sophisticated science process of *classification*.

Children can also arrange objects in order on the basis of the degree to which they have certain properties. For example, objects can be arranged in order from the largest to the smallest or from the darkest red to the lightest red. This operation is called *serial ordering*, and in science it is a way to find new relationships between objects and materials.

Operational Definitions

Early in their work in science, children should begin to understand and use *operational definitions*. In operational definitions, properties are defined in terms of the operations that are carried out to observe these properties. For example, a chair can be described by saying "The chair is black." Obviously, this description depends on the definition of the term "black," "Black" can be defined operationally as being the color of soot. If the term "soot" requires operational definition, it can be defined as the material that forms on an object held in a candle flame. Operational definitions actually suggest the operations that can be carried out to determine whether an object or material actually has a certain property.

Very often, operational definitions are stated in terms of standards. For example, a chair might be described by saying "It weighs 20 pounds." This description implies that if the chair was suspended on one end of a scale, it would be balanced by a standard 20-pound weight at the other end. Describing the chair as "black" could mean that if the color of the chair was compared to the colors on a standard color chart it would be most nearly like the color black.

By defining objects in operational terms, children learn to become more precise in their descriptions. For example, a child stroked a piece of fur and said, "It is smooth." But, "What do you mean by smooth?" The child stroked the cover of a book and said, "The fur is smoother than the cover of the book." To a certain extent, this child had defined operationally her meaning of the term "smooth."

Matter

Objects consist of matter, and matter can be defined as anything that has mass and occupies space. An operational definition of *mass* can be in terms of resistance to change in motion. For example, it is rather difficult to move a piano. Because of this resistance to change in motion an object is said to have considerable mass. An operational definition of "occupies space" can be that its position can be located with reference to some other object.

There are three states of matter: solids, liquids, and gases. Children will often encounter matter in each of these states and should recognize each example as a form of matter. Most kinds of matter, such as water, can be changed from one state to another (see page 207).

Solids have a definite shape and volume. Usually solids will retain their shape and volume unless force is applied. If solids such as marbles or cubes of ice are poured into another container they will retain their original shape.

A liquid tends to have a definite volume, but it takes the shape of its container. If liquids such as water or milk are poured into differently shaped containers, the volume of the liquid will remain the same, but it takes the shape of its new container.

A gas tends to fill its container. Both its volume and shape will be that of its container. If a gas such as air or carbon dioxide is poured into another container, the volume and shape of the gas will be that of the container. Children sometimes do not consider invisible gases such as air to be matter. In Chapter 8 (see pages 170–177), we suggested a number of activities designed to show that air actually is matter.

Changes in Materials and Objects

Materials can undergo physical changes. Although its appearance may change considerably, the material continues to be the same kind of material after a physical change. Wood may be sawed into sawdust or paper torn up into very small pieces, but the material is still wood or paper.

In chemical changes the nature of the material will change. After a wooden match or a piece of paper has burned, the material is no longer wood or paper. The materials have undergone chemical change, and materials such as carbon and ash have been formed.

The conservation of matter is an important generalization, and it is a concept that can be developed. When a piece of paper is torn into little pieces or some wood is sawed into sawdust, the amount of material remains constant. It is somewhat more difficult to show that the amount of

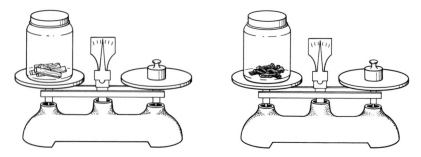

Fig. 11-1 *Matter is conserved, although its form may change—as by burning.*

material remains constant during a chemical reaction. However, if a chemical change takes place within a closed system, the system will weigh the same before and after the chemical action.

THE STUDY OF SYSTEMS

Systems consist of objects that have some relationship to each other. For example, the lungs, bronchi, windpipe, mouth, and nose are objects of the respiratory system of the body, and the battery, alternator, induction coil, and distributor are objects in the electrical system of an automobile. The paints on the canvas of a work of art may be considered to be parts of a system because they have a relationship to each other.

The nature and extent of a system are purely arbitrary. While the paints on canvas may be considered to be the system, in some cases it may be more advantageous to consider the museum where the paintings are housed as the system. The nature and extent of the system will depend upon the purpose of the analysis and study. Artists and art critics would probably focus their attention on the individual paintings, but museum directors would probably consider entire museums as systems for analysis and study.

Delineating the System

A very important step in attacking a problem in science, and in everyday life, is the delineation of the system to be considered. Suppose a compass needle points in an east-west direction rather than north-south. What scheme, or system, should be used in studying why this is so? A very limited system, focusing on the compass may be chosen. Perhaps the needle is stuck, or perhaps it is not magnetized. But to find the answer to the strange behavior of the compass needle it may be advantageous to enlarge the system under consideration. Perhaps there is a strong magnet nearby. Or there may be a piece of steel or iron to which the compass needle, which is a magnet, is attracted. In this example, it will probably be important to enlarge the system beyond the compass in order to find a solution.

The delineation of the system focuses the investigator's attention on those objects that are believed to be pertinent. In the case of the erratic compass needle, the classroom clock or the moon would probably not be considered as parts of the system. On the basis of experience these objects are judged not to be pertinent to the problem being studied; an attempt to find a relationship between the clock or moon and the compass needle would be useless.

Specialization

The deliberate choice of different systems has led to important progress in science. Important contributions to a better understanding of living matter have been made by focusing attention on the cell as the system for study. Other important contributions have come from the study of the compounds that make up the protoplasm of the cell. It is becoming increasingly apparent, however, that an organism, such as the human body, is more than the sum of its cells or the chemical compounds of which it is composed. Thus, the whole organism is also an important system for study. For other purposes it is desirable to broaden the objects being considered beyond the individual organism and consider ecosystems and societies. All of the systems are important, depending on the nature of the studies being undertaken.

Scientists usually specialize in the study of certain systems. For example, cytologists specialize in the study of cells, biochemists specialize in the investigation of the chemistry of living matter, physiologists study the functions that take place in living organisms, ecologists study the interactions that take place in ecosystems, and sociologists specialize in the study of interactions that take place in a society. Such specialization is an important feature of the sciences and it has led to a great increase in the knowledge of man and his environment.

THE STUDY OF RELATIVITY

To many, the term *relativity* connotes a very esoteric theory surrounded with complicated mathematics. Actually, relativity means that observations and descriptions are made in relation to other objects and systems. In describing the size of an object, it is compared to some other object or to some standard of measurement such as a meterstick. The location of an object can be described in relation to other objects or to a coordinate system. Similarly, intervals of time are described relative to such units of time as the second or the year, and motion is described in terms of the motion or the position of other objects.

How various systems are viewed is also of importance. The driver of an automobile usually will not consider a fellow passenger to be moving, but to someone standing on the sidewalk, both the passenger and the driver are moving. To a young child, father always seems tall, but to a taller man, father may not be tall at all. The *reference frame* (see page 295) is a key idea in relativity. The reference frame is the object or system that is used to describe another object or system. "The ball fell" implies that earth is the reference frame. If the sun were the reference frame, the motion of the ball would have to be described in a different way. The stipulation of the reference frame from which observations are made makes possible more useful and precise descriptions.

The following are some ways that the concepts of relativity and reference frame can be used in the description of size, direction, location, time, and motion.

Relative Size

"How long is your science book?" Such a question cannot be answered without reference to some other object or system of objects. The child might say, "My science book is longer than my reading book but shorter than my arithmetic book." He is describing the relative size of the book, and the description is useful if the size of the arithmetic book and the reading book is known.

A more useful answer to the question would be in terms of such standard units of length as the centimeter or inch. If the child lays a ruler alongside the book and says, "The book is 24 centimeters long," he has given an answer that will be understood by students throughout the world. Actually, he is saying that relative to a standard meter accepted by most nations of the world, his book is .24 as long. He has used a standard for comparison that has wide meaning.

Relative Direction

"What is up?" "What is down?" "That's simple," the young student may say as he points into the air to indicate the direction of "up" and toward the ground for the direction of "down." But the questions are complicated when he looks at a globe and is asked, "How about the people in Australia?"

Direction is also a relative matter. In most cases "down" is considered to be the direction toward the center of the earth. A more precise indication of the direction "down" can be obtained by suspending a plumb bob or other weight. The direction "up" may be considered to be exactly opposite the direction of "down."

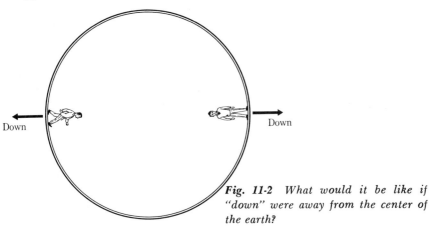

Fig. 11-2 What would it be like if "down" were away from the center of the earth?

Some children may enjoy imagining an earth enclosed in a sphere where all objects fall toward the outside. Then what would be the direction of "down"? Of "up"?

Directions such as east and west are also relative to some other direction. Directions are often determined by finding the direction of north by lining up with Polaris (North Star) or with a magnetic compass. Once the direction of north has been found other directions can easily be determined with a protractor or compass rose.

Fig. 11-3 We use a compass to find directions.

Locations

Locations can only be given relative to other objects and systems. "Where do you live?" The child may answer, "I live in the house next to Mr. Smith's." Note that the location is given relative to some other object.

A more sophisticated way of giving locations is to refer to a coordinate system. The latitude-longitude coordinate system is the one used on maps. If children are given the latitude and longitude of a location they can locate it on a map.

Polar coordinate systems are of special usefulness to children. On polar coordinate systems locations are given in terms of direction and distance from a reference point. The reference direction is usually north, and direction to a location can be given in terms of degrees from the direction of north. The reference point can be the child's own location. The location of some objects may be given degrees from the reference direction and meters from the reference point.

Relative Time

Intervals of time are also compared to other periods of time. The *mean solar day* is often used as a reference time interval. The mean solar day is the average time between successive solar noons. The mean solar day is

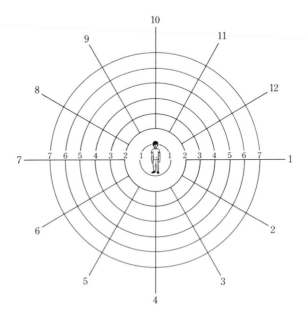

Fig. 11-4 *Polar coordinates are a way of locating positions relative to a reference point.*

customarily divided into 24 hours, 1,440 minutes, and 86,400 seconds. Objects that oscillate periodically such as pendulums, balance wheels, and tuning forks can be used to compare periods of time to the mean solar day or hours, minutes, and seconds.

Because time is relative, children have difficulty in conceptualizing long periods of time. To a six-year-old child, three years is half a lifetime. With such limited experience with time, it is difficult for children to conceptualize the meaning of tens and hundreds of years. To a historical geologist time periods of hundreds of millions of years have meaning, but is difficult for children, and probably most adults, to conceptualize the meaning of such long periods of time.

Relative Motion

The next time you ride in a car drop a rubber ball or a set of keys to the floor. Do they fall directly below where they were dropped? Relative to the automobile, how did the ball fall? But relative to the outside pavement, what was the motion of the ball?

As you sit beside a friend in an automobile moving at 60 mph your friend is not moving relative to you. But both you and your friend have a motion of 60 mph down the highway relative to the pavement and all other "stationary" objects in the environment. Motion is always relative to other objects and systems.

Place two small dolls in a toy truck. Give the truck a push down the floor. Ask the children, "Would the dolls say that they are moving?" "Would the dolls say that they are moving relative to each other?" Cover the dolls with a box and ask the children to imagine that the dolls are sitting on some very fine cushions. "Now could the dolls tell whether or not they were moving?"

Depending on the reference system that is chosen, everyone is moving in some way. The earth spins on its axis, completing one rotation each day. A person at the equator would be traveling at a speed of about 1000 mph as a result of the earth's rotation. But the earth is revolving around the sun at the tremendous speed of 18 miles per second. In turn, the entire solar system is moving around the core of the Milky Way Galaxy at a rate of about 140 miles per second. Then, of course, the entire universe is expanding, and the Milky Way Galaxy is moving away from other galaxies. "How are we moving?" The way that motion is described depends on the reference system chosen.

Reference Frames

The reference frame is the object or system that is used to describe another object or system. It is a common experience that objects and systems appear differently when viewed from different reference frames. For example, one way to get a picture of how a town or village is laid out is to look down upon it from a high hill or from a helicopter. Football teams often have observers at the top of the stadium where they can see the action on the field from a different perspective. Similarly, in science it is often useful to try to view phenomena from different reference frames.

Ordinarily the sun, moon, and planets are viewed from man's platform in space, the earth. One of the observations that can be made, and this was an observation that was difficult for early astronomers to explain, is that the planets seem to move back and forth against the background of stars. Venus, for example, is sometimes seen in the early evening, while at other times it can be seen early in the morning. Copernicus suggested that these retrograde motions of the planets could be explained if it was assumed that the planets revolved around the sun. In essence he suggested a different reference frame. In this reference frame, the sun is considered to be near the center of the system, and all of the planets, including the earth, revolve around it. By changing the reference frame so that the sun is near the center of the solar system, it became much simpler to explain the motions of the planets. This sun-centered model of the solar system has been a most useful model for the explanation of events that take place in the solar system.

Fig. 11-5 *Children gain an understanding of perspective when asked how objects such as these would appear to the doll.*

It is useful for children to try to view objects and systems from reference frames other than their own. One of the ways to do this is to use a doll or picture cutout and ask the children to try to imagine what an object or a system looks like when viewed from the position of the doll. For example, children can be asked where the doll would report an object such as a book to be in relationship to the doll. Of, if the doll is placed on its side on the table and a ball is rolled directly toward its eyes, what would the doll report with regard to the motion of the ball? In a somewhat different task, pupils can be asked to place the doll in the position where it would see other objects in a certain way. For example, "place the doll so that the book would appear to him to be in front and below him." All such tasks lead the child to imagine what objects and systems look like from vantage points other than his own.

By conceptualizing reference frames other than his own a child can be led to recognize that objects and systems may appear to be quite different when viewed from perspectives other than his own. Sometimes, the shift to a different reference frame can help children to see new relationships. In relations with other people, it is often helpful to try to see a situation as it appears to another person. Practice in shifting reference frames may enhance the child's ability to "see things from the other fellow's point of view."

Observations and statements in science tend to be relative rather than absolute. Observations of size, position, time, and motion are made relative to other objects and time periods. The nature of these observations will depend upon the reference frame from which they are made. For children to begin to recognize the relative nature of observations, to think in relative rather than absolute terms, and to see new relationships as they shift reference frames is to open up a new, exciting, and rewarding way of looking at the world.

APPROACHES TO TEACHING

Some of the goals for study in this area can best be achieved through emphasis on the following matters:

1. In descriptions, place stress on physical properties. Descriptions of physical properties are generally more useful than teleological descriptions that emphasize purposes and functions.
2. In discussions, encourage students to make statements in relative terms. Often there is a tendency to be absolute and arbitrary, but it is more useful to recognize the relative nature of knowledge and to express it in relative terms.
3. In experiments, investigations, and discussions, help children to develop the ability to recognize what is pertinent and not pertinent to the question or problem being studied.

These kinds of behavior are desirable in other areas of life in addition to science, and they should be stressed in other appropriate branches of the curriculum as well.

What is the system?

In each of the following demonstrations ask the children to state the objects that should be considered in the system.

1. Inflate a rubber balloon and suspend it from a support by a string. Place a magnet underneath the balloon. Rub a comb with a piece of wool or nylon. Bring the comb near the balloon. What happens? What are the objects in the system? Is the magnet in the system?
2. Sprinkle some ashes on a cube of sugar and with a pair of forceps hold the sugar in a flame. Are the ashes a part of the system? (Try burning a cube of sugar without the ashes present. The ashes are a catalyst that makes possible the chemical reaction.)

298

3. With a wet finger make a damp streak on the chalkboard. Have the children observe the streak. What happens? What objects are in the system? What are some objects that are probably not in the system?

What is down? What is up? What is the direction of Polaris?

A plumb bob is often used to find the direction of "down." Stick a large pin or nail into a soft board that is clamped sideways to a chair or table. With a string, suspend a weight from the pin so that it is free to swing. The direction indicated by the string from the pin to the bob is "down." The direction indicated by the string from the bob to the pin is "up."

The direction of Polaris (North Star) can be used to indicate true north and the latitude of a location. (See page 127 for directions for locating Polaris in the northern sky.) Place a sharpened stick in the ground. At a distance of five or six feet move a second stake about to find the position where you can line up the two stakes and Polaris in a straight line. Insert the second stake in the ground at that point and stretch a string between the two stakes. The taut string indicates a north-south direction.

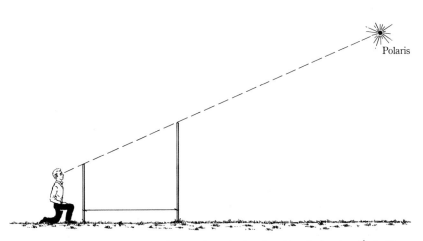

Polaris

Fig. 11-6 *Lining up two stakes with Polaris (the North Star) will indicate true north.*

Now fasten a protractor to the soft board behind your plumb bob so that the string passes by the ninety-degree mark and the hole near the outer edge of the base of the protractor. Stick a small pin through a drinking straw and the hole near the base of the protractor. Line up the protractor so that it is parallel with the north-south line. Sight through the drinking straw and pivot the straw until you can see Polaris through it. The angle that the straw makes with the horizontal (which can be read directly from the protractor) is the latitude of your location.

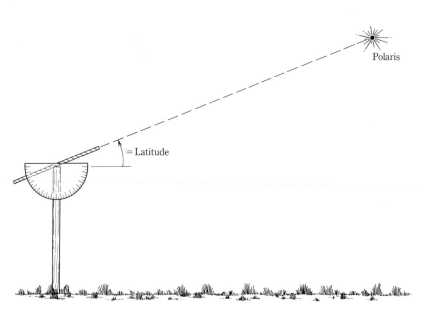

Fig. 11-7   *The angle that a line of sight to Polaris makes with the horizontal is equal to the latitude of the observer's location.*

Where is it?

By tipping the protractor into a horizontal position, the angle between a north-south line and any direction can be ascertained. With this information and the distance, the location of objects can be plotted on a system of polar coordinates. Plot the location of an object using the protractor and drinking straw to obtain the angle from a north-south line and a tape measure to get the distance of the object from the reference point.

How do objects and systems appear from other reference frames?

Children should have practice in imagining how objects and systems would appear from other reference frames. This can be done by using a doll or picture cutouts and asking the children to state how the objects and systems would appear to this other observer. Ask the children to describe the objects as they would appear in relationship to the other observer. For example, the observer might describe an object as being "In front and below me." Place the doll in such positions as the following:

1. In front of a toy truck. Ask, "Where is the truck from the doll's point of view?"
2. In a position so that the truck is to the observer's left and beneath him. Ask the same question.
3. Lying on the floor so that the truck is on the floor above its head.
4. Held upside down above the truck on the floor.
5. In the truck with another object. Ask, "How is the other object moving?"

In another version of this exercise, the children can be asked to place the doll so that another object would appear in a certain way to the doll. Place the doll in the following positions:

1. The truck would appear to the doll to be above his head.
2. The truck would appear to be below and in front of him.
3. The truck and the ball would appear to be moving.

With these as examples, the children should be encouraged to suggest positions for the doll and the objects and to describe them from these reference frames.

INVESTIGATION

In what different ways can a falling object be observed?

It is sometimes useful for children to try to imagine as many significantly different reference frames as possible in which an event in imagination can be viewed. Children should describe the reference frame and try to imagine how an event would appear when viewed from this reference frame.

Drop a ball to the floor and ask the children, "From what different reference frames could this event be viewed?" Limit them to reference frames that are significantly different from each other. Be sure that they remember to place the observer of the ball as one reference frame.

List the suggested reference frames on the chalkboard and then ask, "What would appear to be happening as this event is viewed from each of these reference frames?" Encourage the children to give as complete and accurate descriptions as possible.

Selected References

COLEMAN, JAMES A., *Relativity for the Layman*. New York: New American Library, 1952.

GARDNER, MARTIN, *Relativity for the Millions*. New York: The Macmillan Co., 1962

JACOBSON, WILLARD J., KLEINMAN, GLADYS, HIACK, PAUL S., SUGARBAKER, JOHN, AND CARR, ALBERT, *Science: A Way of Knowing*. New York: American Book Co., 1969.

READINGS FOR THE PRIMARY GRADES

JACOBSON, WILLARD J., AND COWE, EILEEN, *Beginning Science*. New York: American Book Co., 1967.

READINGS FOR THE INTERMEDIATE GRADES

ADLER, IRVING AND RUTH, *Atoms and Molecules*. New York: John Day Co., Inc., 1966.

JACOBSON, WILLARD J., LAUBY, CECILIA J., AND KONICEK, RICHARD D., *Changes in Matter*. New York: American Book Co., 1968.

LANDAU, L. D. AND RUMER, G. B., *What is Relativity?* New York: Basic Books, Inc., 1959.

12 The Study of Interactions

Objects interact. When a string or chain is pulled to raise a flag to the top of a flagpole, there is an interaction between hands, the chain, and the flag. When a certain button is pressed, there is an interaction which causes the clapper on a bell to move back and forth. When another button is pressed, a light may go on or a heater may begin to generate heat. When words are spoken they may lead other people to reply or to take other actions. All of these are examples of interactions between objects.

What proves that an interaction has taken place? The "evidence of interaction"—the changes that have taken place—can be observed. When the chain on the flagpole was pulled, the flag was raised. The change in position of the flag was evidence of interaction. The sound generated when the clapper struck the bell was evidence that an interaction had taken place as a result of pushing the button. Changes that take place—changes in position, temperature, light, sound, shape, color—are evidence that interactions have taken place.

The conservation of matter and energy is an important generalization used in the study of interactions. For example, if a match is placed in a closed bottle and sunlight is concentrated upon it with a magnifying glass, the match will ignite and burn. The flame and the change in form of the match are evidences that an interaction has taken place. But if the system is weighed before and after the interaction, no change in weight will be found. Matter has been conserved. Similarly, in a closed system energy will also be conserved. The generalization that the amount of matter and energy in a closed system remains constant is a powerful tool for the study of interactions.

A great deal of effort in science is devoted to the study of interactions. In fact, entire sciences have been developed around the study of certain kinds of interactions. The emphasis in chemistry, for example, is devoted to the study of chemical interactions, while in nuclear science the major concern is with interactions between nuclear particles. This chapter is concerned with some of the most basic kinds of interactions and how children can be led into a study of some of these interactions.

SIMPLE MACHINES AND DIRECT INTERACTION

There are a number of devices in a classroom that are used to perform various functions. A string is pulled through a set of rollers to raise or lower Venetian blinds. A knob is turned to open or close the catch in a door. We climb up inclined stairs, open a container with a can opener, sharpen a pencil with a pencil sharpener, and lift a set of books with arms. These are all examples of machines and direct interactions.

Machines are devices through which force is applied. A downward force applied to the string in the Venetian blinds is used to raise the blinds. In this case it is convenient to be able to pull downward to raise the blinds. In the can opener, a force is applied over a considerable distance in order to push a blade a short distance through the top of a can. This simple machine is used to increase the amount of force that can be applied. In other cases, machines are used to increase (or decrease) the speed of motion. Machines are used to apply forces in different ways, usually advantageous to man.

The interactions that take place using simple machines can be called direct interactions. When sufficient force is applied at one point of a machine, usually some kind of motion is generated at some other point. However, there is a direct and visible connection between the point where the force is applied and where the motion occurs. In the Venetian blinds the string is connected directly to the blinds, and in the can opener a metal bar connects the point where the force is applied and the effect.

Mechanical Advantage

Machines are often used to exert a greater force. For example, most men cannot lift one end of an automobile off the ground, but with the help of a jack it can be done. The jack makes it possible to multiply the amount of force that can be exerted. The mechanical advantage, M.A., of a machine is a comparison of the force exerted by the machine and the force applied.

$$(\text{M.A.}) = \frac{\text{force exerted by machine}}{\text{force applied}}$$

If we apply a force of 30 pounds to raise a weight of 600 pounds, the machine has an actual mechanical advantage of 20.

$$\text{M.A.} = \frac{600 \text{ lb}}{30 \text{ lb}} = 20$$

It should be recognized that a price is paid for the increase in the amount of force that is exerted. This can be observed in the *inclined plane*. In a typical inclined plane, a load is moved over a long slope in order to lift it a shorter distance. Stairs, ramps, loading chutes are examples of inclined planes. In loading a truck, a ramp may be used. This may make it possible to lift a 500-pound barrel while exerting a force of 100 pounds. This inclined plane will have a mechanical advantage of 5.

The theoretical mechanical advantage, T.M.A., is the increase in force that should be available as a result of using a machine. This is a ratio of the distance over which the force is applied as compared to the distance the resistance is moved.

$$\text{T.M.A.} = \frac{\text{distance force is applied}}{\text{distance resistance is moved}}$$

In the case of an inclined plane, if the force is applied over a distance of 8 feet to raise a resistance 2 feet, the inclined plane has a theoretical mechanical advantage of 4.

The Machine Principle

Machines can be used to increase the amount of force that is exerted. For example, a long lever can be used to lift a resistance such as a very heavy rock. But the force must be exerted over a comparatively long distance in order to move the rock just a little. There is a relationship between the forces and the distances they are exerted that is called the machine principle.

Force × distance force moves = resistance × distance resistance moves

This is another example of conservation. It is possible to use a machine to move a large resistance with small force, but the resistance will move only a short distance as compared to the distance through which the force is exerted. Conversely, a small resistance can be moved through a greater distance if a much larger force is exerted. Work is equal to force times distance.

$$\text{Work} = \text{force} \times \text{distance}$$

Theoretically, the amount of work done with a machine is equal to the work put in. Actually, because of losses due to friction, less work is obtained from a machine than the work put into it.

The machine principle can be demonstrated with an *equal arm balance*. Find the point at which a piece of wood such as a meterstick or yardstick balances and suspend the piece of wood by a string attached at this point. Near each end of the wooden stick attach hooks made from paper clips. A rider made from a paper clip or piece of wire can be moved along the top of the equal arm balance to bring it into fine balance. Weights can be attached to the hooks at each end of the balance and moved along the bar until they are in balance. Then multiply the weights times their distance from the balance point. Are the two products equal?

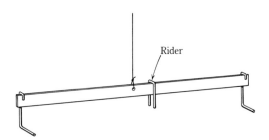

Rider

Fig. 12-1 *Is the weight times the distance on one side equal to weight times the distance on the other?*

There are three different classes of levers depending on where the support or *fulcrum* is placed. Which of these three classes of levers could have the greatest mechanical advantage? In which class lever will the mechanical advantage be less than one?

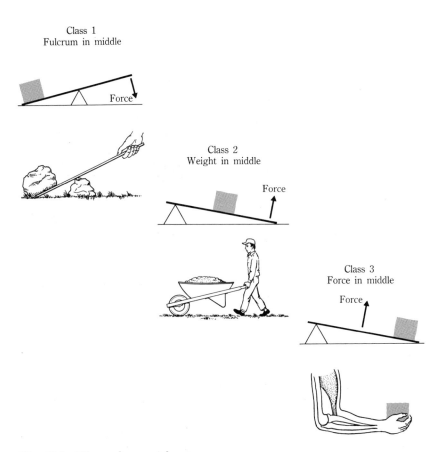

Fig. 12-2   Three classes of levers.

Pulleys can also be used to illustrate the machine principle. In addition to increasing the applied force, pulleys are useful for changing the directions in which a force is applied. Four different pulley arrangements are shown in the illustration.

As with other machines, the theoretical mechanical advantage of a pulley system can be determined by comparing the distance the force is applied to the distance the resistance is moved. However, a close approximation of the theoretical mechanical advantage can be obtained by counting the number of strands that support the resistance. How many strands support the resistance in each of the pulley systems in Figure 12-3? What are the theoretical mechanical advantages?

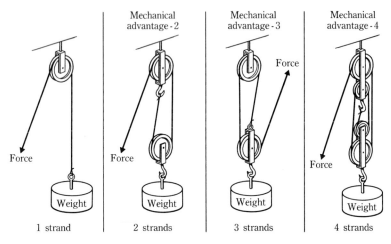

Fig. 12-3 *The mechanical advantage of a pulley system is roughly equal to the number of supporting strands.*

Inertia and Friction in Machines

Inertia is the tendency of an object at rest to remain at rest and of an object in motion to remain in motion in a straight line. When a stalled car is pushed, it is much more difficult to start it to roll than it is to keep it rolling. On the other hand, once it has started rolling it will tend to continue to roll, and a force will have to be applied to stop it. When an automobile is accelerated rapidly, you will feel the car cushion pushing against your back as your body tends to stay at rest. However, if a fast-moving automobile is braked suddenly, you may continue to move forward. The major function of seat belts in automobiles, of course, is to prevent riders from slamming into the interior of automobiles in case of a sudden stop or from being thrown out of the vehicle in case of an accident.

Inertia is a property of matter. The amount of inertia an object possesses depends upon its mass. The more massive the object the greater the inertia. Although all objects have inertia and its effects can be measured, the question "What is inertia?" cannot be answered. Is inertia due to the interaction between an object and all other matter in the universe? The answer is not known. Like the force of gravitation, which it resembles in many respects, effects of inertia are experienced every day and these effects can be described with great precision, but very little success in delving into the nature of inertia has been achieved.

A ball will continue to roll after it has been shoved. A logical question might be, why does the ball continue to roll after the impetus has ceased? This is explained in terms of inertia or the tendency of objects in motion to continue in motion in a straight line. Then why doesn't the ball continue to roll forever? Another force is acting on the ball, the force of friction.

The force of friction is encountered in all machines. If a block of wood is pulled at a constant velocity with a spring scale, the force of friction that has to be overcome can be measured. If some weights are placed on top of the block of wood, the force of friction is increased proportionally. However, if the block is turned on its side so that the area of contact is reduced, the force of friction remains the same. However, if the nature of the surfaces is changed, the force of friction will also change. For example, if a piece of sandpaper is fastened to the bottom of the block, the amount of friction is almost always increased. However, if lubricants such as oil are used, friction is reduced.

In many machines, every effort is made to reduce the amount of friction. Usually, rolling friction is less than sliding friction. If some round pencils or marbles are placed under the block of wood, the amount of friction will be greatly reduced. In many machines, roller bearings and ball bearings are used to reduce the amount of friction. Oil and other lubricants are also used to reduce friction.

In many cases, however, friction is essential. Walking would not be possible without friction. A much-advertised characteristic of automobile tires is the "grip" (friction) between the tire and the road. Of course, an important use of friction is in stopping motion. The ball stopped moving because of friction. Friction is used to stop bicycles, cars, and ourselves as we walk or run.

Because of friction, more work must be put into a machine than the work obtained from a machine. The ratio of the work put out by a machine to the work put in is called the efficiency of the machine.

$$\text{Efficiency} = \frac{\text{Output}}{\text{Input}}$$

Usually this number is multiplied by one hundred to give the efficiency in per cent. By using various means to reduce friction, the efficiency of machines can be increased. However, it has been impossible to build machines that are 100 per cent efficient.

APPROACHES TO TEACHING

What is the mechanical advantage of an inclined plane?

Make an inclined plane by raising one end of a board or plank approximately six feet long to a height of three feet above the floor.

With a spring scale, weigh a small cart or wagon and a heavy object. This weight is the force that has to be exerted to lift the cart and the object.

Now use the spring scale to pull the cart and the object up the inclined plane. How much force has to be exerted? Calculate the mechanical advantage of the inclined plane.

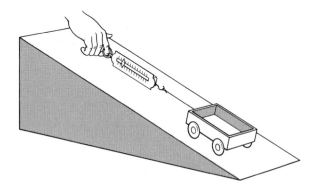

Fig. 12-4 *How much force has to be exerted to pull the cart up the inclined plane at a constant speed?*

Measure the height to the top of the inclined plane and the distance that the cart has to be pulled along the inclined plane to reach that height. What is the theoretical mechanical advantage of the inclined plane? How do the actual and the theoretical mechanical advantages compare?

Adjust the inclined plane so that there is a more gradual incline. How does this affect the mechanical advantage? What happens when the incline is made steeper?

What is the mechanical advantage of a lever?

Place an object such as a small roller or broom handle under a board about a third of the way from the end. Place an object of known weight at the short end. Find out how much weight must be placed at the long end to raise this weight. What is the mechanical advantage of this lever? (To be more precise, consideration must be given to the weight of the lever on each side. Unless the lever is very heavy as compared to the weights used, for practical purposes this factor can be disregarded.)

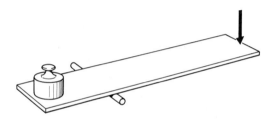

Fig. 12-5 *What is the mechanical advantage of this lever?*

Measure the distance that the long end of the lever must move in order to raise the weight at the short end one inch. What is the theoretical mechanical advantage of this lever? How does it compare with the actual mechanical advantage?

Move the roller to different positions under the board. How do these positions affect the mechanical advantage?

How can the machine principle be used to predict the minimum amount of force needed to move a resistance?

Set up an equal arm balance as shown in Fig. 12-1 on page 308. Place an object of known weight, such as one hundred grams, at a known distance, such as forty centimeters, from the fulcrum and calculate where another object with a weight such as two hundred grams must be placed to bring it into balance. Conduct the experiment. Was your calculation correct?

Examine whatever balances used for weighing that may be at hand. How is the machine principle used in the construction of such balances?

Set up two pulley systems, one having two supporting strands and the other four supporting strands. Predict how much force will be needed to hold a one hundred gram weight off the table in each of the systems? With a spring scale measure the amount of force needed.

What are some effects of inertia?

Tie a string to a heavy object. If you pull slowly, you will probably be able to lift the object without breaking the string, whereas a quick sharp pull will break the string.

Place a piece of paper so that about half of it is hanging over the edge of a table. Place an object on top of the paper. (Try placing a ruler upright on the paper.) Grasp the edge of the paper with one hand and with the other give the paper a sharp blow. What happens to the object on the paper?

Place a brick or a small block at the lower end of an incline. Put an object such as a small doll in a cart. Allow the cart to roll down the incline and be stopped abruptly as it strikes the block. What happens to the object in the cart?

On what factors does the force of friction depend?

Attach a string to a block of wood. To carry out these experiments, the block of wood should be pulled across a wooden board at a constant velocity. (If the block is pulled at a constant velocity, the inertia of the block can be disregarded.) The amount of force necessary to pull the block can be measured with a spring scale. This experiment will also give children practice in handling data as they record the forces that are exerted.

First pull the block along the board several times. Each time note the force that is necessary to pull the block at a constant velocity. Ask the children what figure we should use for the force necessary to pull the block across the board. (They may suggest that the figures be averaged.)

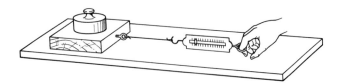

Fig. 12-6 *How does the force required to pull the block at a steady rate increase as the weight on the block is increased?*

Turn the block of wood over on its side and pull it along the board. How does this affect the force necessary to pull the block?

Now place progressively greater weights on the block of wood and in each case measure the force needed to pull it across the board. Have the children graph the force required as the weight is increased. What relation-

ship is there between the force of friction and the force pressing the surfaces together?

Tack a piece of sandpaper to the front edge of the block of wood and
then bend the sandpaper underneath the block of wood. Pull the block
of wood along on this sandpaper surface. Does changing the nature of the
surfaces in contact change the force of friction?

Put dowel sticks or round pencils under the block of wood. How does
this affect the amount of friction?

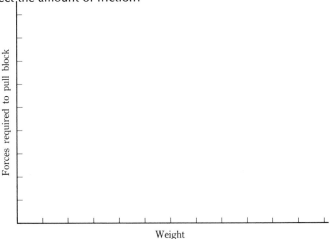

*Fig. 12-7 The relationship between weight and force of friction may be seen
with the help of a graph.*

What is the efficiency of a machine?

The efficiency of a machine can be determined by dividing the work
output by the work input. Since work equals the force times the distance
it is exerted, by measuring these factors both input and output work can be
determined. The inclined plane is a convenient machine for demonstrating
this.

Weigh the object to be lifted and the cart on which it is to be rolled
and multiply this figure by the height the object is lifted. The result is the
work output in foot-pounds if the measurements are made in pounds and
feet. (In this case the weight of the cart is considered as part of the load.
In some cases this might be excluded in calculating the work output.)

With a spring scale, measure the force required to pull the cart and the
object at a constant velocity up the inclined plane. Multiply this figure by
the length of the inclined plane to determine the work input. Calculate
the efficiency of the machine

$$\text{Efficiency} = \frac{\text{Input}}{\text{Output}} = \frac{\text{Weight X distance}}{\text{Effort force X distance}}$$

The efficiency of other machines can be determined in much the same way.

MAGNETISM AND INTERACTION AT A DISTANCE

The Greeks noticed that certain rocks attracted other objects. These rocks were called *lodestones*, and it is now known that they are composed of a mineral that is a natural magnet. Now many kinds of magnets, with a variety of uses, can be made.

Magnets and Interaction at a Distance

If a magnet is brought near a steel paper clip, the paper clip is affected before it is touched by the magnet. This is an example of what is called interaction-at-a-distance. If a person pushed a paper clip with a pencil, the paper clip would move, and this might be considered interaction-at-a-distance. The person and the paper clip have interacted through the medium of the pencil. However, the terminology interaction-at-a-distance is often limited to interactions, such as those between the magnet and the paper clip, in which there is no visible connection between the objects that are interacting. Gravitation and electrical attraction and repulsion are other examples of interaction-at-a-distance.

What kinds of materials interact with a magnet? Children should be encouraged to try to find out for themselves. Have them determine whether such materials as paper, iron, wood, steel, and copper are attracted to magnets. Sometimes children will generalize that metals are attracted to magnets. If they do, have them try aluminum, brass, and copper. Substances that interact with magnets are called *magnetic materials*. Iron and steel are two of the most common magnetic materials.

If a paper clip that is suspended from a strong magnet touches another paper clip, this second paper clip will also be attracted. This phenomenon is called *magnetic induction*. A magnetic material, such as the steel in a paper clip, when near a strong magnet becomes another magnet and will interact with other magnetic materials. In fact, a crude but effective way that children can compare the strengths of magnets is to see how long a chain of paper clips can be formed with a magnet.

Magnets can be used to make other magnets. If a piece of steel or iron, such as a piece of steel wire cut from a wire coat hanger, is stroked in one direction with one end of a magnet, it will be magnetized. It is important that the piece of iron or steel always be stroked in the same direction with the same end of the magnet. An electric current can also be used to make stronger magnets.

Magnetic Poles

If paper clips are spread over a table and a magnet is placed on top of them, when the magnet is raised more paper clips will tend to adhere to some parts of the magnet than others. The places on a magnet where the magnetic effect seems to be concentrated are called the *magnetic poles*. Many magnets have two poles, but magnets may have more poles. Often the poles are located near the ends of the magnets, but they can be located anywhere on the magnet.

If a bar magnet is suspended with a piece of string around the center and if there are no other magnets nearby, the suspended magnet will tend to line up in a north-south direction. The section of the magnet that is north is called the *north pole* and the one in the south the *south pole*. If one pole of another bar magnet is brought near it, one end of the suspended magnet will be attracted and the other end repelled. The north pole of one magnet will attract the south pole and repel the north pole of another magnet. Similarly, a south pole will attract a north and repel a south pole. These interactions are manifestations of the basic principle of magnets: *Unlike magnetic poles attract and like magnetic poles repel.*

This basic principle of magnets provides us with a means of determining whether or not an object is a magnet. That an object attracts other objects such as paper clips is not sufficient evidence; it might be that the paper clips are magnets. However, only a magnet will repel one pole of a known magnet. To find out if an object is a magnet, simply bring a magnet that is free to move near the object and note whether one pole of this magnet is repelled by some section of the object.

The earth is a magnet. One end of the terrestrial magnet will attract one pole of a magnet and repel the other. If the suspended bar magnet is turned so that the end that was toward the north is now to the south, the poles of the terrestrial magnet will repel these ends of the magnet, and the bar magnet will tend to line up as before. Some students may question how, if the principle of magnets holds, the north pole of the magnet can be attracted to the north. This can be confusing, but it is a matter of definition. The north pole of a magnet is defined as being the one that tends to line up to the north. Another way to think of it is that the magnetic pole to be found in the northern reaches of the earth is a "south pole."

Small bar magnets mounted so that they can turn easily are called *compasses* and are useful for determining north-south directions and for determining whether or not another object is a magnet. A compass is moved alongside an object, and if some section of that object tends to repel a pole of the compass, then that object is a magnet.

If magnets are broken or cut into two pieces, both pieces are magnets. A piece of wire can be cut off a wire coat hanger with a pair of pliers and magnetized by pulling it along a strong magnet. If a compass is moved along the wire, it will be found to have a north pole at one end and a south pole at the other. However, when the wire is cut in two, both pieces will be found to have a north pole and south pole; both are magnets.

A Modern Theory of Magnetism

With the help of a magnet, children can easily determine that some substances such as iron, steel, and nickel are magnetic, while other substances such as copper, zinc, lead, wood, and glass are non-magnetic. But why are some substances magnetic while other substances are not? What are the differences between magnetic and non-magnetic substances? A modern theory of magnetism must help to answer such questions.

To understand magnetism, there must be an understanding of the structure and make-up of matter. All matter is made up of very small particles called *atoms*. Atoms are the smallest unit of any chemical element. Atoms, in turn, are made up of atomic particles. More than thirty atomic particles have been identified. However, in the consideration of the structure of matter only three need to be considered: electrons, protons, and neutrons. Almost all of the matter in an atom is concentrated in the protons and neutrons, and the neutrons and protons are all in the small, relatively hard nucleus of the atom. Around the nucleus are found the electrons; there are as many electrons as protons in every electrically neutral atom. These electrons are arranged in shells. In the first shell there are two electrons; the second shell has eight electrons; and the third shell has eighteen electrons.

Each of the electrons in an atom is spinning, and because of this spin, each electron is a very small magnet. Usually there are an equal number of electrons spinning in each direction, and the magnetic effects of the electrons tend to cancel each other. Atoms with an odd number of electrons, however, must have at least one more electron spinning in one direction than in the other. Therefore, these materials are slightly magnetic.

In the iron atom there are four more electrons spinning in one direction than in the other. The iron atom can be depicted as in Fig. 12-8. As the diagram shows, in the third shell of the iron atom there are believed to be ten electrons spinning in a clockwise direction while only six electrons are spinning in a counterclockwise direction. It is this feature of the iron atom that makes it a magnetic substance.

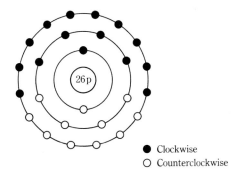

Clockwise
Counterclockwise

Fig. 12-8 The magnetic properties of iron are believed due to there being four more electrons spinning in one direction than in the other.

However, all objects made of iron are not magnets. The iron object has to be magnetized before it becomes a magnet. What is the process whereby an iron object is magnetized?

The large numbers of iron atoms in a region are called *domains*. These domains are very small magnets. However, in an unmagnetized piece of iron, these domains are lined up in a helter-skelter fashion so that their magnetic effects cancel. If a test tube is filled with iron filings and tested to see whether it is a magnet, the result is usually negative. But if the test tube is stroked with a magnet, it will become magnetized. The iron filings, which are small magnets, become lined up so that the north poles tend to lie in one direction and south poles in another direction. In a similar way if the domains in a piece of iron or steel can be lined up so that the north poles tend to be in one direction and the south poles in the other, the iron or steel object becomes a magnet.

A magnetic substance can be magnetized by stroking with another magnet, storing in a magnetic field, or by an electric current. In each case, the magnetic domains become lined up. A magnet can be demagnetized by heating or pounding. This tends to rearrange the domains again into a helter-skelter arrangement.

This modern theory of magnetism has been useful in explaining why some substances are magnetic but others non-magnetic and the process whereby some substances can be magnetized. In recent years it has also been useful in the search for ways to make more powerful magnets.

APPROACHES TO TEACHING

Through what kinds of materials do magnets attract?

Suspend a strong magnet from some kind of support. Tie a piece of thread to a paper clip and adjust and fasten the thread to the bench or table so that the paper clip is held in space a short distance below the magnet.

Now have the children pass various materials such as paper, wood, aluminum, and plastic between the magnet and the paper clip. Have them move their hand through the space. Then try a piece of iron or steel. Which materials affect the interaction?

Where are the poles of a magnet?

One way to find the poles of magnets is to move compasses alongside. Gather together a variety of magnets and move a compass along their sides. Where are the poles located? See Fig. (12-9.)

Another way to locate magnetic poles in magnets is to use iron filings. Place a piece of cardboard or a manila folder over a magnet and sprinkle iron filings onto it. Tap the cardboard gently; and the iron filings will be seen to form lines that are defined as magnetic lines of force. The points where the lines seem to converge indicate the positions of the magnetic poles. (See Fig. 12-10.)

Cut a fairly long piece of wire from a wire coat hanger. Stroke both ends of the wire outward with the same end of a strong magnet. Try to locate the poles on the wire using both the compass and iron-filing methods. How many magnetic poles does the wire have? Where are they located? Try stroking other pieces of wire in other ways and locating the magnetic poles.

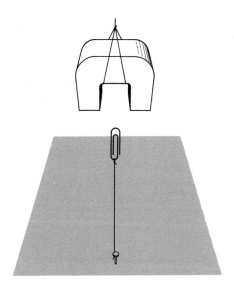

Fig. 12-9 *What happens when various kinds of materials are passed between the magnet and paper clip?*

What is the nature of the earth's magnetic field in your locality?

A compass needle will line up parallel to magnetic lines of force and can be used to indicate the direction of the earth's magnetic lines of force. First it is necessary to find the direction of true north. This can be done by sighting along two stakes and setting them so that they are in positions in

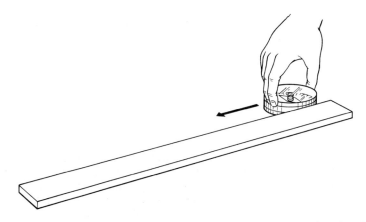

Fig. 12-10 *To locate the magnetic poles move a compass alongside the object.*

line with Polaris, the North Star. Stretch a string between the two stakes and place a compass on top of the string. With a protractor measure the angle between the north-south line and the compass needle. This angle is called the *magnetic declination*.

The earth's magnetic lines of force also are at an angle with the horizontal. The angle of *magnetic inclination* can be measured with a homemade dipping needle. Obtain an unmagnetized steel knitting needle or a straight

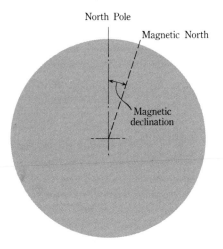

Fig. 12-11 *The angle between a north-south line and the direction a compass needle points is the magnetic declination.*

piece of steel wire cut from a coat hanger. (If neither end of a compass needle is repelled by the needle, it is not magnetized.) Slip a small piece of rubber tubing to the center of the knitting needle. Push a pin through the rubber tubing, place it on a stand and move the rubber tubing back and forth to find the point at which the needle is balanced. Hang a protractor from the pin so that the ninety-degree mark hangs straight down.

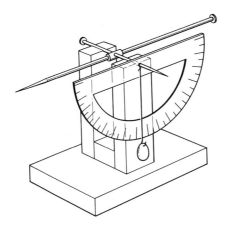

Fig. 12-12   *A dipping needle.*

Magnetize the knitting needle by stroking it in one direction with a pole of a strong magnet. Place the knitting needle back on its stand and line it up so that the knitting needle is parallel with a compass needle. When the knitting needle is released it should dip. Using the protractor, read the angle that the needle makes with the horizontal. This is the magnetic inclination for your locality.

Check the magnetic declination and inclination for your region in the *Handbook of Chemistry and Physics.* How do your findings compare with these?

How are magnetic substances magnetized?

Fill a test tube with iron filings, cork it, and then shake. Bring the bottom of the test tube near both poles of a compass needle. If either pole of the compass needle is repelled, the test tube of iron filings is a magnet and should be shaken again until neither pole of the compass needle is repelled.

Now stroke the test tube with one end of a strong magnet. Notice what happens to the individual iron filings. It is believed the magnetic domains in a bar of iron behave similarly under the influence of a magnetic field.

Now bring the bottom of the test tube near the compass needle. Is either end of the compass needle repelled?

Shake the test tube again and test to see if it is still a magnet.

How can the earth's magnetic field be used to magnetize a piece of iron?

Obtain a soft iron rod and check to see if it is a magnet. If it is, hold it in an east-west direction and pound it with a hammer until it is demagnetized.

To use the earth's magnetic field to magnetize the rod, hold the rod so that it is parallel with a compass needle and a dipping needle. In this position, the rod is parallel with the earth's magnetic lines of force. (This experiment should be done away from the influence of any other magnets.) Pound the bar with a hammer. Check to see whether the bar has been magnetized. If it has, how can the process by which it has been magnetized be explained?

ELECTRICITY AND INTERACTION AT A DISTANCE

Sometimes when hair is combed the hair seems to stick to the comb and a slight crackling noise may be heard. Garments made of wool or certain synthetic fibers seem to collect dust and lint. If a nylon garment is removed in the dark, flashes of light may be seen. All of these are electrostatic phenomena.

Electrostatics, as the word implies, refers to electric charges that tend to remain stationary. A great deal can be learned about electricity by studying electrostatic charges. Consider the following two experiments that children can do. Explanations of electrostatics will have to explain the results of such experiments as these.

Tear some very small pieces of paper and place them on the table. Rub a rubber rod with a piece of plastic and bring the rod next to the pieces of paper. The pieces of paper will probably be attracted to the rubber rod. Some pieces of paper may seem to be alternately attracted and repelled by the rubber rod.

Rub a rubber rod with a piece of plastic and bring it near a rubber balloon suspended from a string. The balloon is attracted to the rubber rod. Now rub both the balloon and the rod with the plastic. Usually, the balloon will be repelled by the rod. However, if the rubber rod is rubbed with plastic and the balloon with some other material, such as wool, the balloon will usually be attracted to the rod.

Electric Charges

The electrostatic phenomena just described are due to the transfer of electrons from one material to the other. Ordinarily, materials have an equal number of negatively charged electrons and positively charged protons. However, when some materials are rubbed together, electrons are rubbed off one material leaving it positively charged and are transferred to the second material making it negatively charged. When a rubber rod is rubbed with a piece of wool, the electrons are rubbed off the wool and onto the rod making the rubber rod negatively charged. However, the electrons are held more tightly in most plastics, and when a rubber rod is rubbed with plastic, some electrons are transferred to the plastic leaving the rubber rod positively charged.

Objects that are electrically charged often interact. When the rubber balloon and rubber rod were rubbed with the same material, they had the same kind of electric charge and they repelled each other. However, when the balloon was rubbed with wool and the rubber rod with plastic, they were left with unlike electric charges and were attracted toward each other. These interactions illustrate a basic principle of electricity: *Objects having unlike electric charges are attracted and objects having like charges are repelled.*

This basic principle can be used to help explain the interaction between the charged rubber rod and the small pieces of paper. When the positively charged rod is brought near the pieces of paper, some of the electrons on the paper tend to move toward the side of the paper nearest the rod. This makes this part of the paper negatively charged, and the paper is attracted to the positively charged rod. However, when the paper comes in contact with the rod, some of the electrons may rub off onto the rod leaving the paper positively charged. Then, since like charges repel, the paper will be repelled by the positively charged rod. The principle that like charges repel and unlike charges attract is used often in explaining electrical phenomena.

Some children may notice considerable similarity between electrostatic phenomena and magnetism. Some may, in fact, suggest the rubber rod is a magnet. While there are striking similarities, they are different phenomena. An obvious difference is that different kinds of materials are involved. Only magnetic materials such as iron and steel are attracted to magnets while non-magnetic materials such as paper are attracted to electrically charged objects.

Electricity and Magnetism

While electricity and magnetism are different phenomena, there are very important relationships between them. The Danish physicist H. C. Oersted noticed that when a compass was left near a wire bearing an electric current, there was an interaction between the electric current and the magnetic compass needle. Children can observe the effects of this interaction by placing a wire connected to the posts of a dry cell over a compass needle and parallel to the needle. Have them observe the movement of the needle when the switch is closed and an electric current is sent through the wire.

This interaction between a magnetic needle and an electric current is the essential interaction in the *galvanometer* which is a sensitive device for detecting an electric current. Wrap several turns of wire around a compass. Whenever an electric current flows through the wire, it will interact with the compass needle and cause it to move. This is the basic principle on which galvanometers are based.

If a magnet, such as a compass needle, is caused to move when an electric current is sent through a nearby wire, then something should happen in a wire if a magnet is moved near it. This was the brilliant thought that Michael Faraday had, and he suggested that an electric current might be generated in the wire. Wind several feet of insulated wire into a coil and connect the ends of the wire to a galvanometer. Then pass a strong bar magnet through the coil. Is there any indication that an electric current is generated in the coil?

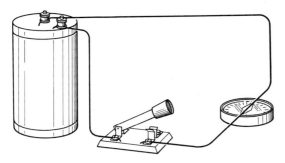

Fig. 12-13   The wire is held parallel to the compass needle. What happens when the switch is closed?

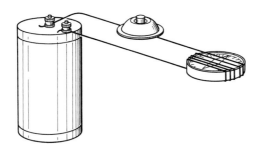

Fig. 12-14   The magnetic needle can be used to detect an electric current flowing through the coil.

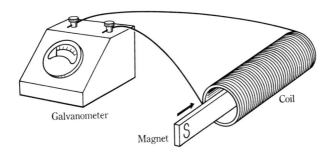

Fig. 12-15   When a magnet and a coil move relative to each other, an electric current is generated.

The Generation of Electricity

The dry cell is the most important source of electricity for elementary school science. It is convenient and completely safe. It is an example of the chemical generation of electricity, and children can make a similar cell using chemicals that can be obtained at most drugstores.

Place about two ounces of ammonium chloride (sal ammoniac) in a glass jar and fill the jar with water. Sprinkle some potassium permanganate on a piece of cloth 4 inches by 6 inches and wrap and tie this cloth around a carbon rod taken from an old dry cell. Connect a flashlight bulb to the carbon rod and to a piece of zinc such as found in dry cells. Insert the zinc and the carbon rod into the ammonium chloride solution. Sufficient electric current should be generated to light the flashlight bulb.

In this chemical generation of electricity, the zinc reacts with the ammonium chloride faster than the carbon. As a result of the chemical reaction, electrons are released on the zinc. Since like charges repel, the electrons are repelled through the wire and the bulb as an electric current.

However, the most important method of generating electricity involves the conversion of mechanical energy into electrical energy. Essentially, magnets and coils of wire are moved relative to each other. Usually, either the coils of wire or the magnets are turned inside the other as shown in the sketch of a simple generator. An *alternating current* is generated by this kind of generator. In an alternating current, the electrons move back and forth: this is the most widely used kind of electric current.

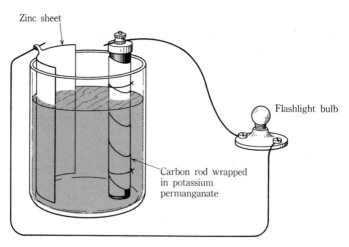

Fig. 12-16   An electric cell.

The Transmission of Electricity

One of the great advantages of electricity as a form of energy is that it can be generated at one location and then transmitted for use at a distant location. Before the harnessing of electrical energy, factories had to be located at places where energy such as that from waterfalls could be transmitted by belt and drive shaft. Now the use of electricity has made it possible to locate factories at more convenient locations.

Electricity is transmitted through conductors. A *complete circuit* is needed. It is as if the electrons require a "round trip ticket." They must be conducted from the source to the point where the electricity is used and back to the source. The flow of an electric current can be stopped and started with *switches*. A circuit is protected from carrying too large a current by *fuses* and *circuit breakers*.

Electricity and Other Forms of Energy

Another great advantage of electricity is that it is readily convertible into other forms of energy such as heat, light, and mechanical energy. Inevitably, in each of these conversions some of the electrical energy is changed into a form, usually heat, that cannot be used. However, this energy "loss" is often compensated for by the convenience of electricity.

Fasten one end of a wire to one post of a dry cell. Hold the other end against the second post. Does the wire begin to feel hot? As soon as it does, remove the wire from the post. The passage of an electrical current through the wire generated heat. Most electrical heating appliances, such as toasters and hot plates, generate heat in this same way.

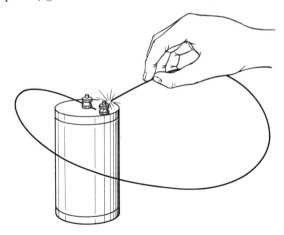

Fig. 12-17   *Electrical energy can be transformed into heat energy.*

Connect one thin strand of picture wire between the bared ends of two copper wires. When the other ends of the copper wires are connected to a dry cell, the picture wire will glow and give off light. (This will be most evident if this experiment is carried out in a darkened room.) If the wires are left connected the picture wire will soon "burn." Light is generated in a similar way in an ordinary light bulb. Electricity is passed through a thin wire of wolfram. However, the light bulb is filled with an inert gas, such as argon, and the thin wire does not "burn."

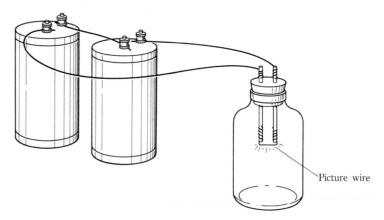

Picture wire

Fig. 12-18 *Electrical energy can be transformed into light.*

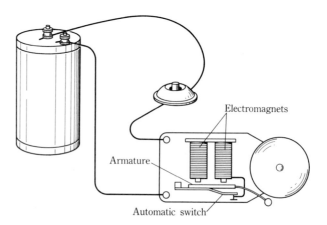

Electromagnets

Armature

Automatic switch

Fig. 12-19 *An electric bell is a simple motor.*

The *electric motor* converts electrical energy into mechanical energy. The electric bell is perhaps the simplest motor, and children can examine it to find out how an electric motor works. Basically, an electric bell consists of electromagnets, an armature to which the clapper is connected, and an automatic switching device. When an electric current flows through the electromagnets, the armature is attracted and the clapper strikes the bell. However, when the armature is attracted, the circuit is broken and the armature springs back to complete the circuit again. In the bell this making and breaking of the circuit goes on very rapidly. A similar kind of action takes place in most direct current motors.

APPROACHES TO TEACHING

What is the electric charge?

The way that a charged object interacts with an object that has a known electric charge will indicate the nature of the electric charge. For example, if a rubber balloon is rubbed with wool, the balloon will acquire a negative charge. The balloon will be repelled by a negatively charged object and attracted to one that is positively charged.

The *electroscope* is a sensitive instrument for the study of electric charges. It consists essentially of two thin metal leaves, ordinarily made of gold or aluminum, that diverge when the system is charged. The electroscope shown in the illustration can be made using the thin aluminum foil from gum wrappers.

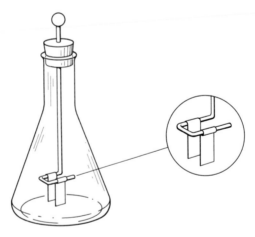

Fig. 12-20 *An electroscope for detecting electrical charges.*

If a rubber rod is charged negatively by rubbing it with a piece of wool and brought near the knob of the electroscope, electrons are forced out of the knob onto your finger when you touch the knob. Because some of the electrons have been removed, this leaves the electroscope positively charged. If a negatively charged rod is brought near the knob of the

Fig. 12-21 Charging an electroscope by induction.

electroscope, electrons will be forced into the leaves, and they will come together. A positively charged rod, on the other hand, will attract electrons out of the positively charged leaves, and they will diverge even farther.

In this way, the electroscope becomes a sensitive and convenient instrument for detecting electric charges and determining whether they are negative or positive.

Rub a rubber rod with such materials as wool, silk, paper, plastic, and rubber. In each case, what kind of charge is generated on the rod? Rub other kinds of materials together. What are the charges generated?

What materials will conduct an electric current?

Connect a dry cell, flashlight bulb, and a pair of nails in a manner so as to insure that there is a gap between the two nails. A conductor placed across the two nails will close the circuit, and the flashlight bulb will give off light.

Try placing a wide variety of materials, such as iron, steel, wood, paper, glass, lead, graphite, string, plastic, and leather, across the two nails. By turning the board and nails upside down they can be immersed in such liquids as water, salt water, and kerosene. Which of these many materials are good conductors of electricity?

How is electricity conducted in a flashlight?

The flashlight is a convenient device for studying electrical circuits. Have the children take a flashlight apart and trace the complete circuit. Have them note how the switch makes and breaks the circuit. After they become familiar with the flashlight circuit, pose problems for them by turning one of the dry cells around, removing the spring at the rear, or placing a non-conductor over the center post of one of the dry cells. See if they can repair the flashlight.

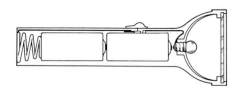

Fig. 12-22   Have the children trace the circuit in a flashlight.

What are some characteristics of series and parallel circuits?

Fig. 12-23 illustrates two different ways of connecting several bulbs or electrical appliances into a circuit. Connect two flashlight bulbs in series and two in parallel. Close the circuit and note how bright the lights are. Add a third bulb to each of the circuits. How is the intensity of the light affected in each of the circuits? Unscrew a bulb in each of the circuits. How does this affect each of the circuits? Which kind of circuit would be best for use in homes and factories?

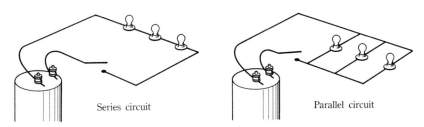

Fig. 12-23 *Have the children use such circuits to find answers to the questions posed on the opposite page.*

In what ways are electromagnets like and unlike permanent magnets?

An electromagnet can be made by wrapping a number of turns of insulated wire around a nail and connecting the wire through a switch to one or more dry cells.

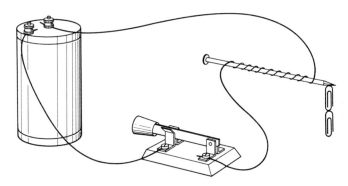

Fig. 12-24 *Graph the relationship between the number of turns in the coil and the length of the paper clip chain that can be suspended.*

Lower the electromagnet down onto paper clips spread over the table. Does the electromagnet appear to have poles?

Hold the ends of the electromagnet next to the ends of a compass needle. Is one end of the compass needle repelled?

Unwind the electromagnet and then wind the wire around in the opposite way. How does this affect the poles of the electromagnet?

Reverse the connections of the wires on the dry cell. How does this affect the polarity of the electromagnet?

Pick up some paper clips with the electromagnet. Then open the switch. Does the electromagnet continue to be a magnet? What happens when the switch is closed again?

LIGHT AND INTERACTIONS WITH RADIATION

Seeing is perhaps the most important way of obtaining information about the environment. Objects can be seen only as a result of the interactions between them and light. A burning match, an incandescent bulb, and the sun are sources of light. Many other objects can be seen because they reflect light. Such interactions make it possible to learn about the environment, and, therefore, the nature of light and how it interacts is of special importance.

The Nature of Light

Strange as it may seem, the nature of light is not completely understood. Some interactions can be explained by assuming that light is a wave phenomenon. However, other interactions can only be explained if it is assumed that light consists of a beam of particles. A few simple experiments that can be undertaken by children will give considerable information about light and illustrate the dilemma of trying to explain the nature of light.

If holes are cut in three pieces of cardboard and lined up so that the children can see a light through them, it will be found that the holes are lined up in a straight line. This can be checked to see if a string can be stretched through the holes without touching the sides. *Light travels in a straight line.* This is an important characteristic of light. However, this characteristic could hold for light as either a wave or a particle phenomenon.

If the beams of two flashlights are aimed so that they cross each other, the beams do not seem to affect each other in any way. In a somewhat similar way, if two pebbles are dropped in still water, the waves that are formed will cross each other with no apparent effect. This observation supports a wave theory of light.

If a beam of light from a flashlight or slide projector is aimed through a spherical flask filled with water, the beam of light will be concentrated upon a sheet of paper held a few inches away. Similarly, sunlight can be concentrated with a magnifying glass on a piece of paper or tinder to start a fire. This bending and concentrating of light is an example of *refraction* and can best be explained by considering light to be a wave phenomenon.

When a light meter or photoelectric cell is held in the light, a small electric current is generated which causes the needle on the light meter to deflect. This *photoelectric effect* can best be explained by assuming that light consists of a stream of particles and that these particles knock off electrons in the photoelectric material. The small electric current is the flow of these electrons.

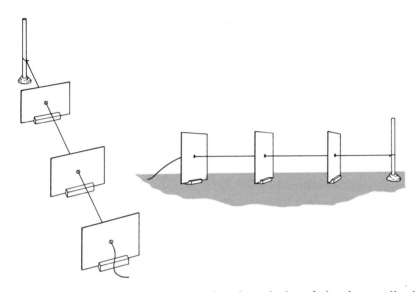

Fig. 12-25 *Can you stretch a taut string through three holes that are lined up by sighting through them?*

Light is now considered to be both a wave and a particle phenomenon. It has been suggested that light could be considered to consist of small particles traveling in waves. This is not the kind of explanation that is looked upon with favor in science—a simpler explanation is much to be preferred. But in order to explain various interactions associated with light it is still necessary to consider light as primarily a wave phenomenon under certain conditions and a particle phenomenon under other conditions.

Reflection

When a rubber ball is thrown against a wall, it bounces back. If the wall is smooth, the direction the ball will bounce can be predicted. But if the wall is rough, it is more difficult to tell in which direction the ball will go. Similarly, light is reflected from most surfaces. From a very smooth surface, such as that of a mirror, light will be reflected in a very predictable manner. Clear images are reflected from such surfaces. However, from most surfaces, such as the surface of this page, light is reflected in such a diffuse manner that we cannot see images.

There are three kinds of common mirrors. *Concave mirrors* are like hollow spheres. The mirrors in large astronomical telescopes are concave, and they gather in light from distant sources and reflect it back to a point. The reflectors in automobile headlights are also concave. They are shaped so that the light from the bulbs is reflected outward in parallel rays. *Convex mirrors* are shaped like part of the outside of a ball. Light that strikes convex mirrors is spread out over a wider area as it is reflected, although a larger area can be surveyed by the use of a concave mirror. The large mirrors that are sometimes seen suspended in stores are concave mirrors as are some rearview mirrors in automobiles. In the *plane mirror*, which has a flat surface, light is reflected evenly.

Refraction

Place a coin in a coffee cup and then move your eye to the point where the coin can no longer be seen over the edge of the cup. Have someone slowly pour water into the cup. As the water rises in the cup, you will be able to see the coin again. To explain this observation, the *refraction* of light must be considered.

Light travels at a velocity of about 3×10^{10} centimeters per second in a vacuum. Its velocity in air is about the same, but in a denser medium such as water its velocity is somewhat less. Therefore, light reflected by the coin will tend to be bent toward the observer as it leaves the water at an angle and enters the air. This makes it possible for the observer to see the coin even though his eyes are below a straight line from the coin past the edge of the cup.

Fig. 12-26 *When water is poured into the cup, the reflected light from the coin is bent so that the coin can be seen by the eye.*

Perhaps the best way to explain refraction to children is to use an analogy. If the right wheels of an automobile rolling down the highway were to strike soft sand, the automobile would tend to swerve to the right. The velocity of the automobile in sand would tend to be reduced as compared to that on the smooth highway. Similarly, the edge of a ray of light that first strikes a dense medium such as water will tend to be slowed and the entire ray will be bent. Conversely, the edge of a ray that first enters a less dense medium such as air will go faster than that part of the ray still in the water. This ray will then be bent away from a line perpendicular (the normal) to the denser medium.

This analogy can be used to explain how a beam of light can be concentrated with water in a spherical flask. As the center of the beam strikes the flask it is slowed. However, the edges of the beam continue to travel at a greater velocity for a short distance in air, and they tend to be bent inward. The outer edges of the beam also emerge from the water sooner and are bent farther toward the center.

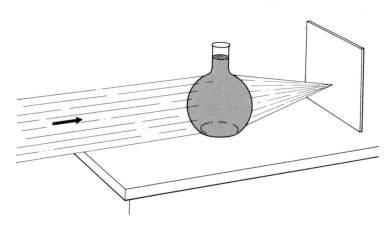

Fig. 12-27 The water in the flask acts as a lens concentrating the light.

If a thin beam of light is reflected from a mirror placed at an angle in a pan of water as shown in the illustration, a *spectrum* consisting of the colors of the rainbow will be projected onto the wall or ceiling. The colors of the spectrum, which make up white light, travel at slightly different velocities. Because of these slightly different velocities, the colors that make up white light are slightly dispersed into a spectrum as they enter and leave a triangular-shaped *prism* such as the water over the mirror. The colors can be recombined into white light by passing them through another prism.

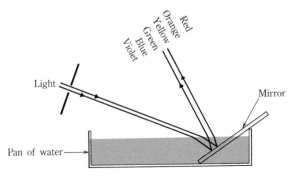

Fig. 12-28 *The water serves as a prism to refract the thin beam of light.*

Many children will notice that the colors of the spectrum of white light are the same as those of the rainbow. Rainbows are formed in very much the same way. As sunlight shines into water droplets left in the air after a rainstorm, the light is spread slightly into a spectrum. This is reflected at the opposite edge of the raindrop. As the light leaves the raindrop it is dispersed even more. The refraction and reflection of light by large numbers of raindrops produce the rainbows that sometimes can be seen after a rain shower.

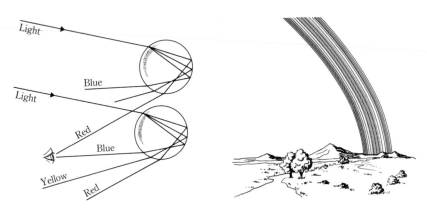

Fig. 12-29 *How a rainbow is formed.*

The Eye and the Camera

Since eyes are probably the most important sense organ, part of the study of light should be devoted to a consideration of the structure of the eye and how we see. One of the best approaches to the study of the eye and seeing is to use the analogy of the camera. The children should have access to cameras and be able to examine them as they study the eye.

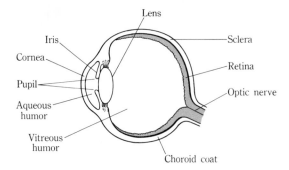

Fig. 12-30 *Cross section of the eye.*

Essentially, both the eye and the camera are instruments for transforming light energy into other forms of energy. In both, light is transformed into chemical energy. In the eye this chemical energy is transformed into electrical nerve impulses.

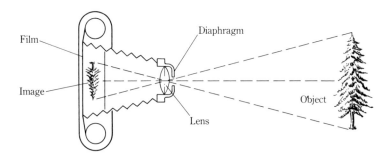

Fig. 12-31 *Cross section of a camera.*

In both the eye and the camera, the light enters through a small hole in the front. The size of the *pupil* of the eye is automatically controlled by the intensity of the light; in some sophisticated cameras there is a similar automatic control of the size of the opening. *Lenses* focus the light on the back of the eye and the camera. In the eye, the shape of the lens is changed by muscles that contract and relax. No way has been found to do this with the glass or plastic lenses used in cameras. Instead, the lenses are moved backward and forward to focus the image on the film at the back of the camera.

The image formed in both the eye and the camera is inverted. This inverted image can be seen in the pinhole camera and in cameras that have ground-glass backs. Although the image in the eye is inverted, man has long since learned to interpret this image as "right side up." In fact, it has been learned that subjects who have worn special glasses that invert the image can within a short time become adjusted to them and then adjust again when the glasses are removed.

In the camera, the light of the image interacts with chemicals of the photographic film. In one kind of interaction, the light interacts with a compound of silver to cause a color change. In the eye, the image is cast upon the *retina* at the back of the eye. The retina is composed of *rods* and *cones*. Under bright light, the cones are able to distinguish colors, and under these conditions everything can be seen very clearly. Under very dim light, such as starlight and dim moonlight, only the rods are stimulated. The rods cannot distinguish colors, and this is why objects seen in dim light appear to be different shades of gray.

The interaction between light and the rods and cones of the retina set up chemical reactions. In some way these chemical reactions set up electrical impulses that are carried by the optic nerve to the brain. These impulses are interpreted in the brain. Not only are the specific impulses involved in the interpretations, but past experience is also involved. The most obvious example of this is that the world is not viewed as being upside down. A host of experiences with other senses help us to interpret the visual impulses.

APPROACHES TO TEACHING

*How can a pinhole camera be used to show that
light travels in a straight line?*

In a pinhole camera, all light except that which can pass through the
very small pinhole is excluded. This makes possible the projection of a
clear, but dim, image of the light source or brightly illuminated object
on the screen.

Using a pinhole-camera principle, make a small pinhole in one end of
an empty cereal box and cover the other end with waxpaper. In a dark
room, point the pinhole toward a burning candle. What kind of an image
appears on the waxpaper? How was this image formed? How does this
show that light travels in a straight line?

How is light reflected by a plane mirror?

With small pieces of clay or wood, set a small plane mirror upright on
a piece of paper. Lay a protractor on the paper alongside the mirror. Draw
a line on the piece of paper perpendicular to the mirror at the center of
the protractor.

Tape a piece of black paper with a small hole or slit in it over the face
of a flashlight so that only a thin beam of light will be projected.

Shine the beam of light so that it strikes the plane mirror immediately
above the small hole in the protractor. Note the angle between the beam
of light and the perpendicular line. This is called the *angle of incidence*.
Move a small card back and forth to locate the reflected beam and note
the angle between the reflected beam and the perpendicular line. This is
called the *angle of reflection*. How does the angle of incidence compare
to the angle of reflection?

Repeat the experiment using different angles of incidence. Is there a
consistent relationship between the angle of incidence and the angle of
reflection?

343

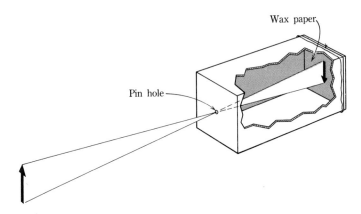

Fig. 12-32 How an image is formed in a pinhole camera.

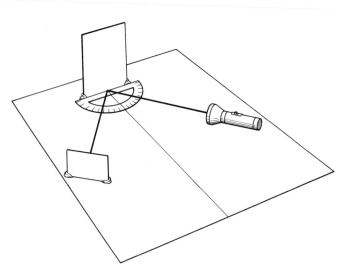

Fig. 12-33 A way to study the relationship between the angle of incidence and the angle of reflection.

How can a spectrum be projected?

To project a spectrum it is desirable to have a thin beam of white light and a prism such as the one shown in the illustration. The light can be sunlight or from a projector. The thin beam can be arranged for by cutting a thin slit in a piece of black paper and taping the paper over a window or in front of the projector. When this thin beam of light shines through the prism, it is dispersed into the colors of the rainbow. By adjusting the beam and the prism, the spectrum can be projected onto a screen or other convenient place.

Have the beam of light pass through different colored cellophane. How does the insertion of different colors affect the spectrum?

Place different colored pieces of paper so that the spectrum will be projected upon them. How does the spectrum appear when projected onto different colors?

*What happens when light passes through various kinds of
lenses or is reflected by various kinds of mirrors?*

The bending and reflection of light rays can be studied in a smoke box. An empty aquarium can be used. On the rear side tape a piece of black paper. On one end of the box, tape a piece of black paper through which slits have been cut so that a light from a projector or flashlight can shine through it. On the bottom of the box place a block of wood or plasticene on which lenses or mirrors can be placed. The lenses and mirrors should be adjusted so that the beams of light shining from the side will strike them. Fill the box with smoke from a smoldering punk. (A punk can be made by twisting a paper towel into a tight rope, igniting it, and then putting out the flame so that the paper smolders.) Cover the box with a piece of wood or cardboard so that the smoke will not escape.

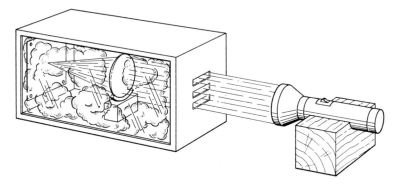

Fig. 12-34 *The refraction and reflection of light can be studied in a smoke box.*

Place the following kinds of lenses and mirrors in the smoke box so that the beams of light will shine upon them: plane, concave, and convex mirrors; convex and concave lenses. In each case, how are the beams of light affected? Where is the focal point of the beams?

How does the size of the pupil of the eye change with the changes in the intensity of light?

In this experiment two people observe the changes in each other's pupils as the light in the room is changed. First dim the light in the room as low as possible. Estimate the diameter of your partner's pupil. Now quickly make the room as bright as possible. What happens to the size of your partner's pupil? Now what is the diameter of your partner's pupil? What happens when the room is dimmed again?

What happens when the retina tires?

Shine a bright light on a piece of red paper taped onto a white screen. Stare intently at the red paper for two or three minutes and then quickly remove the red paper. What do you see?

After your eyes are rested again, stare intently at a piece of green paper for two or three minutes and then quickly remove it. What do you see now?

It is believed that the cones sensitive to a particular color tire after a few minutes of exposure. When exposed to white light, the retina is not as sensitive to that part of white light as it is to the complementary color. (Complementary colors are two colors that when mixed give white light.) Therefore, the complementary color is usually seen until those cones are rested again.

CHEMICAL INTERACTIONS

The purpose of having children become acquainted with chemical interactions is not to involve them in sophisticated chemistry. Instead, it is to have them become aware of another kind of interaction and to illustrate how some of the important generalizations of science also hold for these interactions. One way to investigate the nature of chemical interactions is to study the candle and what happens when it burns.

Physical and Chemical Changes

When a piece of string is cut into pieces and some wax is shaved from a candle, the shape and size of the string and the wax are changed. They can be mixed together and even heated to melt the wax. But, when the solution cools again, the wax is still wax and the string is still string. These are physical changes. Although there may be changes in the size and shape of materials as a result of physical changes, the identity of the materials does not change.

However, if a candle is ignited, the materials in the wick and wax are changed into new and different materials. In chemical changes materials are formed that are different from those that went into the interaction.

The Study of a Burning Candle

The burning candle is an interesting and instructive example of a chemical interaction. Perhaps the best way to study the burning candle is to approach it as a cooperative investigation in which the entire class observes and suggests experiments that can be undertaken, and then the teacher, or one of the students with the help and guidance of the teacher, carries out the operations necessary for the various experiments.

First the children should observe the burning candle. What is the color of the flame? Is it the same color throughout? How big is the flame? Does the flame flicker? If it does, what seems to cause the flickering? What are the obvious materials that are involved in the burning?

What is burning? Some students may suggest that is is the wick or string that is burning. A similar piece of string may be held with a pliers or forceps and ignited. It will burn, but it will be all gone in a very short time. Others may suggest that it is the liquid wax. The wick can be pushed down into the liquid at the top of the candle, and it usually will go out. Perhaps, it is a gas that is formed that burns? A piece of glass tubing can be held with one end in the dark part of the flame and usually the gas that emerges at the other end will burn when ignited. To test this hypothesis further, snuff out the flame and see if the gas that emerges from the wick can be ignited.

Are there materials other than the obvious wax and wick that are involved in the burning? Put a glass jar, such as a large pickle jar down over a burning candle. The candle will eventually go out. This can be repeated with other jars. The candle will always go out, and usually the smaller the jar the sooner the candle will be extinguished. There is considerable justification for concluding that there is something in the air that is necessary for burning and that eventually there is an insufficient supply of it under the jar to sustain burning.

But if this is a chemical change taking place, then there must be products formed that are quite different from the materials that entered into

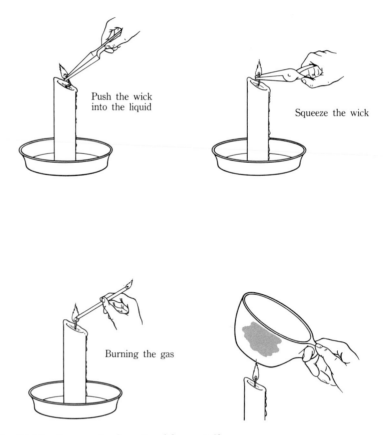

Fig. 12-35 Some experiments with a candle.

the interaction. What is the nature of some of these products? If a clean, dry glass jar is placed down over a burning candle, the sides of the jar will begin to fog, and some small droplets may be produced. This product of the burning is water. If the top of the jar is touched, it will be quite hot for one of the products is heat energy. And, of course, the light energy that is given off can be seen. If the glass jar is removed and some clear lime-water is poured into it and swished around, the limewater will turn a milky color. (If carbon dioxide is exhaled through a straw into limewater, it will also turn milky.) This is a test for the presence of carbon dioxide, and one of the products of the burning of the candle is carbon dioxide. If a cup or some other such surface is held in the candle flame, it will turn black. This black soot is another product, and it is quite different from the wick or the wax of the candle. The interaction that takes place when a candle burns produces materials that are quite different from those that went into the interaction.

APPROACHES TO TEACHING

What are some evidences of chemical interaction?

Pour some copper chloride solution into a beaker or tumbler. Observe its color and measure its temperature with a thermometer. Examine a small (four- by six-inch) sheet of aluminum foil. Note its color and size. Place the aluminum foil into the copper chloride solution. What evidences of chemical interaction do you see?

INVESTIGATIONS

What objects in the environment are magnets?

Objects made of magnetic substances, such as iron and steel, may become magnetized by the earth's magnetic field. Objects that are often magnetized are flagpoles, steel fence posts, table legs, and water pipes.

Whether an object is magnetic can be ascertained by seeing whether any part of an object will repel one end of a compass needle. Children can make a list of objects in their classroom and at home that have been magnetized.

What electrical charge is generated on a rubber rod or comb when it is rubbed with different materials?

By definition, a negative charge is generated on a rubber rod or comb when it is rubbed with wool or cat's fur. To conduct this investigation, charge an electroscope positively by touching the knob while a negatively charged rod is held nearby. A negatively charged rod brought near the knob of the electroscope will cause the leaves of the electroscope to converge, while a positively charged rod will cause them to diverge. (This investigation can be carried out with a suspended rubber balloon that is charged negatively by rubbing it with wool or cat's fur.)

Rub a rubber rod or comb with a variety of materials such as silk, paper, nylon, plastic, rubber, and the skin of your hand. In which cases is there an electric charge generated on the rod? What kind of charge is generated?

Selected References

Jacobson, Willard J., Kleinman, Gladys, Hiack, Paul S., Sugar-baker, John, and Carr, Albert, *Force and Motion, Electricity and Magnetism*, and *Energy and Waves*. New York: American Book Co., 1969.

Karplus, Robert, *Introductory Physics*. New York: W. A. Benjamin, Inc., 1969, Chapters 3 and 4.

READINGS FOR THE PRIMARY GRADES

Adler, Irving and Ruth, *Machines: the Reason Why Book*. New York: John Day Co., Inc., 1965.

Glemser, Bernard, *All About Biology*. New York: Random House, Inc., 1964.

Jacobson, Willard J., Lauby, Cecilia J., and Konicek, Richard D., *Forces and Magnets*. New York: American Book Co., 1969.

Jacobson, Willard J., Lauby, Cecilia J., and Konicek, Richard D., *Machines*. New York: American Book Co., 1969.

Jacobson, Willard J., Lauby, Cecilia J., and Konicek, Richard D., *The Sounds You Hear*. New York: American Book Co., 1969.

Podendorf, Illa, *The True Book of Energy*. Chicago: Childrens Press, Inc., 1963.

Russell, Solveig Paulson, *Sound*. Indianapolis, Ind.: Bobbs-Merrill Co., Inc., 1963.

Showers, Paul, *Follow Your Nose*. New York: Thomas Y. Crowell Co., 1963.

UBELL, EARL, *The World of Push and Pull*. New York: Atheneum Publishers, 1964.

ZIM, HERBERT S., *Lightning and Thunder*. New York: William Morrow & Co., Inc., 1952.

READINGS FOR THE INTERMEDIATE GRADES

ADLER, IRVING, *Electricity in Your Life*. New York: John Day Co., Inc., 1965.

ANDERSON, M. D., *Through the Microscope*. Garden City, N.Y.: Natural History Press, 1965.

FREEMAN, MAE AND IRA, *Fun and Experiments With Light*. New York: Random House, Inc., 1963.

GALLANT, ROY A., *The A B C's of Chemistry*. Garden City, N.Y.: Doubleday & Co., Inc., 1963.

HIGHLAND, HAROLD JOSEPH, *The How and Why Wonder Book of Light and Color*. New York: Grosset & Dunlap, 1963.

HOLDEN, RAYMOND, *All About Fire*. New York: Random House, Inc., 1964.

HYDE, MARGARET O., *Molecules Today and Tomorrow*. New York: McGraw-Hill Book Co., Inc., 1963.

JACOBSON, WILLARD J., LAUBY, CECILIA J., AND KONICEK, RICHARD D., *The Atom and Nuclear Energy*. New York: American Book Co., 1969.

JACOBSON, WILLARD J., LAUBY, CECILIA J., AND KONICEK, RICHARD D., *Electricity*. New York: American Book Co., 1968.

JACOBSON, WILLARD J., LAUBY, CECILIA J., AND KONICEK, RICHARD D., *Energy from the Sun*. New York: American Book Co., 1968.

JACOBSON, WILLARD J., LAUBY, CECILIA J., AND KONICEK, RICHARD D., *Energy to Do Work*. New York; American Book Co., 1968.

JACOBSON, WILLARD J., LAUBY, CECILIA J., AND KONICEK, RICHARD D., *Light and Heat*. New York: American Book Co., 1968.

KEEN, MARTIN L., *The How and Why Wonder Book of Magnets and Magnetism*. New York: Grosset & Dunlap, 1963.

PIPER, ROGER, *The Big Dish, the Fascinating Story of Radio Telescopes*. New York: Harcourt, Brace & World, Inc., 1963.

SANDER, LENORE, *The Curious World of Crystals*. Englewood Cliffs, N.J.: Prentice-Hall, Inc., 1964.

SELSAM, MILLICENT E., *How Animals Tell Time*. New York: William Morrow & Co., Inc., 1967.

IV
Processes of Science

The processes of science are an integral part of the structure of science.[1] They are among the most powerful intellectual tools available to man. It is through the use of these processes that man has developed the scientific world view with the broad generalizations that are so useful to scientists in the attempt to find explanations for phenomena. These processes are also of value to laymen in dealing with some of the problems of daily life.

In science, problems arise to which the scientist does not have a satisfactory answer. Similarly, most children raise questions to which they do not have answers. To both the child and the scientist the problem arises out of the problem situation—the great variety of activities in which they are engaged—and often the very nature of the problem is very ephemeral and only sensed in a general way. To both the scientist and the child one of the most critical and difficult steps to problem solution is to frame and state the question or problem clearly. There is no clear-cut procedure for delineating and defining a problem. The ability to do so for both the scientist and the child comes out of the observations and impressions that are gained when they are immersed in the problem situation.

Possible answers or solutions are suggested, and these hypotheses are intellectual tools that can be used in the investigation of the problem. The difference between a pedantic, tradition-bound scientist and one who is creative and successful is largely a matter of the relative imaginativeness of the hypotheses that are suggested. Exuberant, energetic children are often quite imaginative. This imaginativeness should be nurtured and cultivated. Alas, it is too often lost.

The logical consequences of hypotheses are deduced and observations and experiments are undertaken to test for these consequences. The hypotheses are accepted or rejected on the basis of whether or not the logically deduced consequences meet the observational and experimental tests.

[1] See Chapters 1 and 2 for a discussion of how the processes of science are related to broad generalizations and basic assumptions in the structure of science.

This can involve a number of skills such as predicting, observing, classifying, serial ordering, measuring, and recording data. Children can become quite skillful with many of these processes early in the elementary school.

However, it is not enough to collect a mass of data; the data must be interpreted. In science this often takes the form of relating the findings to the generalizations of the conceptual structure of science and the formation of models into which the information that has been gathered fits.

The processes that are so useful in dealing with problems in science can also be useful in dealing with the questions and problems that arise in everyday life.[2] Certainly, it is important to clarify as much as possible the nature of the problems and to suggest imaginative possible solutions. The search for relevant and reliable information and evidence may sometimes be more difficult in dealing with the problems of everyday life than it is in science, but certainly it is important to try to get relevant and reliable information. To make sense out of this information is often difficult but always important. Experiences with such processes of science in the elementary school may, hopefully, help some children to become more effective in dealing with the problems they will eventually face.

In the following chapters there is a more detailed discussion of some of the processes of science. In most cases, the discussion is built around science activities that can be undertaken with children.

[2] For a more detailed discussion of problem solving in science and in everyday life, see Willard J. Jacobson, "Helping Young People to Deal with Their Problems" in Lester D. Crow and Alice Crow, *Readings in Child and Adolescent Psychology* (New York: Longmans, Green & Co., 1961), p. 571.

13 Observation, Classification and Measurement

Observation is the basic process by which information is obtained. Objects, changes in objects, and the evidences of interactions between objects can be observed. In science, observations are often carried out in a very systematic way. In observing classroom behavior, for example, the observer may try to record everything that is said and done for one minute every ten minutes. In this way the observer may hope to get a fair sample of all the behavior. In experiments, one or more factors are altered so that the effect of that change can be observed. For example, the kind of fertilizer used on soil may be changed so that the effect of this change on plants will be evident.

OBSERVATION SKILLS

Observation involves all of the senses. In elementary school science children should be helped to become more sensitive and better able to discriminate between various kinds and levels of sensory stimuli. The program should include experiences in which children use their senses of seeing, hearing, feeling, and smelling to make observations. Under some circumstances they may use their sense of taste, but in science this should be done with great care because many of the chemicals and other substances used are very harmful if taken into the mouth.

In some cases instruments are used to extend the range and sensitivity of the senses. The magnifying glass is an example of such an instrument; it permits the observation of small objects and phenomena better. Every child should have a magnifying glass available and in the upper grades it is highly desirable that children have access to a microscope, which extends much farther the range of the sense of sight.

Observing is an act in which the observer is deeply involved. There are those who have thought that the observer in science is very much like a camera recording everything that is seen. This is simply not so; what is seen depends very much upon the observer. A skilled observer of animal behavior, for example, will see much more in the behavior of animals than the unskilled; a fond lover of animals may see only one aspect of animal behavior. It is important that children recognize that they are a part of the art of observing. What they will see will depend, among other factors, upon their sensory acuity, previous experiences, and expectations. Even what the camera records depends upon the direction it is pointed, the amount of light that is shining, and the kind of film that is used.

The nature of observations will depend upon the hypotheses that have been formed. These hypotheses can lead to observations that might otherwise be missed. Charles Darwin is reputed to have said, "How odd it is that anyone should not see that all observation must be for or against some view, if it is to be of any service." Darwin was arguing for the use of hypotheses as guides in observation. On the other hand, it is important for the observer to recognize that he is using the hypotheses as an intellectual tool and not as blinders to shield unwanted facts from his eyes. Both children and scientists can become wedded to a favorite hypothesis and blinded to observations that contradict that hypothesis. "What greater pain must man endure than the wrecking of his favorite hypothesis."

It is important that children begin to recognize the factors that may influence their observation. It may be the perspective from which they view an object or phenomena. Of it may be the limitations of their senses and the instruments they are using. Of greater importance, different people may see things in different ways because of the particular backgrounds and values that they bring to the observation. If children could begin to have an understanding of "the way that the other fellow sees things," it would be an important outcome of their experiences in elementary school science.

CLASSIFYING

Observations can be interpreted through comparison. One dog is larger than another dog. A mineral is harder than several other kinds of minerals. One kind of animal has a backbone while another does not. Certain plants are found in swampy areas while others never are. At one point during the baseball season Frank Robinson was batting .327 while Roberto Clemente was batting .347. Through comparisons, one set of observations can be related to other observations, and this is an integral process in the development of the conceptual structure of science.

Comparisons can be systematized through systems of classification. Many systems of classification are based upon the physical properties of objects. For example, minerals are usually classified on the basis of such physical properties as color, hardness, cleavage, streak, and luster. However, it should be recognized that different kinds of classification systems are possible. It is possible and sometimes desirable, for example, to build systems of classification based upon geographic location. Or upon the ways that objects are used. Systems of classification are devised to be useful.

The following example shows how systems of classification can be devised. These examples can be used with children to help them gain a better understanding of the process of classification. Leaves are used as the objects to be classified because they are available almost everywhere.

Yes-No Classification

Many systems of classification are "yes-no" systems in which objects are grouped on the basis of whether or not they have certain properties. Children can examine a sample of leaves and group them into "yes" groups and "no" groups on the basis of whether or not they have such physical properties as the following:

1. Leaves are needlelike.
2. Leaves have parallel veins.
3. Leaves have smooth edges.

Children should be encouraged to suggest additional properties by which leaves could be grouped.

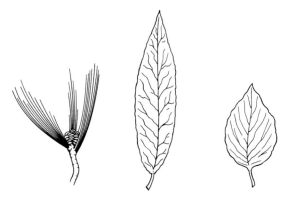

Fig. 13-1 *We can use a "yes-no" system of classification to classify leaves such as these.*

Building a System of Classification

In a system of classification, a series of questions are asked that can be answered by "yes" or "no." For example, one of the questions that can be asked about leaves is "Are the leaves needlelike?" When all the leaves in a sample are examined in terms of this question, two groups of leaves are formed: Those that are needlelike and those that are not. However, these two large groups can be divided into smaller subgroups in response to questions such as the following:

Are the leaves needlelike and bunched in a cluster?
Are the leaves not needlelike and have parallel veins?

The diagram below shows the beginnings of a classification system for leaves. Children can copy this diagram on a large sheet of paper and then classify each of their leaves into the appropriate subgroups. The subgroups can be classified still further. However, it is suggested that the children be asked to propose the properties by which these subgroups can be classified into smaller subgroups.

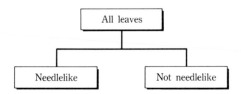

Fig. 13-2 *You might ask children to extend this classification system.*

Although systems of classification are arbitrary and devised to be useful, their probable usefulness can be predicted on the basis of such characteristics as the following:

1. Are there enough subgroups to accommodate all the original items? The usefulness of a system of classification will be limited if there are a large number of items that cannot be classified.
2. Are the subgroups mutually exclusive? Each item should be clearly assignable to only one subgroup.
3. Is the system of classification based on properties that are comparatively stable? If the properties change rapidly. it becomes difficult to use them as a basis for classification.

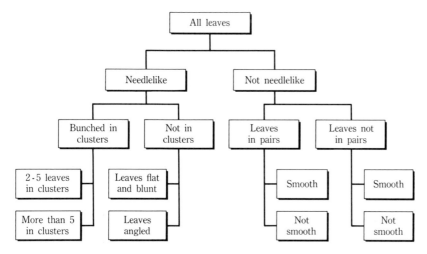

Fig. 13-3 *A system of classification can be built by continually dividing groups of leaves into two subgroups.*

Systems of classification have been of great usefulness. Perhaps the best known and most useful has been the Linnean system of classification devised by the Swedish botanist Carl von Linné. This is a binomial system much like the one that is described for classifying leaves. The Linnean system of classification makes it possible to classify and identify all living organisms. Since there are more than 650 thousand known species of insects and large numbers of species of other kinds of organisms, the importance of a system of classification that can help to organize observations becomes apparent.

SERIAL ORDERING

Another kind of comparison consists of ranking materials and objects according to the degree to which they possess certain properties. For example, objects can be ranked according to size, color, or the number of certain features that they have. This ranking is called serial ordering. Sometimes serial ordering can make it possible to see new and important interrelationships between materials and objects.

The Periodic Table of the Chemical Elements was developed by Dmitri Mendeleev by arranging the known chemical elements in serial order on the basis of comparative weight. Mendeleev noticed that certain chemical properties appeared periodically in the list. Based on these observations, Mendeleev devised the Periodic Table. He had sufficient confidence in his

Periods: 1-7
Families: IA-O

LIGHT METALS

	IA	IIA	IIIB	IVB	VB
1	1 ¹ **H** Hydrogen 1.00797				
2	3 (2,1) **Li** Lithium 6.939	4 (2,2) **Be** Beryllium 9.0122			
3	11 (2,8,1) **Na** Sodium 22.9898	12 (2,8,2) **Mg** Magnesium 24.312			
4	19 (2,8,8,1) **K** Potassium 39.102	20 (2,8,8,2) **Ca** Calcium 40.08	21 (2,8,9,2) **Sc** Scandium 44.956	22 (2,8,10,2) **Ti** Titanium 47.90	23 (2,8,11,2) **V** Vanadium 50.942
5	37 (2,8,18,8,1) **Rb** Rubidium 85.47	38 (2,8,18,8,2) **Sr** Strontium 87.62	39 (2,8,18,9,2) **Y** Yttrium 88.905	40 (2,8,18,10,2) **Zr** Zirconium 91.22	41 (2,8,18,12,1) **Nb** Niobium 92.906
6	55 (2,8,18,18,8,1) **Cs** Cesium 132.905	56 (2,8,18,18,8,2) **Ba** Barium 137.34	57 (2,8,18,18,9,2) **La** Lanthanum 138.91	72 (2,8,18,32,10,2) **Hf** Hafnium 178.49	73 (2,8,18,32,11,2) **Ta** Tantalum 180.948
7	87 (2,8,18,32,18,8,1) **Fr** Francium (223)	88 (2,8,18,32,18,8,2) **Ra** Radium 226.04	89 (2,8,18,32,18,9,2) **Ac** Actinium 227		

LANTHANIDE SERIES

58 (2,8,18,20,8,2) **Ce** Cerium 140.12	59 (2,8,18,21,8,2) **Pr** Praseodymium 140.907	60 (2,8,18,22,8,2) **Nd** Neodymium 144.24

ACTINIDE SERIES

90 (2,8,18,32,18,10,2) **Th** Thorium 232.038	91 (2,8,18,32,20,9,2) **Pa** Protactinium (231)	92 (2,8,18,32,21,9,2) **U** Uranium 238.03

Fig. 13-4   In developing the Periodic Table of the chemical elements the elements were arranged in serial order on the basis of comparative weight.

table to suggest that there were blank spaces where there were chemical elements that had not yet been discovered and even suggested some of the properties that these missing elements might have. Later, when these elements were discovered, it was remarkable how closely they resembled Mendeleev's predictions.

The Periodic Table of the Chemical Elements has been one of the most useful conceptual models in the science of chemistry, and it was developed through the process of serial ordering.

RIODIC TABLE OF THE ELEMENTS

INERT GASES — 0

KEY

Atomic Number — 6 ... 2 4 — Electron Distribution

Element — C — Symbol

Carbon 12.01115 — Atomic Weight

	2	2
	He	
	Helium	
	4.0026	

---NONMETALS---

IIIA	IVA	VA	VIA	VIIA
5 2 3 **B** Boron 10.811	6 2 4 **C** Carbon 12.01115	7 2 5 **N** Nitrogen 14.0067	8 2 6 **O** Oxygen 15.9994	9 2 7 **F** Fluorine 18.9984	10 2 8 **Ne** Neon 20.183
13 2 8 3 **Al** Aluminum 26.9815	14 2 8 4 **Si** Silicon 28.086	15 2 8 5 **P** Phosphorus 30.9738	16 2 8 6 **S** Sulfur 32.064	17 2 8 7 **Cl** Chlorine 35.453	18 2 8 8 **Ar** Argon 39.948

TRANSITION ELEMENTS:

---HEAVY METALS---

	VIIB		---VIII---			IB	IIB

25 2 8 13 2 **Mn** Manganese 54.9380	26 2 8 14 2 **Fe** Iron 55.847	27 2 8 15 2 **Co** Cobalt 58.9332	28 2 8 16 2 **Ni** Nickel 58.71	29 2 8 18 1 **Cu** Copper 63.54	30 2 8 18 2 **Zn** Zinc 65.37	31 2 8 18 3 **Ga** Gallium 69.72	32 2 8 18 4 **Ge** Germanium 72.59	33 2 8 18 5 **As** Arsenic 74.9216	34 2 8 18 6 **Se** Selenium 78.96	35 2 8 18 7 **Br** Bromine 79.909	36 2 8 18 8 **Kr** Krypton 83.80
43 2 8 18 13 1 **Tc** Technetium (99)	44 2 8 18 15 1 **Ru** Ruthenium 101.07	45 2 8 18 16 1 **Rh** Rhodium 102.905	46 2 8 18 18 **Pd** Palladium 106.4	47 2 8 18 18 1 **Ag** Silver 107.870	48 2 8 18 18 2 **Cd** Cadmium 112.40	49 2 8 18 18 3 **In** Indium 114.82	50 2 8 18 18 4 **Sn** Tin 118.69	51 2 8 18 18 5 **Sb** Antimony 121.75	52 2 8 18 18 6 **Te** Tellurium 127.60	53 2 8 18 18 7 **I** Iodine 126.9044	54 2 8 18 18 8 **Xe** Xenon 131.30
75 2 8 18 32 13 2 **Re** Rhenium 186.2	76 2 8 18 32 14 2 **Os** Osmium 190.2	77 2 8 18 32 15 2 **Ir** Iridium 192.2	78 2 8 18 32 17 1 **Pt** Platinum 195.09	79 2 8 18 32 18 1 **Au** Gold 196.967	80 2 8 18 32 18 2 **Hg** Mercury 200.59	81 2 8 18 32 18 3 **Tl** Thallium 204.37	82 2 8 18 32 18 4 **Pb** Lead 207.19	83 2 8 18 32 18 5 **Bi** Bismuth 208.980	84 2 8 18 32 18 6 **Po** Polonium (210)	85 2 8 18 32 18 7 **At** Astatine (210)	86 2 8 18 32 18 8 **Rn** Radon (222)

RARE EARTH ELEMENTS

| 62 2 8 18 23 8 2 **Sm** Samarium 150.35 | 63 2 8 18 24 8 2 **Eu** Europium 151.96 | 64 2 8 18 25 9 2 **Gd** Gadolinium 157.25 | 65 2 8 18 25 8 2 **Tb** Terbium 158.924 | 66 2 8 18 27 8 2 **Dy** Dysprosium 162.50 | 67 2 8 18 28 8 2 **Ho** Holmium 164.930 | 68 2 8 18 29 8 2 **Er** Erbium 167.26 | 69 2 8 18 30 8 2 **Tm** Thulium 168.934 | 70 2 8 18 31 8 2 **Yb** Ytterbium 173.04 | 71 2 8 18 32 9 2 **Lu** Lutetium 174.97 |
| 94 2 8 18 18 32 24 8 2 **Pu** Plutonium (242) | 95 2 8 18 32 25 8 2 **Am** Americium (243) | 96 2 8 18 32 25 9 2 **Cm** Curium (247) | 97 2 8 18 32 26 9 2 **Bk** Berkelium (249) | 98 2 8 18 32 28 8 2 **Cf** Californium (251) | 99 2 8 18 32 29 8 2 **Es** Einsteinium (254) | 100 2 8 18 32 30 8 2 **Fm** Fermium (253) | 101 2 8 18 32 31 8 2 **Md** Mendelevium (256) | 102 2 8 18 32 32 8 2 **No** Nobelium (254) | 103 2 8 18 32 32 9 2 **Lw** Lawrencium (257) |

MEASURING

"My dog is bigger than your dog" is an old refrain. But how much bigger? To find out, it would be necessary to measure. In serial ordering objects are compared in terms of the degree to which they have certain properties; to determine the degree to which objects have these properties they must be measured. Measurement is a process that provides greater precision in observation, comparison, and communication.

Units of Measurement

Measurement is a form of comparison. When one nail is placed along-side another and it is determined that one is longer, the process is measurement. To achieve more effective measurement, however, certain *standard units* are selected and defined and measurements are based upon them. For example, the short nail could be used as the standard unit and it could be said that the long nail is so many "short nails" long. If the long nail happened to be a convenient multiple of the short nail in length, say three, then it, too, could be used as a standard unit. The length of a desk might

Fig. 13-5 How many "nails long" is your desk?

then be expressed in such terms as, "It is ten 'long nails' and two 'short nails'." The length of the short nails and the long nails could be standard-ized, accurate copies made, and this system of measurement could be used widely. These units would have a more reliable base than some of man's early standard units. At one time, the yard was defined as the distance between the point of King Henry's nose and the end of the thumb of his outstretched arm. The foot was simply the length of a man's foot. These standards are considerably less reliable than "short nails" and "long nails."

Our basic units of measurement have been very carefully standardized. In the metric system, the standard unit of length is the *meter*. The meter was once based on the length of a metal bar kept in the International Bureau of Weights and Measures in France. Carefully made copies of the standard meter were made available for use elsewhere. Now, however, the meter is based on the wavelength of the orange-red light emitted by a krypton-86 lamp. This standard unit can be made available anywhere. The unit of mass, the *kilogram*, is based on a platinum-iridium cylinder which is kept in the International Bureau of Weights and Measures. The standard unit of time is the *second* and it is defined as 1/86,400th of a mean solar day.

Length, mass, and time are basic physical quantities, and many other quantities are based upon them. Volume, for example, is based upon measurements of length. Temperature is usually measured by noting the length of the liquid in a thermometer. The average velocity of an automobile or object can be obtained by dividing the basic quantity distance by the time taken to travel the distance.

Tools for Measurement

Distance is the space between two points and a basic unit for measuring it is the meter. Distances are measured with metersticks or tapes. A necessary characteristic of tools used to measure distance is that their length remains as constant as possible. Obviously, reliable measurements of distance using an elastic tape could not be made.

While metersticks and tapes are convenient for measuring distances along a straight line, sometimes in elementary school science the problem of measuring the distance along a crooked path or around an uneven object such as a hole in the ground are encountered. One way that children can do this is to lay out a string along the crooked path or around the uneven object. The length of the string can then be found by stretching it out and measuring its length with a meterstick or tape.

In some cases it is more convenient to measure distances in terms of time. Air travelers usually consider the distance between two cities in terms of the time it takes to fly it. The tremendous distances in outer space are usually expressed in *light-years* which is the distance that light, with a velocity of about 186 thousand miles per second, will travel in one year.

The mass of objects is measured in grams with balances. While the gram is standardized in terms of a standard kilogram at the International Bureau of Weights and Measures, for practical purposes it is equal to the mass of one cubic centimeter of water. The mass of an object can be determined directly by seeing how many grams or kilograms are necessary to balance it on an equal arms balance (see page 308 for a simple equal arms balance). In most cases in the elementary school, a double or triple beam balance is the most convenient instrument for determining mass.

While the basic unit of time, the second, is based on the mean solar day, there are more convenient ways of measuring time in the classroom. Most clocks are based on the periodic swing of a pendulum, an escapement mechanism as in many watches, the fixed frequency of small tuning forks as in some electric wristwatches, or on the very regular alternations in alternating current that are used in electric clocks. In the elementary school classroom a wall clock with a sweep second hand can be used by all the children to measure periods of time. A stopwatch should also be available for more accurate measurements.

The Accuracy of Measurements

It is important that children gain some understanding of the potentialities and limitations of their measuring instruments. Several children might be asked independently to measure the length of a desk or of this book. After they have finished, ask them for their results and write them on the board. Almost certainly the children will report different measurements. Why are the results of the measurements different? What are the limits to the accuracy of instruments?

The illustration shows a meterstick with part of it magnified. The meter is divided into 100 centimeters and the centimeters in turn into 10 millimeters. In measuring the length of the book, it is clear that it is more than

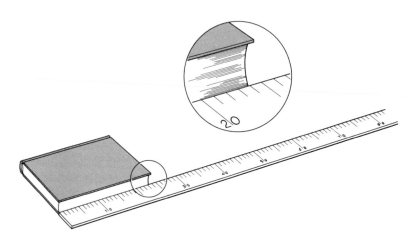

Fig. 13-6   What is the last significant digit?

23 centimeters long. All would probably agree that it is more than 8 millimeters beyond the 23. But beyond this its length becomes less certain. It can be estimated to the next tenth, perhaps .4 of the distance between the millimeter marks, but this is the last *significant digit*. Then the length of the book could be stated as 23.84 centimeters. But now that the limit to the accuracy of the meterstick has been reached, there might not be agreement on the last digit. More accurate measurements cannot be made with this

instrument. Although finer and more precise instruments could be used, there will always be a limit to the accuracy of a measuring instrument.

The limitations of the measuring instruments must also be considered in handling data. Suppose the width of the book is 19.32 centimeters. To find the area of the cover it would be necessary to multiply the length times the width.

$$\text{Area} = \text{length} \times \text{width} = 23.84 \times 19.32$$

The answer cannot be written as 460.5888 square centimeters because this implies an accuracy of measurement that simply is not available. Usually the answer, whether it be a product or a quotient, is the smallest number of significant figures in the numbers that have been multiplied or divided. In the example used, there were four significant figures in the two numbers that were multiplied. Therefore, four significant figures, or 460.5 square centimeters, would be kept in the answer.

APPROACHES TO TEACHING

The following activities and investigations can be undertaken to give children experiences with the processes of observing, classifying, and measuring.

How can we arrange objects in serial order? Are there new relationships between the objects that become apparent?

A variety of objects that differ in several ways can be used. The sample of leaves used for classification can also be used for this exercise. It is suggested that not more than five objects be included in the first attempts at serial ordering.

Mark the objects by lettering them or a card on which they are placed. Now arrange the objects in order on the basis of such properties as length, over-all size, greenness (or the degree to which they have any other color), number of veins, and roughness. Each of the orders should be recorded. Children should be asked to suggest additional properties by which the objects can be ordered.

Are there relationships between the objects? For example, are the largest objects also the greenest? Or, are the smallest objects also the smoothest? The various relationships that are perceived should be recorded. When children look for these relationships, they are, in a sense, doing on a small scale what Mendeleev did. They are being creative.

How can distance be measured on curved and uneven surfaces?

Sometimes it is necessary to measure distances that are not in a straight line. Children can gain experience in doing this by measuring the distance around a basketball, around a hole in the ground, and along a curved path.

A simple way to measure distances that are not in straight lines is to use a cloth or flexible steel measuring tape and lay it along the curved path. If this cannot be done, lay a string along the curved line. Then measure the string with a meterstick or yardstick.

How are scale drawings made?

Measure the length and width of the classroom. Make a scale drawing of the classroom using a scale of one inch = five feet.

Measure the distance from one corner of the scale drawing to the other and multiply this distance by five to find out the distance in feet from one corner of the classroom to the other. Compare this figure with that which is obtained when the distance between corners is measured with a measuring tape.

Make a scale drawing of the classroom using a scale of one inch = ten feet and determine the distance from corner to corner. With which scale do you obtain the figure that is closest to that obtained using a measuring tape?

How can distances to inaccessible places be measured?

A method known as *triangulation* can be used to measure distances to inaccessible places such as across a river or the height of a tree. Triangulation is also used to measure the distances to the planets and nearby stars. Children can become familiar with the technique by measuring the distance to the back of the classroom.

To measure angles use a protractor and a drinking straw. A small pin can be pushed through the drinking straw and the hole at the center of the base of the protractor. The drinking straw can be pivoted on the protractor to indicate the angle.

Select a spot near the center of the opposite wall on which to sight. Adjust the straw so that it points through the ninety-degree mark on the protractor. Then move the protractor along the front of the room until the point where the spot on the opposite wall can be seen through the protractor. This is one end of the *base line*. (Actually, the base line can be located anywhere along the front wall, but it is a little simpler if one of the angles sighted is ninety degrees.) Now hold one end of a six-foot-long string at the hole of the protractor and have another person hold the other end so that the string passes over a zero-degree mark on the protractor. The end of the taut string indicates the other end of the base line.

Sight through the drinking straw at the other end of the base line to find the angle that a line-of-sight to the point on the opposite wall makes with the base line.

Make a scale drawing of the base line. A convenient scale might be one inch = two feet. At one end draw a line perpendicular to the base line. At the other end draw a line at the angle of the line-of-sight to the point

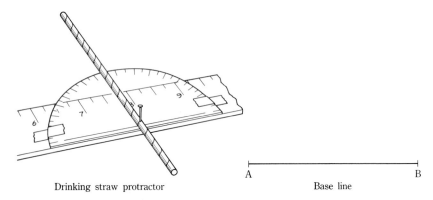

Drinking straw protractor   Base line

Fig. 13-7 *By sighting the angle to X from both A and B at the ends of the base line and making a scale drawing, the distance to the inaccessible point X can be determined.*

on the opposite wall. On the scale drawing, the point where this line and the perpendicular line cross represents the point on the opposite wall. The distance to the opposite wall can be found by measuring the length of the perpendicular line and multiplying by the scale of the drawing. The children may wish to check their accuracy by comparing their measurements with those made with a ruler or measuring tape.

Some of the children may wish to use this method of triangulation to measure the height of a flagpole or the distance to some inaccessible place.

How can a pendulum be used to measure time?

Attach a small weight to a string and hang it so that the weight is free to swing and the length of the pendulum can be adjusted.

Pull the weight back, release, and count the number of swings in either direction in ten seconds. Now adjust the length of the pendulum until the pendulum makes ten swings in either direction in ten seconds. Since this pendulum requires one second to complete a swing in one direction it is called a *seconds pendulum.* (Since a *period* is the time required to complete a swing in both directions, the period of a seconds pendulum is two seconds.) Measure the distance from the center of the weight to the point where the string is attached. You may wish to compare the length of your "seconds pendulum" with that given for your latitude in the *Handbook of Physics and Chemistry.*

Use the seconds pendulum to measure the length of time it takes someone to carry out such operations as reading the page of a book, heat a given amount of water until it boils, and dissolve a chemical such as salt in a liquid.

Fig. 13-8 Adjust the length of the pendulum so that it makes ten swings in either direction in ten seconds. How long is the pendulum?

INVESTIGATION

How can the living organisms to be found in a small area be classified?

In many places a considerable variety of living organisms can be found in a square meter of lawn or woodland. In this investigation an attempt is made to find the different kinds of organisms existing in such a restricted area and to develop a system for classifying them.

Collect or observe and describe the various organisms to be found in a square meter. Remember to look both on and in the soil.

Try to devise a system of classification using the "yes-no" approach to classification. An obvious first question is, "Is the organism an animal?" Suggest further questions that will divide the subsequent groups into subgroups until only similar organisms are in each category.

Make a schematic diagram of the system of classification that has been developed. How does this system rate in terms of characteristics of useful systems of classification listed on page 362?

Selected References

JACOBSON, WILLARD J., AND KONDO, ALLEN, "Classification and Serial Ordering: A Laboratory Exercise" in *SCIS Elementary Science Sourcebook*. Berkeley, Calif.: Science Curriculum Improvement Study, University of California, 1968.

JAFFE, BERNARD, "Mendeleef" in *Crucibles: The Story of Chemistry*. New York: Simon & Schuster, Inc., 1948.

YOUDEN, W. J., *Experimentation and Measurement*. New York: Scholastic Book Services, 1962.

READINGS FOR THE PRIMARY GRADES

CLEMONS, ELIZABETH, *Rocks and the World Around You*. New York: Coward-McCann, Inc., 1960.

COLBY, C. B., *The First Book of Animal Signs*. New York: Franklin Watts, Inc., 1966.

DARBY, GENE, *Jerry Finds Ants*. Austin, Tex.: The Steck Co., 1964.

GEORGE, JEAN, *The Hole in the Tree*. New York: E. P. Dutton & Co., Inc., 1957.

LIBERTY, GENE, *The How and Why Wonder Book of Time*. New York: Grosset & Dunlap, 1963.

READINGS FOR THE INTERMEDIATE GRADES

BRONSON, WILLFRID S., *Beetles*. New York: Harcourt, Brace & World, Inc., 1963.

JACOBSON, WILLARD J., LAUBY, CECILIA J., AND KONICEK, RICHARD D., *Distances in Space.* New York: American Book Co., 1968.

JACOBSON, WILLARD J., LAUBY, CECILIA J., AND KONICEK, RICHARD D., *Insects and Senses.* New York: American Book Co., 1968.

KONDO, HERBERT, *Adventures in Space and Time: the Story of Relativity.* New York: Holiday House, Inc., 1966.

RIEDMAN, SARAH R., *Naming Living Things.* Chicago: Rand McNally & Co., 1963.

SWAIN, SU ZAN, *The Doubleday First Guide to Insects.* Garden City, N.Y.: Doubleday & Co., Inc., 1964.

WATTS, MAY THEILGAARD, *The Doubleday First Guide to Trees.* Garden City, N.Y.: Doubleday & Co., Inc., 1964.

14 Experimentation

Information about the materials, objects, and phenomena of the environment is gained through observation. But sometimes more can be learned by making changes to see what the effects will be. For example, it may be observed that an object is red, but whether the redness is due to the nature of the object or the kind of light that shines upon it must be determined. So another light that is known to be white is shined upon the object to see if it continues to appear red. In experimentation, changes are made and the effects of these changes are observed and studied.

GOALS AND RESULTS OF EXPERIMENTATION

One kind of experimentation involves "try it and see." Young children may squeeze or press a balloon to see what will be the effect. This kind of "try it and see" experimentation is a very important process in the development of a child. He starts this kind of experimentation very early in life; everyone probably continues to a certain extent to do this kind of experimenting. However, there are definite limitations to what can be learned through this kind of experimentation.

At a more sophisticated level, the experiment is designed to test hypotheses suggested by theory. For example, in the seventeenth century Torricelli developed the theory that the earth was surrounded by an ocean of air. This ocean of air could be expected to be denser at low elevations than at high elevations. From this theory a hypothesis could be deduced. A higher column of mercury should be supported by air pressure at sea level than on a mountaintop. An experiment could be designed to test this hypothesis: determine the height of the column of mercury supported by air pressure at the same time at sea level and on top of a mountain. If a higher column is measured at sea level than on the mountaintop, this would tend to confirm the hypothesis and support the theory. This measurement, of course, has been made many times and the hypothesis confirmed. In fact, modern altimeters used in airplanes are based upon this "fact."

The results of experiments help to build the conceptual structure of science. The experimental study of how air pressure varies with altitude has helped in the development theories to explain convection in the atmosphere, winds, and the broad, encompassing theories that are used to predict weather. The conceptual structures of science have been developed on the basis of the results of great numbers of experiments.

Sometimes the results of experiments lead to a questioning of parts of the conceptual structure of science. For example, a theory suggested that inert gases such as helium and xenon would not combine with other elements to form compounds. But in 1962, it was found that the inert gas xenon could be made to combine, under conditions that could be duplicated in a well-equipped high school chemistry laboratory, with the very active gas fluorine to form xenon tetrafluoride. This discovery led to a questioning of some aspects of chemical theory. Similarly, the results of experiments have led to reconsideration of theory in other sciences, and this process can be expected to continue.

New instruments and materials make it possible to carry out experiments that had not been possible when a hypothesis was first formulated. Aristarchus of Samos had suggested more than two thousand years ago that, if the earth revolved around the sun, an apparent shift of the stars over a six-month period should be observed. But neither he nor the observers who followed in his footsteps could detect this relative movement. This failure to observe parallax was one of the major reasons the Greeks continued to believe the sun revolved around the earth. However, with the invention and refinement of the telescope it became possible for Bessel to detect this relative displacement of nearby stars. This observation, made with the help of a new instrument, supported the Copernican or sun-centered view of the solar system.

Experimentation involves taking some action to test ideas. What ideas that have just been discussed were tested by action? First, the idea that the color of an object is due to the kind of light that shines upon it was tested by shining a light that was known to be white. The idea that the atmosphere at low elevations would exert greater barometric pressure than at higher elevations was tested by taking barometric readings at sea level and on top of a mountain. The suggestion that an inert gas could be made to combine with another element was tested by bringing xenon and fluorine together at a high temperature. A common characteristic of experiments is that the experimeter takes some action to test an idea.

In most experimentation, and especially in experimentation in elementary school science, all factors but the one factor that is being studied are controlled. In the study of the effect of elevation upon barometric pressure, it is important to take the barometric readings at the same time; otherwise any differences in readings might be interpreted as being due to differences in time of the readings. Also, it would be best to use the same kind of barometer for the readings and to have calibrated the barometers against each other. Unless all factors but one are controlled, it becomes difficult to ascertain whether or not any changes that are observed are due to the factor being studied. In working with children it is important to lead them into considering what factors should be controlled if the effect of an action is to be observed.

In experimentation it is a common procedure to have a *control*. A control consists of the materials, objects, or phenomena on which no action is taken and to which the experimental results can be compared. For example, if the effect of a certain kind of fertilizer on corn production is to be studied, a similar plot of corn of the same size with the same kind of soil, using the same kind of seed, and receiving the same amount of water, is used as a control. The production of the two plots can be compared, and if all relevant factors have been controlled, any differences in production should be due to the fertilizer.

Sometimes the situation as it was before the experiment was undertaken is the control. For example, the corn production after application of fertilizer could have been compared to production on the same plot the previous year. This procedure has obvious weaknesses. For example, there might have been more rain or more sunshine or a longer growing season one year than the other. In some cases, this is the only kind of control possible. In the study of the effect of seeding clouds to generate rain, for example, the amount of rainfall has to be compared with the average rainfall over a period of years to see if cloud seeding had any effect.

A very important outcome of some experimentation is that other fruitful experiments are suggested and become possible. The successful combining of xenon and fluorine has led to attempts to combine other inert gases with fluorine and also other elements. In science one of the criteria for judging the importance of an experiment is the extent to which additional experimentation has grown out of the results of the experiment.

THE CHILD AND THE EXPERIMENT

One of the aims in elementary school science is to provide children with experiences that will enable them to make the transition to the formal level of intellectual operations. A key feature of the formal level of operations is the ability to suggest hypotheses, deduce logical consequences of the hypotheses, and devise experiments and plan observations to test these consequences. It is becoming apparent that the transition from the concrete stage of operations to the formal level does not take place automatically as a result of the ordinary experiences that children have in their lives. Instead, many children need special kinds of experiences such as the science experiences they should have in the upper grades of the elementary school.[1]

Experimentation is one of the key experiences through which children gain the intellectual skills to move onto the formal level of operations. The "try it and see" experimentation is important during the concrete level of operations, but as soon as possible children should be led to suggest hypotheses, deduce possible consequences of these hypotheses, and then design experiments to test for the deduced consequences. In setting up the experiments, they should be led to think through the factors that should be controlled if the results of the experimentation are to be meaningful. These are all skills that contribute to the development of abilities to carry out logical, formal operations.

Observing, Hypothesizing, Inferring, and Predicting

To show how experiences to foster these key abilities can be developed, consider how a commonplace phenomenon can be analyzed and investigated in an attempt to get an explanation that is consistent with observation. Dip a finger in water and make a wet streak on the chalkboard. Ask the children to observe and describe what happens. As they describe the evidences for interaction, lead them to limit themselves to descriptions of what they actually observe and not to make inferences. For example, some child may say, "The water evaporated." This is an inference for which there is no direct evidence. An important dimension of this experience is to challenge hastily suggested answers.

After the children have given a careful description of what they observed, ask them to suggest as many possible explanations for their observations as they can. It is important that they be encouraged to be imaginative. As in all areas where creativity is desirable, it is important in science to broaden the range of what is considered to be possible beyond ideas that "have always been thought to be true." The children may suggest such possible explanations for the disappearing streak as the following:

---

[1] For a further discussion of the stages of intellectual development and their implications for elementary school science, see Chapter 3.

1. The water went into the chalkboard.
2. The water went into the air.
3. The water was absorbed by the chalk.
4. The water just disappeared.

What are the logical consequences of each hypothesis? Very often children need considerable experience before they are able to deduce the logical consequences of hypotheses. However, this is one of the critical operations in formal thought. As examples, the children may make such deductions as the following:

Hypotheses	*Logical Consequences*
Into the chalkboard	a. The water might soak through to the other side of the chalkboard.
	b. The chalkboard will be heavier after the water has soaked in.
Into the air	a. If the wet streak has no contact with the air, then it should not disappear.
	b. The relative humidity of the air around the streak should rise as the streak disappears. (Actually suggested by a sixth-grade youngster.)
Absorbed by chalk	If all chalk is removed from the chalkboard, the wet streak should not disappear.
Just disappeared	This is an interesting hypothesis because it attacks a basic assumption on which all of science is based, namely, that there are logical, consistent explanations to all phenomena (see Chapter 1).

Now it may be possible to design and carry out experiments to test to find out if the logical consequence of a hypothesis actually does occur. Usually it is more efficient to try to predict on the basis of theory which hypothesis is the most likely. To gain experience in designing experiments, children may be asked to try to suggest experiments to test each of the logical consequences that have been listed.

On the basis of theory and prior experience, the children may suggest "The water went into the air" as the most likely hypothesis; they may design and set up experiments related to this hypothesis first. For example, the following experiment might be designed to test the logical consequence "If the streak has no contact with the air, then it should not disappear":

Place some Scotch tape over part of the wet streak so that part of the streak does not have contact with the air. Does that part of the streak disappear?

One of the critical tests of a hypothesis is whether it can be used to make further predictions. Suppose the experimental evidence supports the hypothesis "The water went into the air." What might be some predictions that could be made and checked on the basis of this hypothesis?

It might be predicted that if the streak came into contact with more air, as it would if it were fanned, it would disappear faster. The children might be asked to design an experiment, with careful attention to controls, to test this prediction.

If a hypothesis that has stood up under experimental test of deduced consequences can also be used to make predictions that hold up, this provides powerful support for the hypothesis as the explanation of the phenomenon.

Throughout their elementary school years children should have ample opportunities to use their imaginations to suggest hypotheses, deduce consequences of these hypotheses, design experiments to test them, and make predictions on the basis of these hypotheses. It is through these experiences that children will achieve the ability to carry out formal, logical operations.

Setting Up an Experiment

There are a variety of approaches to setting up experiments. The best way for children to become conversant with various procedures is through actual experience. The following are examples of three kinds of procedures that are often used.

A suitable way has to be found to gather data

The question was asked, "Which of two solutions has the most salt?" Most of the children in the class suggested that equal amounts of the two solutions could be evaporated over a hot plate. The solution containing the greater amount of salt would leave more residue.

One youngster suggested that another way would be to put strips of paper toweling into samples of each of the solutions. From previous experience he knew that the liquids would move up the toweling and evaporate, leaving a residue. He reasoned that the liquid having the higher concentration would leave the most residue.

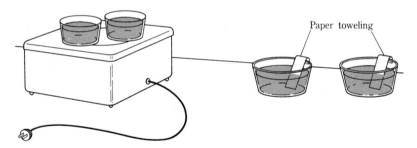

Fig. 14-1 *Two ways of finding out which solutions have the most salt.*

Some answers can be found by first trying the extremes and then working toward an answer

This process has sometimes been called "zeroing in." When a glass jar is placed over a burning candle, the candle eventually goes out. "How high could the glass jar be raised from the table and still have the candle go out?"

In this experiment it is useful to work from extremes and zero in on the answer. One extreme is when the jar over the candle rests on the table. Another extreme could be to support the jar so that its opening is above the flame of the candle. Next try a height halfway between these two extremes. With this zeroing in procedure the experimenters can find the height at which the candle will just continue to burn.

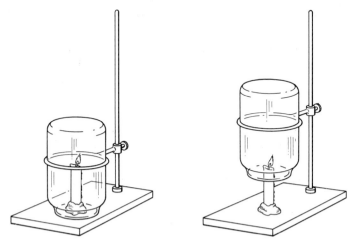

Fig. 14-2 *How high can the glass jar be raised before the candle will not go out?*

In many experiments all factors but one have to be controlled

The effect of changing one factor is determined by comparison with a control which is similar in every way except for the one variable factor.

"How does making a surface black affect its temperature when exposed to sunlight or a source of radiant heat?"

One way that this experiment can be carried out is to record and compare the rise in temperatures in a large test tube that has been blackened

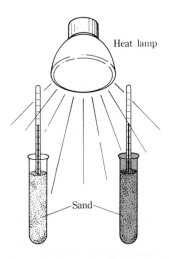

Heat lamp

Sand

Fig. 14-3 *What factors have to be controlled to find out the effect of blackening of the surface on temperature, when exposed to a source of radiation?*

by holding it in a candle flame and a test tube that has not been blackened when both are exposed to a source of radiant energy. The children should try to control all other pertinent factors. The following are some factors that should be considered:

1. The two test tubes should be the same distance from a source of radiant energy. Possible sources are sunlight, heat lamp, or a hot plate tipped up on its side.
2. Both test tubes should be filled with the same materials. Sand is suggested.
3. The same temperatures at the start.
4. Exposed for the same length of time.
5. Heat transfer by means other than radiation should be minimized, e.g., if test tubes are placed over hot plate there will be heat transfer by convection.

If all such factors are controlled, then any difference in temperature should be due to the difference in the color of the surface of the test tube.

The Role of the Hypothesis

A hypothesis is a suggested answer to a question. It is an important intellectual tool, for hypotheses are used to direct investigation. Usually, experiments are set up to test the deduced consequences of hypotheses, and results of experiments are interpreted in terms of whether or not they support the hypothesis.

Although the imaginativeness of the hypotheses that creative scientists suggest is one of the characteristics that distinguishes them, relatively little is known of the process by which hypotheses are formulated. Von Helmholtz reported that his most imaginative hypotheses came to him as he was walking in the woods after a long period of unsuccessful wrestling with a difficult problem. Many have reported that they have arrived at hypotheses after leaving a problem that they have struggled with for some time. For many people it may be that such an "incubation period" is necessary for imaginative ideas to emerge. Sometimes ideas come out of discussions where people with a variety of backgrounds bring different perspectives to the problems. In team research, different groups sometimes deliberately approach the problems in different ways. For example, one group might approach the problem by reading all the pertinent literature, while another group tries to come up with hypotheses without reference to the literature. As children struggle with questions and problems, they should be encouraged to reflect upon the ways that they have arrived at suggested answers. When and how did imaginative new ideas emerge?

Ways in which hypotheses can be used as intellectual tools are illustrated by an investigation that a group of children undertook of the question "Are there any differences between the air you breathe in and the air you breathe out?" Children can easily repeat these experiments.

Hypothesis 1

Some differences may be seen if a quantity of the air breathed in and a quantity of the air breathed out can be examined and compared. One plastic bag was filled using an air pump, such as is used to pump up a basketball, and the other with exhaled air. The gases in the two bags were examined for differences in color, water content, weight, and so on.

Hypothesis 2

The exhaled air may form an acid when bubbled through water while inhaled air does not. This and the following hypothesis probably came from the readings of some of the children. Bromothymol blue is a sensitive and convenient indicator of acidity. The students put one-hundred milliliters of water in each of the two beakers and then added eight drops of a concentrated bromothymol blue solution into each. Exhaled air was forced through a straw and bubbled through one solution. Air was pumped through the other solution. If an acid is formed the bromothymol blue will change color.

Hypothesis 3

The exhaled air contains more carbon dioxide than does the inhaled air. A common test for carbon dioxide is to bubble gas through limewater. Carbon dioxide will cause limewater to change to a milky color. The openings of two plastic bags were tied around one-hole rubber stoppers. Plastic drinking straws were inserted into the rubber stoppers, and the bags were

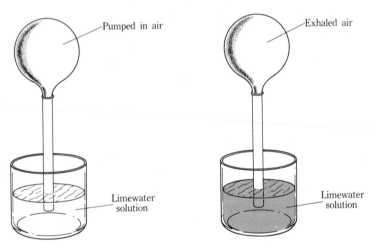

Fig. 14-4 *Which kind of air has the greatest effect on limewater?*

filled with air from a pump and exhaled air respectively. The contents of each of the bags were then forced through separate beakers containing equal quantities of limewater and the degree of milkiness of each sample of limewater was compared.

The use of hypotheses to direct inquiry changes random, undirected probing and trying from which little is learned into systematic investigation which can be the most efficient approach to the solution of a problem. Some times "experimenting" carries the connotation of "trying anything once." Instead, experimentation involves careful thought leading to the suggestion of the most likely possible answer and then the systematic testing of the answer.

Recording and Interpreting Data

The following are some of the ways that children can record and interpret the data that is acquired through experimentation:

Describing

In some cases, results take the form of verbal descriptions. A result of the examination of the plastic bags containing samples of inhaled air and exhaled air would be a verbal description. These descriptions might be recorded in writing or in pictures. Pictures are an especially important form of recording for young children.

Counting

In an experiment to find out the comparative strength of magnets, children tried to form chains of paper clips suspended from the magnets. The numbers of paper clips that could be suspended from each magnet were counted.

Comparing

Samples can be compared qualitatively. Two samples of limewater can be held up to the light and their milkiness compared.

Recording measurements

The temperatures of samples of sand in test tubes exposed to heat radiation can be periodically determined with thermometers and recorded.

Yes-No tests

Often there are "yes-no" tests to hypotheses. If a wet streak still disappears when placed on a chalkboard where the chalk is not present, the disappearance of the streak was not due to the chalk, and there is a simple "no."

Histograms

A histogram is the simplest kind of graph in which a mark is made for each time a certain result is noted. For example, Figure 14-5 is a histogram showing the number of serrations or notches on the edges of leaves in a sample. Children can make histograms by simply recording the numbers they count. This type of recording helps children to see how various counts are distributed.

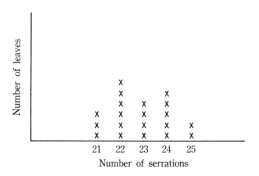

Fig. 14-5 *A histogram of numbers of leaves having different numbers of serrations.*

Graphs

   Simple line or bar graphs can help children to see relationships between two or more factors. The line graph in Figure 14-6, for example, shows the relationship between notches at the edges of leaves and the length of leaves.

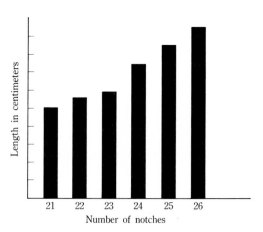

Fig. 14-6 *Graphs are useful in studying relationships between two factors.*

Histograms and graphs are especially useful when there are no clear-cut "yes-no" answers as to whether hypotheses should be accepted or rejected.

Experiments Lead to New Experiments

The value of experiments can be judged by the extent to which they open up new avenues of investigation. The discovery of radioactivity by Becquerel, for example, opened up a veritable Pandora's box of investigation. Many of the subsequent investigations into the nature of matter stemmed from his discovery of radioactivity, and on this basis it must be considered to have been a very important experiment.

The concept that scientific investigation leads to new investigations is a very important one. Science may be thought of as having an "endless frontier." Scientists do not seek final answers. True, they seek better understanding, but they also seek new fields to conquer.

APPROACHES TO TEACHING

As children complete certain experiments, they can be asked to suggest new lines of investigation that seem to have opened up. In some cases, they may wish to pursue some of these investigations.

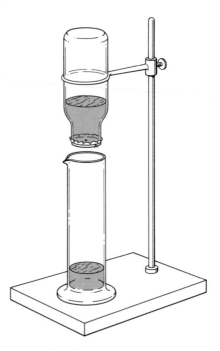

Fig. 14-7 *How long does it take for 50 cc. of water to flow out of different-sized holes?*

INVESTIGATION

*How is the rate at which water flows out of a bottle
related to the size of the opening?*

There are several different ways in which this problem can be studied in addition to the one described here. After completing the investigation, ask the children to try to design other ways that the investigation can be carried out.

Out of material such as aluminum foil, make bottle caps that have holes with diameters of 1, 2, 3, 4, and 5 millimeters, respectively. Fill a flask completely with water. Fasten the cap over the top, and with a finger over the hole invert the flask. Place a graduated cylinder under the flask. Remove the finger and find the time in seconds necessary for fifty cubic centimeters of water to run through the hole. Repeat using caps with different size holes.

Make a line graph showing the relationship between the time in seconds and the diameter of the hole. What relationship seems to exist? How can it be explained?

Selected References

GABRIEL, MORDECAI L., AND FOGEL, SEYMOUR, *Great Experiments in Biology.* Englewood Cliffs, N.J.: Prentice-Hall, Inc., 1955.

SHAMOS, MORRIS H., *Great Experiments in Physics.* New York: Holt, Rinehart and Winston, 1959.

READINGS FOR THE PRIMARY GRADES

JACOBSON, WILLARD J., LAUBY, CECILIA J., AND KONICEK, RICHARD D., *Energy to Do Work.* New York: American Book Co., 1968.

JACOBSON, WILLARD J., LAUBY, CECILIA J., AND KONICEK, RICHARD D., *Fire and Temperature.* New York: American Book Co., 1968.

MILGROM, HARRY, *First Experiments With Gravity.* New York: E. P. Dutton & Co., Inc., 1966.

NOTKIN, JEROME, AND GULKIN, SIDNEY, *The How and Why Wonder Book of Beginning Science.* New York: Wonder Books, 1960.

SELSAM, MILLICENT E., *Greg's Microscope.* New York: Harper & Row, Publishers, 1963.

READINGS FOR THE INTERMEDIATE GRADES

BARR, GEORGE, *Research Ideas for Young Scientists.* New York: McGraw-Hill Book Co., 1958.

BEELER, NELSON F., AND BRANLEY, FRANKLYN M., *More Experiments in Science*. New York: Thomas Y. Crowell Co., 1950.

BRANLEY, FRANKLYN M., AND BEELER, NELSON F., *Experiments With a Microscope*. New York: Thomas Y. Crowell Co., 1957.

FABELL, WALTER C., *Nature's Clues*. New York: Hastings House, Publishers, Inc., 1964.

HENDRICKSON, WALTER B., JR., *Winging into Space*. Indianapolis, Ind.: Bobbs-Merrill Co., Inc., 1965.

ROSENFELD, SAM, *The Magic of Electricity: 100 Experiments With Batteries*. New York: Lothrop, Lee & Shepard Co., Inc., 1963.

ROSENFELD, SAM, *Science Experiments With Water*. Irvington-on-Hudson, N.Y.: Harvey House Inc., Publishers, 1965.

SCHWARTZ, JULIUS, *It's Fun to Know Why*. New York: McGraw-Hill Book Co., 1952.

SILVERBERG, ROBERT, *Scientists and Scoundrels*. New York: Thomas Y. Crowell Co., 1965.

WYLER, ROSE, *The First Book of Science Experiments*. New York: Franklin Watts, Inc., 1952.

YOUNGPETER, JOHN M., *Winter Science Activities*. New York: Holiday House, Inc., Publishers, 1966.

SELECTED FILM

Language of the Bees. Moody Institute of Science. A description of Von Frisch's classic experiments in the study of how bees communicate.

15 Model Formation

Ernest Rutherford bombarded a thin sheet of gold with very small particles called *alpha particles*. When he placed a particle detector on the other side of the gold sheet, he found that most of the stream of particles passed straight through the gold sheet. But when he moved his particle detector around, he found that some of the particle stream had been deflected. Surprisingly, when he put his particle detector on the same side of the gold sheet as the source of the particles, he found that some of the particles actually had been reflected. It was as if the particles had hit something solid and bounced back. When the gold sheet was removed, no particles were detected at this position. What did these observations mean? How could they be explained?

Models are "pictures" that are developed to explain observations. While models are based on observations, they may also involve a great deal of imaginative thought. Rutherford, for example, explained his observations by developing a nuclear model of the atom. In his model, the atom was presumed to be made up largely of empty space. The particles that streamed through the thin gold leaf passed through this empty space. However, within the atom, he suggested, there is a dense, hard nucleus. The particles that hit the dense nucleus were deflected and in some cases were reflected. This model seemed to explain Rutherford's observations. Although this model has been refined in many ways, it is still basically the model that is used to explain the nature and structure of the atom.

Models help us make "sense" out of disparate observations. The development of useful models that are consistent with observations is one of the most creative dimensions of science. For example, there are many seemingly disparate observations related to gases such as air. It has been found that these gases can exert pressure against the walls of a container as air exerts pressure against the sides of a balloon, that the amount of pressure increases when heated and decreases when cooled, and that the volume that the gas will tend to occupy will increase as the temperature is raised and decrease as the temperature is lowered. These and other observations can be interpreted using a model in which gases are assumed to be composed of very small particles that are constantly in motion. The velocity of their motion is a function of the temperature. These particles will bounce off each other and the walls of the container. The sum of these bounces constitutes the pressure. Although this model has been refined in many ways, it has been extremely useful in interpreting observations related to gases and is still the basic model used in interpreting gas phenomena. The development of a model such as the gas model may be considered a major event in science. New and radical models are sometimes called "scientific revolutions."

There are two kinds of models: *physical models* and *theoretical models*. In a physical model, an actual physical representation is made. For example, physical models of atoms have been made using wire and small rubber balls. Theoretical models are mental pictures. Theoretical models may be expressed in words or in mathematical expressions.

Since the formulation of models is such an important process of science, it is important that children become cognizant of the nature of some models, some of the observations that are explained by models, and some of the criteria that are used to judge the relative adequacy of models. Children, of course, cannot be expected to formulate new models to replace existing models. Most scientists do not do this but instead are engaged in refining models. However, children can be helped to become aware of some of the factors that went into the formulation of some of the important models. Children can also have some experience in formulating models that can be used to explain observations that they make. In the sections that follow, examples are given of the two types of models. Some of the observations that led to the formulation of the models are described, and children are asked to devise models that will explain their observations.

PHYSICAL MODELS

Physical models are made out of concrete materials. Some physical models duplicate on a small scale something that is large and difficult to study. A physical model of San Francisco Harbor has been constructed. With this model it is possible to study the probable effects of proposed changes in the harbor. Other physical models provide a picture of what conditions will be like after certain changes are made. It is a common procedure to develop models showing what different sections of a city will look like after urban renewal. Physical models also help prevent mistakes.

As a safety feature in chemistry laboratories it is common practice to provide showers which can be used in case chemicals are accidentally spilled on someone. The failure to provide a drain under the shower in one laboratory might have been prevented if a physical model had been constructed.

An important advantage of physical models is that the effects of certain features can be studied. Many factors such as weight distribution and pilot vision have to be considered in planning a new type airplane. However, physical models that are constructed for tests in wind tunnels are used to study only the effects of different kinds of aerodynamical design. This, of course, is only one feature that needs to be considered in the design of new aircraft.

The Hydrologic Cycle

Children can make a variety of observations related to water in their environment. Rain falls; where does it come from? Water runs off in streams and rivers and sinks into the soil; where does it go? Water in mud puddles or left in open containers eventually disappears; what happens to it? Will the lakes and oceans also disappear like the water in the mud puddle? Clouds are usually seen when it rains; what are they made of? Will we ever run out of water for rain?

The hydrologic cycle is a model that helps to explain many observations related to water in the environment. In this model, almost all water in the atmosphere, on the earth's surface, and in the soil is considered to be in the water cycle.

The hydrologic cycle can be represented in a physical model. In this physical model (see Figure 15-1), heat from the lamp or bulb will speed up the evaporation of the water from the pan somewhat as solar energy brings about evaporation from lakes and oceans. The water vapor condenses on the plastic cover to simulate the condensation of water vapor in the atmosphere. The drops of water may fall to the surface like rain. This water runs off the inclined surface to return to the body of water. This physical model helps to visualize the various changes that take place, the possible travels of a drop of water, and then to interpret some of the observations that can be made of the environment.

THEORETICAL MODELS

Theoretical models are "mental pictures" of how a person conceives of phenomena. For example, a young child when asked where the water for the bathtub comes from, replied, "It comes from the wall." This was a

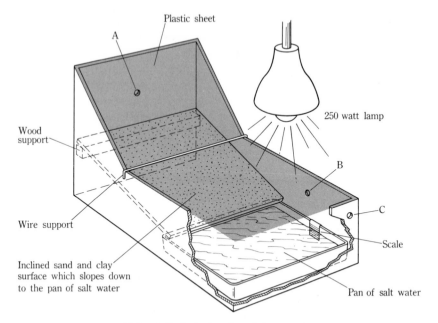

Holes A, B, C, for insertion of thermometer

Fig. 15-1 *A physical model of the hydrologic cycle. Water circulates through-out the system.*

theoretical model that explained his observations and was based on his experiences with water. In a much more sophisticated way, Rutherford developed the nuclear model of the atom to explain his observations.

While theoretical models are mental pictures, they have to be expressed in some way if they are to be communicated to others. In the elementary school theoretical models are usually described with words or such representations as diagrams and pictures. At a more sophisticated level, the models may be expressed in mathematical terms. An advantage of mathematical models is that they can be easily manipulated. With the aid of such devices as the computer, theoretical applications of a model can be tried out without actually carrying out experiments or trials.

It should be remembered that theoretical models are abstractions and not reality. No one has "seen" an atom or its nucleus. However, the nuclear model of the atom is so consistent with observation and has been so successful for prediction that one nuclear scientist said, "I know the nuclear atom is only a theoretical model, but for me, I'm afraid, it really exists."

But since models are often modified and sometimes, in major scientific revolutions, new and more effective models are proposed, it is best to remember that models are abstractions rather than reality.

Emotional attachments are formed with theoretical models, and divorce from them is difficult. Fred Hoyle, a world-renowned astrophysicist, has been a leading proponent of the steady-state model of the universe. In brief, in this model the universe is seen as having had no beginning and always having been very much as it is now. After years of championing this theoretical model, Hoyle stepped before a major scientific meeting and stated that recent astronomical observations made it necessary for him to extensively modify this model. This kind of a statement is relatively rare in science. The emotional attachments to a theoretical model are often too strong.

The following are three important theoretical models and some of the observational and experimental evidence to support them.

Models of the Solar System

The ancients watched the sun rise in the morning and follow a path across the sky until it set in the late afternoon. The path changed somewhat with the seasons. For the people in the Northern Hemisphere it was lower in the sky in the winter and higher in the summer. In the evening, many of the stars also seemed to move across the sky from east to west. Some of the stars in the northern sky circled a star, Polaris, that appeared to be stationary in the sky. At times, the moon followed a path across the sky somewhat like that of the sun. What kind of theoretical model would explain these observations—observations that shepherds in the field and dwellers in unlighted villages were much more aware of than are the inhabitants of the fluorescent-lit cities of today?

An obvious model, and one that seemed most consistent with observation, was that the sun, stars, and moon actually moved across the sky. In this model the earth was considered to be at the center of the universe and all other celestial objects might be considered to be moving around it. There were some remarkable regularities in that the stars always remained in the same position relative to each other. The sun and the moon moved in relationship to these background stars, but these movements were regular and could be predicted. This model was a common-sense model consistent with most of the observations that can be made by any observer of the nighttime sky. It was also an ego-staisfying model in that it placed man and the earth at the center of the universe.

But there is another possible model. It could be that the stars and sun are relatively stationary and it is the earth that spins (see pages 295–297 for a discussion of relative motion). This possible model was suggested very early by the Greeks and others. This model would also explain most of the observations that can be made. It is somewhat like the air traveler who flies through the sky at night. He sees lights passing beneath him. This could be explained by assuming either the lights were moving or the plane was moving. Both are possible explanations. In the case of the airplane, other objects, such as the stars, can be noted in order to analyze the nature of the relative motion. Similarly, in the case of the relative motion of the earth, the sun, and the stars, some other reference was needed.

If the nighttime sky is observed over a period of time, it will be noticed that there are bright objects that do not stay in the same position relative to the stars. They "wander" across the sky; the Greeks named them *planets* or "wanderers." Which of the models could be used to best explain the motions of the wanderers? Perhaps, the "wanderers" were the objects that could be used to clarify the relative motions of the earth, the sun, and the stars.

Attempts were made to explain the motions of the "wanderers" with both models. In the earth-centered model, the planets were assumed to revolve in small epicycles as they revolved in larger circles around the earth. But predictions based on the epicycles were not always consistent with observations. Epicycles had to be piled on top of epicycles. Still, the predictions were not completely accurate and the model became very clumsy and complicated.

First Aristarchus of Samos and later Copernicus suggested that the motions of the planets could be explained if it was assumed that they, like the earth, revolved around the sun. While this model was not as consistent with "common sense" and the egocentric desire of man to be at the center of the universe, it was conceptually a simpler model, and it served as a better basis for predicting the positions of the wandering planets. In this case, as with the airplane in the night sky, a better understanding of relative motion could be attained by referring to a third set of objects, namely the planets.

The heliocentric model of the solar system is the model that has been found to be most useful. But models are refined and improved. Based on the very meticulous observations made by Tycho Brahe, Johannes Kepler found that the actual positions of the planets were not exactly where they should be if it was assumed that the earth and the planets revolved around the sun in circles. He suggested a heliocentric model of the solar system in which the planets revolve around the sun in ellipses rather than in circles.

This theoretical model has been very successful. Coupled with Newton's law of gravitation it can be used to predict with accuracy the paths of artificial satellites as well as natural satellites such as the moon.

Models to Explain Inheritance

Elephants beget elephants and wheat grows from wheat seed. Also, children tend to resemble parents, and, sometimes, "Little Peter is the 'spittin' image of his great-grandfather." These are common observations, and they suggest that there is a connection between generations.

Plant and animal breeders for a long time have had an operational, common-sense understanding of ways that traits are transmitted from generation to generation. On an Egyptian tomb constructed about 2000 B.C. there is a model of a greyhound which must have been developed by selective breeding. Farmers and plant and animal breeders have been able to develop better breeds through careful selective breeding.

Although man has known for a long time that physical traits are transmitted from generation to generation, and how to develop plants and animals with desirable traits, it is only within the last century that models have been developed that help to explain the mechanism of inheritance. Gregor Mendel made a highly significant contribution in developing these models. It is instructive to consider the way that Mendel carried out his experiments, especially the way he developed a theoretical model from his data. (Compare the discussion of genetics and inheritance, pp. 252–253.)

Mendel worked with peas. Peas have definite and differing characteristics. While Mendel studied seven different physical characteristics, only the shape of the pea will be considered here.

Mendel carefully raised some pea plants so that they bred true, that is, the offspring always were like the parents. Some of the plants always had round seeds, others always wrinkled seeds. Mendel made controlled matings of plants that always had round seeds with plants that always had wrinkled seeds. All of the seeds that resulted from this mating were round.

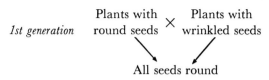

Now Mendel planted these seeds and allowed self-fertilization to take place, that is, they were not crossed. Instead, the pistils in the flowers were pollinated with pollen from the same plant. In this case, Mendel got the following results:

Table 15–1: MENDEL'S EXPERIMENTS

2nd generation	No. Round	No. Wrinkled	Ratio of Round to Wrinkled
plant 1	45	12	3.75 to 1
plant 2	27	8	3.37 to 1
plant 3	24	7	3.43 to 1
plant 4	19	10	1.90 to 1
plant 5	32	11	2.91 to 1
Total	147	48	3.06 to 1

What did these results mean? How could they be explained?

One obvious dimension of the theoretical model is that factors can be transmitted by individuals even though those individuals do not show the characteristic. None of the first generation were wrinkled, but some of their offspring were.

To explain why the first generation showed only the characteristic of "roundness," Mendel suggested the law of dominance, which has become known as Mendel's first law of heredity: *When an organism with a purebred dominant trait is crossed with an organism having a purebred recessive trait, all of the offspring will show the dominant trait.* In the case of the peas, "roundness" was a dominant trait and all of the first generation had this trait.

The results of Mendel's second experiment indicated the ratio of round to wrinkled was about three to one. In fact, as larger numbers of plants are used the ratio comes closer to three to one. This led Mendel to state his second law of heredity, the law of segregation: *In the second generation the ratio of the number of offspring with the dominant trait to the number with the recessive trait will tend to be three to one.* If "R" represents the trait of roundness and "r" represents wrinkledness, this disgram (Figure 15-2) can be formulated:

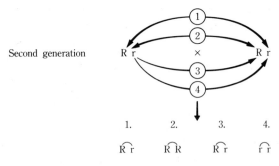

Fig. 15-2 *All of the second generation must carry factors for both traits, but round is dominant.*

Note that in all the combinations where the dominant trait "R" appears (3) the seeds will be round. However, two of these also carry the recessive trait "r." In the one combination (r r) where the dominant factor does not appear, the seeds will show the recessive trait of being wrinkled. This aspect of the theoretical model explained the three to one ratio that was found in the second generation.

In some of his experiments, Mendel followed two or more traits. For example, he followed the traits of roundness and color with round being the dominant shape and green the dominant color. He found that offspring could have all possible combinations of traits. Apparently, the various traits were transmitted independently, and one trait did not affect the transmittal of other traits. (Exceptions to this were noted later.) This feature of inheritance has been called the law of unit characters: *Each trait is inherited independently of other traits.* These three laws served as a theoretical model to explain many of the observations related to inheritance and the model could be used to predict the probable results of various crosses. The model has been extremely useful in plant and animal breeding.

It should be remembered that Mendel did all of his work without the benefit of the science of genetics. In fact, the beginnings of the science of genetics can be traced to the year 1900, and one of the key features was the rediscovery of Mendel's original papers by three biologists working independently. Since many others had made observations of the inheritance of physical traits, it is useful to note some of the characteristics of Mendel's work that enabled him to formulate the theoretical model that helps explain many of these observations:

1. Mendel focused on a few characteristics rather than trying, like many of his predecessors, to follow all characteristics.
2. Mendel chose for his experiments organisms that had definite characteristics that differed. The shape of the peas was one such characteristic. Most of the peas were round, but a few were wrinkled. It has been suggested that Mendel was lucky in his choice of organisms; if this is so, it is well to be lucky.
3. Organisms in which the parents could be specified with certainty and with many offspring were necessary. With the peas the crossings could be controlled through controlled pollination. From a mathematical standpoint it is easier to see patterns when there are many offspring as there are in peas.
4. Mendel was willing to spend long hours at the tedious work to carry out his experiments and analyze his result. Although it may be contrary to the television image of science that many children have, important contributions in science often involve very hard work.

The theoretical model of inheritance suggested by Mendel has been of great importance in the biological sciences. But it didn't receive much recognition when it was published. True, it was published in a very obscure journal, and the attention of biologists at that time was focused on Darwin's *Origin of Species*. Yet it seems as though the world was not ready for Mendel's theoretical model until thirty years later.

The Atomic Model

What is the nature of matter? The answer may seem simple—"matter is stuff." A table may appear to be made up of solid pieces of wood. But how about a liquid such as water or gases such as air? What is the nature of this kind of matter?

Actually, two theoretical models of the nature of matter seem possible. Matter might be considered to be "continuous." This model might seem to be consistent with most of everyday experiences with solids, although there may be some difficulty in explaining how solids can be cut or broken. Matter might be considered to be "particular" in nature, that is, made up of particles. A difficulty with this model is that, in most cases, the particles cannot be seen. Which of these two possible theoretical models is most consistent with observations of the nature of matter? The following are some observations that must be explained by a theoretical model of the nature of matter:

1. Some solids dissolve in liquids. If some sugar is placed in water, it will disappear and the water will taste sweet.
2. Many liquids diffuse in other liquids. If a few drops of food coloring are placed in a container of water, the food coloring will diffuse throughout the container. The rate can be speeded up by stirring.
3. Liquids and gases diffuse in gases. A little ammonia placed in a container will soon be smelled throughout a room. The fragrant aroma of perfume can also be sampled at a distance.
4. Some liquids seem to fit within each other to a certain extent. If fifty centimeters of alcohol are added to fifty centimeters of water, the resulting volume will be less than one hundred centimeters.
5. Solids intermix. If a bar of gold is placed on top of a bar of lead, in a few months there will be some gold in the lead and some lead in the gold.
6. There are certain materials called chemical elements that are always alike and cannot be changed to other elements by any ordinary means. If wood, paper, or sugar are burned or charred, carbon is formed. In each case the carbon is the same.

7. Chemical elements can be combined to make other materials. Carbon and oxygen can be combined, for example, to form carbon dioxide, and there is always a definite proportion of carbon and oxygen in carbon dioxide.

8. Many materials will react with each other. If a strip of aluminum foil is dipped into a solution of copper chloride, copper will be removed from the solution and coat the aluminum foil. Often the application of heat will speed up chemical reactions.

Which of the two models, the "continuous" model of matter or the "particular" model of matter, best explains these various observations? It is now generally agreed that matter is "particular." The early Greek philosopher Democritus suggested that all matter is made up of very small particles called atoms. However, the foundations of the modern atomic theory were laid in the early nineteenth century by the British chemist John Dalton. Now the atomic model of matter is so widely accepted and used that, although no one has ever seen an atom in any literal sense of the word "seeing," for many scientists, "the atom now seems to be real."

In the atomic model, all matter is made up of chemical elements. There are ninety-two chemical elements that occur naturally, and a few more have been made using high-energy accelerators. These chemical elements are made up of atoms, and all the atoms of an element are alike chemically, that is, all carbon atoms are alike as all copper atoms are alike. (There are small differences in mass between different isotopes of elements.) The atoms of elements often combine with each other or with the atoms of other elements to form *molecules*. Atoms of carbon, for example, combine with atoms of oxygen to form molecules of compounds such as carbon dioxide.

The small particles of materials, atoms or molecules, are in motion. This motion explains the diffusion of materials into other materials. The rate at which particles move depends upon their energy; their average velocity can be increased by heating. Temperature is a measurement of the average velocity of the particles that make up a substance. Usually an increase in temperature will lead to an increase in the rate at which chemical reactions take place.

The theoretical model that has been described helps explain phenomena associated with the materials that can be experienced in elementary school classrooms and in everyday life. However, the model has been greatly refined. The atom has been probed and has been found to consist of a dense nucleus surrounded by electrons. The nature and arrangements of the electrons and their effects have been studied. With sophisticated devices such as high-energy accelerators, the nature and structure of the nucleus has been probed. The relentless probing of the atom, the formulation of new and imaginative theoretical models of the atom, and the testing of the logical deductions of these models has been among the most active and rewarding undertakings in science in the twentieth century. These undertakings have been based on the "particular" model of the nature of matter.

Models and Children

One of the primary functions of the teacher is to help children derive meaning from their experiences. Scientific activities are fine for children, but what do they mean? What can be learned from them? What is their significance? Models, both physical and theoretical, are ways of deriving meaning from experience.

All models are abstractions. When children construct a diorama to represent their community, school grounds, or the classroom, the physical model is an abstraction; it represents. A theoretical model, such as a verbal description of what the inside of a black box may be like, is even more of an abstraction. These abstract models are useful in explaining observations and sometimes in making plans for action. A diorama of a community, for example, might help in ascertaining what the community might be like if certain changes were made.

At appropriate times, children should be asked to consider what is meant when someone says, "It is *really* like this." For example, it is quite common for witnesses of an accident to differ markedly in their descriptions of what occurred. In observation, a person's previous experiences and personal predilections are factors. While it is not true that a person sees only that which he wishes to see, these factors do color and condition what he sees. (One of the very important aims of an elementary science program is to help youngsters to become more objective observers.) Reality differs from individual to individual, but in the sciences there are checks upon the individual. To a certain extent, reality might be considered to be the consensus of what the scientists that work in a certain area consider to be true. Children can also try to reach a consensus as to the nature of the "reality" of some of the objects and phenomena that they observe. As they do this they will have an experience somewhat like that of scientists as they strive for a shifting and ever-changing consensus.

Models are checked against experience and tested in the fire of empirical observation and experimentation. The earth-centered model of the solar system proved to be ineffective in explaining the motions of the planets. A child suggested that one of the objects in the black box was a steel ball, but he had to reject this model when he was unable to influence the ball with a magnet. Models have to withstand such empirical tests, and much of the work in the sciences is devoted to testing and refining models to make them consistent with empirical evidence. Occasionally, new models or radical changes in old models are suggested, and these may be considered scientific revolutions.

Another test of models is *simplicity*. Simplicity does not necessarily mean that the models are easy to understand; some simple models are very abstract and abstruse. Simple models require few assumptions. Since assumptions are statements that must be accepted without necessarily having supporting evidence, a simple model will have a minimum of these and there will be more elements for which there is some evidence. The simple model is also conceptually simple. A solar system model in which all planets revolve around the sun is simpler conceptually than a model in which planets move in a complicated system of epicycles. As they devise models, children should consider their simplicity. For example, which of the possible models for a black box is the simpler?

While there are many advantages to the development and use of models, there are also hazards and drawbacks. Sometimes the model may be mistaken for reality. A word, for example, may be regarded to be the same thing as its referent in the physical world. When carried to an extreme, this confusion between symbol or model and the "real" world becomes a kind of insanity. A much more widespread hazard is that of overcommitment to a model. There are many examples in which scientists have become so committed to a particular model that they have not been able to consider evidence that may lead to serious questioning or even refutation of the model. If a model is not consistent with empirical evidence, it is the model that must give way. As children carry out experiments and investigations in science they may have the experience of becoming overcommitted to a model. To have done this and to have recognized it, is to have had a very profound educational experience.

The formulation of physical and theoretical models and the use of these models to explain observations and to make predictions is important for the intellectual development of children. These are logical operations that are very characteristic of intellectual operations at the formal stage of development. Experiences with these kinds of logical operations in the upper grades of the elementary school may help children to move into the formal stage of operations.

APPROACHES TO TEACHING

The following activities can be used to develop the children's understanding of the various kinds of models discussed in this chapter.

How can we test different designs of air foils?[1]

A variety of gliders can be folded using ordinary paper. First compare wide gliders with thin, sleek gliders. How does the width affect flight?

Try adding and adjusting such surfaces as ailerons, rudder, and elevators. How do each of these affect flight?

What kind of a theoretical model can be used to
explain our observations of the moon?

Prior to undertaking this exercise, the children should have made observations of the phases of the moon. It may be useful to bring out through discussion the succession of changes that take place in the apparent shape of the moon throughout the month.

Paint half a tennis ball or baseball black with paint or shoe polish. With tape, suspend the ball from a string or place it on a stick. As the children demonstrate this model, the ball should always be held so that the white side is toward the light.

At one end of a partially darkened room place a projector or flashlight. Have one child direct the light so that it is always shining at the ball.

Have two children, who represent the earth, stand together near the opposite end of the room. With tape or chalk, mark a circle about two meters in radius around them. (The moon's orbit is almost a circle.)

---

[1] The *Scientific American* has sponsored competition in the design of such gliders. Some of the gliders might be tried by children.

Now have another child hold the ball between the two observers and the light with the white side of the ball toward the light. Ask the children, "How much of the white side of the ball do you see?" "Is there any time of the month when we cannot see the moon?"

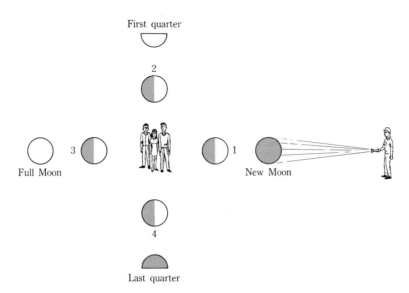

First quarter

2

Full Moon   3

New Moon   1

4

Last quarter

Fig. 15-3   *A Model depicting the phases of the moon.*

Have the child move the ball along the circle a quarter of the distance around the observers keeping the white side in the direction of the light. "Now how much of the white side of the ball do you see?" Have one of the observers trace on the chalkboard the shape of the white part of the ball that they see. Repeat the procedure for each succeeding quarter distance around the observers.

Are the observations of the white part of the ball something like the observations of the phases of the moon? Is this demonstration of a theoretical model of the earth-moon system consistent with observations? Is it simple? Has it been used for prediction?

How are unit characteristics assorted?

Some understanding of the assortment of unit characteristics may be achieved through the flipping of coins. Alternately flip a nickel and a penny and record the results in the first two columns of a chart such as the following:

flip	nickels	pennies	trait
1			
2			
3			
4			
5			

How many "heads" and how many "tails" were there for each? On the basis of these observations alone, what would you predict will be the ratio of heads and tails in each case. Flip five more times. Is the predicted ratio holding up? Flip ten more times. Now what is the ratio? What will happen if a large number of flips are made?

Suppose heads is the dominant trait. In the right-hand column write the trait that would be evident. (Any flip in which a nickel or a penny comes up heads would have the heads trait. If both are tails, the trait would be tails.) What would be the ratio of head traits to tail traits? Are these results similar to predictions made on the basis of Mendel's law of segregation?

What is inside the box?

There are many variations of the "black box" experiment, and most of them are designed to give children experiences in model formation when the nature of the objects cannot be seen directly. This, of course, is analogous to the problem of devising a theoretical model for the nature of matter.

An interesting "black box" can be made by placing a large ball bearing or Ping-Pong ball, a marble, and a penny in an empty shoebox and taping the box shut.

The children should be encouraged to manipulate the box in any way that they wish short of breaking the box. They may wish to use apparatus, such as magnets, to try to find out more about the nature of the matter in the box. They should keep a record of the "questions" they ask of the box, their procedures for answering the questions, and the results. Finally, they should be asked to describe their theoretical model.

INVESTIGATION

What "really" happened?

There are several variations of this investigation, but in all of them children are asked to describe independently what happened, or may have happened, and to compare their descriptions. In one version, two or more children dramatize an accident such as the spilling of a liquid or the dropping of a weight. In another version, a picture showing several people in vigorous disagreement is flashed on the screen. Each child is asked to write on a sheet of paper, without prior discussion with anyone, what they saw or thought they saw happen. When the various descriptions are collected, they can be analyzed in terms of such questions as the following:

1. Which aspects of the descriptions are direct observations and which are inferences?
2. What aspects are common to all of the descriptions?
3. What different elements are there in the various descriptions?
4. Is it possible to reach consensus on a composite description?

Selected References

JACOBSON, WILLARD J., KLEINMAN, GLADYS S., HIACK, PAUL, SUGAR-
BAKER, JOHN, AND CARR, ALBERT, *The Solar System and the Universe: The
Use of Theory and Models in Science*. New York: American Book Co., 1968.
TRIEGER, SEYMOUR, *Atoms and Molecules*. Darien, Conn.: Teachers Pub-
lishing Corp., 1964.

READINGS FOR THE PRIMARY GRADES

JACOBSON, WILLARD J., LAUBY, CECILIA J., AND KONICEK, RICHARD D.,
Exploring the Solar System. New York: American Book Co., 1968.
SCHNEIDER, HERMAN AND NINA, *How Big is Big*? New York: William R.
Scott, Inc., 1950.

V
Science and Man

"Who am I?" "I" am many things: the person who talks in a certain way, believes in certain things, and acts in characteristic ways. "I" always involves the body. "The body is the house in which we live. We must know it, understand it, and care for it if we are to live full and wholesome lives." The elementary school years are not too early for children to begin to understand their bodies and how to care for them.

In teaching about the human body it is important to develop the concept that the same physical and biological principles that are used to explain other phenomena can also be used to explain how the body operates. For example, some of the digested food passes through the membranes of the small intestine in much the same way that soluble minerals pass through root membranes in plants. Also, the rays of light that enter the eye are bent by the lens in the eye in the same way that light rays are bent when they pass through a glass lens. The most important physical and biological principles are general in nature and are believed to be applicable everywhere, including the human body.

In the study of man and his relationships there are opportunities to emphasize the conceptual structures and processes of science. In studying the human body the systems, such as the digestive or circulatory systems, and subsystems, such as the stomach or heart, are almost always considered. Similarly, in studying the environment and how the actions of man affect the environment, it is useful to consider ecosystems and the effects of changes within ecosystems. And, of course, the processes of science, such as observing, classifying and experimenting, can be used to study the human body and the effects of man's actions on the environment. Children can gain experience in using the structures and processes of science as they study in this area.

It is also important to help children learn to care for their bodies. "Health is a state of complete physical, mental, and social well-being and not merely an absence of disease or infirmity." This definition of health by the World Health Organization (WHO) makes health a goal that everyone can strive to approach or achieve. In elementary school science, children should gain an understanding of some of the scientific generalizations that can be used to achieve health.

In many environments, man is usually the most important factor. Most other organisms live in the environment without making critical changes in it. But man cuts the trees and tills the soil; he pollutes the rivers and befouls the air; and he builds great cities to provide a habitat for himself. True, he must change the environment in order to get the food and other necessities that he needs, but he often has done this with a vengeance. And now he is multiplying so rapidly and his demands for matter and energy from the environment are so insatiable that a crisis has developed in the relationship between man and the environment on which he is so dependent. It is essential that the young generation becomes aware of this "Quiet Crisis."

Science is one of the approaches to the study of man and the relationships between man and his environment. (The artist and the poet also approach these subjects in ways that are important for children to understand.) As the study of man and his environment is approached in a scientific framework it is important that the generalizations and processes of science be stressed. For example, the conservation laws apply in the study of man as well as in the study of the burning candle, and there are empirical tests for ideas in this realm as well as in the study of falling objects.

In the chapters that follow there is discussion of the human body and how the human body can be cared for. Descriptions are given of how children can study a few of the systems within the body. Some of the environmental problems that man is encountering are described, and firsthand experiences for children in investigating some of these problems are suggested.

16 The Human Body and How It Functions

The body, like all other matter, is made up of chemical elements. The three main elements are oxygen, carbon, and hydrogen. There are smaller amounts of a number of other elements. It has been said that, even at inflated prices, the chemicals that make up the human body are worth only a little over a dollar. But these chemicals in the complex relationships of living tissue constitute man's most valued possession, his body.

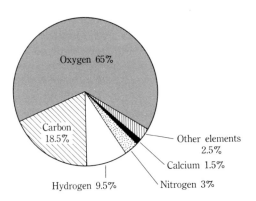

Fig. 16-1 *Percentage by weight of elements composing the body.*

It is not the chemicals that make up the body that are unique and precious. Instead, it is the way that they are organized. Obviously, the study of the organization of the human body can become very sophisticated. However, in this chapter, starting with the cell, the human body will be described in such a way that children can be led into some direct, firsthand

419

experiences with the structures and functions of the human body that are
discussed. As in the sciences related to the human body, the teacher is
helped in his task of teaching and learning about the human body by the
fact that there are analogous structures and functions in other organisms,
both plant and animal.

THE CELL

The basic unit or building block of protoplasm is the *cell*. Some organisms, such as ameba or paramecia, are composed of only one cell. The
human body, however, is composed of a tremendous number of cells. Although there are some differences, there are remarkable similarities between cells in various kinds of living matter.

Structure

Samples of epithelial cells from the body can be obtained by scraping
the inside of the mouth with a spoon or sterile tongue depressor (see page
432). If this material is placed on a slide, stained with a little iodine dissolved in water, and viewed under a microscope, the structure of the cell
can be seen.

Around the outside of the cell is a *cell membrane*. This membrane is semipermeable so that food and oxygen can pass through it into the cell and
the waste products of metabolism can leave the cell. Plant cells differ from
animal cells in that they have a cell wall.

Within the cell there is a spherical body that is more deeply stained than
most other parts of the cell. This is the *nucleus*. The nucleus is involved in
the metabolic processes that take place in the cell, and contains the chromosomes that carry the hereditary characteristics from one generation to the
next.

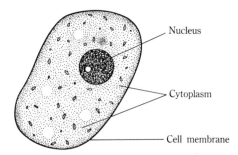

Fig. 16-2 *Diagram of a cell.*

Surrounding the nucleus is the *cytoplasm*. Many metabolic functions take place in the cytoplasm. The energy locked in food is released. Some of this energy is used for muscular work; some of it is used in the chemical operations by which new living material is manufactured.

Reproduction

The body cells reproduce by a process called *mitosis*. In mitosis the parent cell divides to form two daughter cells. Each daughter cell receives the hereditary characteristics of the parent cell.

Every plant and animal has a definite number of chromosomes in its cells. Human body cells contain 46 chromosomes. On these chromosomes are the genes that are believed to carry the hereditary characteristics. In cell division the chromosomes appear to split lengthwise so that each new cell contains all the genes on the chromosomes of the parent cell and in the same order as in the parent cell. To accomplish this a succession of changes takes place within the nucleus in a similar way as that shown in the diagram below.

Each chromosome contains many genes and many particles of an acid called *DNA* (deoxyribonucleic acid). DNA is believed to be the actual carrier of the "hereditary information" that is transmitted from the parent cell to the daughter cells. DNA is a very complicated organic compound in which the various elements are arranged in two threads that are chemically linked. When cell division takes place, it may be that each DNA particle divides into two single threads and each single thread forms a complete double thread. The process of separation and duplication among the DNA molecules may be somewhat similar to that which takes place on a larger scale among the chromosomes.

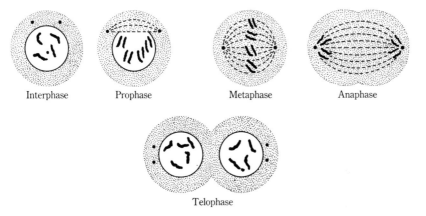

Interphase   Prophase   Metaphase   Anaphase

Telophase

Fig. 16-3   Changes that take place in the nucleus of the cell.

Tissues

A *tissue* is a large group of cells that helps to carry out a certain function. Epithelial tissue, for example, serves as a covering for the body surfaces on both the inside and the outside. Some other kinds of tissues are connective tissue, nerve tissue, and muscle tissue.

Epithelial tissue

Found in the skin which covers the outer parts of the body, epithelial tissue also forms the lining of such inner surfaces as the respiratory and digestive tracts. The skin, of course, is the epithelial tissue that children can examine directly. The outer surface of the skin is called the *epidermis*. The outer cells of the epidermis do not contain nuclei. As they wear off, they are replaced by others. Beneath the epidermis is the *dermis*, which contains the nerve endings, very small blood vessels, and sweat glands. The skin serves to protect the rest of the body and to help regulate body temperatures.

Hair and nails are parts of the skin that children can examine (see page 437). However, they are not living tissue. The nails are horny plates formed from the epidermis. They are related in structure and function to the hoofs and claws of animals. Hairs are developed from the epidermis. As children examine a hair, they will notice a bulb at the end of the root of the hair. This hair bulb is set in the subcutaneous tissue beneath the dermis.

Connective tissue

Supporting and connecting various parts of the body, some of the forms of connective tissue are bone; tendons, which join muscles to bone; ligaments, which join bones; and fatty tissue, which stores fat. The cells in connective tissue tend to be long and narrow and are widely separated. Connective tissue tends to be flexible and wiry to withstand the physical stresses imposed upon the body.

Nerve tissue

The nervous system that serves as a communication system for the body is made up of nerve cells. The nerve cells, *neurons*, have long extensions. Some of these extensions, such as those from the spinal cord into the feet of a man, may be as long as three or four feet. Nerve impulses are conducted to and from the main body of the cell through these long extensions.

Muscle tissue

Muscle tissue helps to move various parts of the body. One kind of muscle tissue helps to move arms, legs, and other segments of the skeleton. In general, the movement of these muscles, which are often called *voluntary* muscles, can be controlled. Other muscles help operate such organs as the kidneys, lungs, and intestines. These *involuntary* muscles cannot be controlled. One of the most important muscles in the body is the heart, which pumps blood throughout the body.

ORGAN SYSTEMS

An *organ* is a unit or structure in the body that performs a certain function. The heart, for example, is an organ that functions to pump blood throughout the body. The stomach is an organ in which certain phases of the digestion of food take place. The organs consist of one or more kinds of tissues that work together to perform certain functions.

However, a number of organs are usually needed to carry out the necessary processes. For example, the entire process of digestion is not carried out by the stomach. The mouth, esophagus, small and large intestines, and liver all carry out important functions in digestion. The organs that work together to carry out a body function are called *organ systems*. Among the important organ systems in the body are the digestive, respiratory, circulatory, excretory, endocrine, and nervous systems.

Digestive System

The function of the digestive system is to prepare the food so that it can be used by the body. To do this, it has to change the food, which may be of a variety of types and states, into a form that can pass through walls of the digestive system and be absorbed into the bloodstream.

Food, of course, enters the body through the mouth. In the mouth the food is broken and ground into small pieces as it is chewed by the teeth. The food is mixed with *saliva*, which softens the food in preparation for its journey through the digestive tract. The enzyme *ptyalin* in saliva converts some starch into sugar. This is what makes food taste sweeter after it has been chewed a while. The food is swallowed and passes down a tube called the *esophagus* into the *stomach*.

In the upper part of the stomach the ptyalin in saliva continues to act upon the food. Later the food is acted upon by hydrochloric acid and such enzymes as *pepsin*, *rennin*, and *lipase*. In the stomach proteins, such as those found in meat, are partially broken down into simpler compounds called amino acids. The digestion of milk is also begun. The partially digested food passes from the stomach into the *small intestine.*

Much of the digestion of food takes place in the small intestine. The small intestine is a relatively narrow tube that in a man is about twenty-one feet long. Here the proteins are further acted upon by enzymes to form the amino acids that can be absorbed through the walls of the intestine. The digestion of starches is completed by converting them to simple sugars, and fats are converted to fatty acids that can pass through the walls of the small intestine. It is from the small intestine that most food materials pass into the bloodstream. The small intestine is lined with a large number of small projections called *villi.* There may be around five million villi in the small intestine of a human being. Among other things, these villi serve to increase the surface area through which absorption can take place. (It has been estimated that the active surface of the small intestine is more than five times as great as that of the skin.) In each of the villi there are blood vessels. The digested food in the form of simple sugars, amino acids, and fatty acids passes through the membranes of the villi and into the blood-stream.

The food that is not absorbed passes into the *large intestine.* The large intestine has a greater diameter than the small intestine, but it is not nearly as long. Much of the water needed by the body is absorbed through the walls of the large intestine. The undigested food, along with some of the body wastes, is passed along the large intestine and excreted from the body.

Respiratory System

The respiratory system serves to make oxygen available to cells for the oxidation of food and to remove from the body such products of oxidation as carbon dioxide and water. In small organisms the oxygen enters the cells directly from the outside atmosphere, and the carbon dioxide is excreted directly into the surrounding air. In larger organisms, such as man, all of the cells do not have direct access to the outside air, and some kind of respiratory system is needed to supply oxygen and remove waste products.

Air enters the body through the nose or mouth, passes through the *trachea* or windpipe, the *bronchi,* and into the *lungs.* In the lungs there are great areas of thin membranes. These membranes contain very small blood vessels. The oxygen is able to pass through these thin membranes and enter the bloodstream. Similarly, carbon dioxide is able to pass out of the bloodstream and into the lungs where it is expelled during exhalation.

To inhale air, the body must reduce air pressure in the lungs. This is done largely by moving the diaphragm, a muscle sheath just below the lungs, downward so that the size of the chest cavity is increased. When the pressure within the lungs is decreased, the greater air pressure outside forces air into the nose or mouth, through the trachea and bronchi, and into the lungs, To exhale, the diaphragm moves upward, decreasing the size of the chest cavity, increasing the pressure within the lungs, and in this way the air containing carbon dioxide is forced out of the lungs (see page 434).

To revive a person who has in some way had his breathing stopped, such as drowning and electrocution, artificial respiration has to be applied. In artificial respiration, air in some way or other is forced into the lungs. The mouth-to-mouth method of artificial respiration is now recommended. In this method, the person giving the artificial respiration blows air from his mouth down into the lungs of the patient.

Circulatory System

The principal function of the circulatory system is to carry food and oxygen to the cells of the body and to carry away the waste products of oxidation. The circulatory system is a closed system consisting of the *heart*, which acts as a pump, and a network of *blood vessels*.

The heart is essentially a muscle that pumps the blood through the circulatory system. It consists of four chambers (see Fig. 16-6). In the upper part of the heart are the right and left *atria* (auricles). Beneath the atria are two larger chambers called the *ventricles*. Between the atria and the ventricles there are valves that control the direction of flow of the blood. The blood returning from the different parts of the body enters the right atrium. From here it flows down into the right ventricle. The right ventricle contracts, the valve between the ventricle and the atrium closes, and the blood is forced through the pulmonary artery to the lungs. In the lungs the blood gives up carbon dioxide and absorbs oxygen. The oxygenated blood leaves the lungs through the pulmonary veins and enters the left atrium. It flows from the left atrium into the left ventricle. As the left ventricle contracts, the valve between the ventricle and the atrium closes, and the blood is forced out through a large blood vessel, the *aorta*, into the various parts of the body. The left ventricle is the most powerful part of the heart; it can exert the pressure necessary to force the blood throughout the body.

The vessels that convey the blood away from the heart are called *arteries*; those that bring the blood back to the heart are called *veins*. The arteries are subjected to considerably more pressure than the veins; so, to withstand this pressure, the walls of arteries are thicker than those of veins. After branching several times, the arteries lead into the very thin blood vessels called *capillaries*. The walls of the capillaries are composed of a single layer of cells. Oxygen and digested food materials can pass through these thin walls to the cells. Similarly, carbon dioxide and other waste materials can pass through the capillary walls and into the circulatory system. The waste materials are carried away from the capillaries by the veins. The veins convey the blood back to the heart.

The remarkable fluid that is pumped throughout the body is called *blood*. In composition, blood is surprisingly like seawater. Interestingly, in very simple organisms living in the sea, the functions carried out in higher animals by blood are performed by surrounding water. Blood may be considered as part of the environment that has been enclosed within the body and in the process changed somewhat.

The blood performs several functions. It carries oxygen and food materials to the cells and removes much waste products as carbon dioxide and urea. It helps regulate body temperature and maintain the water content of the tissues. In addition, it helps protect the body against attacks of bacteria and other harmful organisms. A further function of the blood is the carrying of some of the hormones that help regulate body functions. The liquid portion of the blood is called plasma and is about 90 per cent water. There are three kinds of cells in the blood: *red corpuscles* (help carry oxygen to the capillaries), *white corpuscles* (help defend the body against invading microorganisms), and *platelets* (contribute to the coagulation of blood when there is a wound or other injury).

Excretory System

The waste products of metabolism are removed from the body through the excretory system. While such organs as the lungs and skin do help to remove some of the wastes from the body, the major organs in the excretory system are the *kidneys*. The kidneys remove such waste products as urea and uric acid and help to maintain the body's water balance by eliminating some water when the intake is high.

There are two kidneys; they receive blood directly from the aorta and discharge it into a major vein. The flow of blood through the kidneys is about 1,200 milliliters per minute. From 1,000 to 1,500 milliliters of urine are formed each day. Some of this urine is extracted from the blood by filtration through the thin walls of capillaries and parts of the kidneys. This process of filtration can be illustrated by having the children filter some muddy water through filter paper and pointing out that in the kidney some filtered material is reabsorbed into the bloodstream. However, in the course of a day 1,000 to 1,500 milliliters of urine are removed from the blood and passed out of the body.

Some children have difficulty in controlling the voiding of urine. The kidneys produce urine continuously. However, the urine is stored in the bladder until it is voided. In a baby the voiding of urine is involuntary. How to control emission of urine is learned as the child's body matures. Since this habit involves the development of voluntary control over an involuntary act, it is one of the most difficult learnings any child has to achieve. It is little wonder that it takes time for some children to establish this control.

Endocrine System

The endocrine system consists of such glands as the *pituitary, thyroid, parathyroid, thymus, pancreas, adrenal,* and the *sex glands.* These glands secrete hormones that help to control various body functions. Being ductless, these glands empty their secretions directly into the bloodstream, which carries the hormones to all parts of the body.

The hormones secreted by the endocrine system have critical control functions, so that either a lack or an oversupply of a hormone can have serious consequences. The secretions of the thyroid gland, for example, exercise general control over the metabolic rate. If there is a lack of thyroid hormone, the heart rate is reduced, and the body tends to become fat and sluggish. An oversupply of thyroid hormone leads to an increased metabolic rate, nervousness, muscular tremors, and loss of weight. The adrenal gland is sometimes called the "emergency" gland. In times of stress and danger the secretion from the adrenals stimulates body activity. In similar ways the other endocrine glands carry out control functions.

Nervous System

The nervous system is the central control system of the body. The nervous system serves to integrate the work of the various organs and systems of the body. For example, the heart pumps blood to all parts of the body, and all parts of the body are dependent on it. However, the heart is dependent upon the food derived from the digestive system and oxygen from the respiratory system for the energy needed to keep it beating. The nervous system helps keep all parts of the body working smoothly together.

The nervous system also helps the body respond to changes in the environment. For example, if the weather suddenly becomes colder, this information is gathered in by receptors in the nervous system, interpreted, and the nervous system activates the muscles that may do the work of putting on a coat or sweater.

The nervous system is composed of the *brain, spinal cord,* and 43 pairs of *nerves.* The brain is located at one end of the spinal cord. It may be considered to be an outgrowth of the brain stem to be found in lower animals. A highly developed brain is probably the most important physiological characteristic of man. The brain is connected to the spinal cord that extends down the spinal column. The 43 pairs of peripheral nerves extend from the brain or spinal cord to different parts of the body.

The signals that are conducted by the nerves are believed to be electrical in nature. As was mentioned earlier, nerve cells have long extensions, and nerve impulses are conducted along these extensions.

To illustrate one of the ways that the nervous system functions it may be desirable to describe what occurs in a reflex action. In a reflex action a nerve impulse is set up in a sensory nerve. For example, if a person accidentally touches a hot stove, a nerve impulse is set up. This nerve impulse is transmitted through several neurons to a neuron connected to a muscle. The muscle is actuated, and the part of the body touching the hot stove is pulled away. In this case the nerve impulse travels from the sensory nerve to the nerve connected to the muscle without having to travel to the brain. This reflex action is one of the important ways in which the body protects itself from injury.

In other cases sensory impulses are sent to the brain, where the impulses are interpreted, and voluntary (consciously controlled) responses are made. The details of how these interpretations are made in the brain are not known. However, the fact that many actions can be voluntary and made after considerable thought is one of the most important "human" characteristics.

THE SENSES

The body has specialized receptors that are sensitive to such stimuli as light, sound, taste, smell, and touch. Such specialized receptors are called *senses.*

The Eye

Perhaps the most effective way to describe the eye and its operation is to compare it to a camera. The children should have an opportunity to examine a simple camera and to see the various parts that are comparable to the parts of the eye (see page 341).

The round, dark "dot" in the center of the eye is the *pupil,* and it actually is a hole in the eye through which light enters. (When ophthamologists wish to examine the inner surface of the eye, they look through the pupil with the aid of a bright light.) The size of the pupil is automatically controlled and varies with the intensity of the light (see Fig. 12-30). The part of the eye and the camera that controls the size of the opening is called the *iris*. In the eye the iris is controlled automatically. In some modern cameras, however, the size of the opening has to be controlled manually.

In both the eye and a camera the light passes through a *lens* that focuses the image on a light sensitive surface. In a camera the image is focused by moving the lens back and forth. In the eye, however, the focusing is done by varying the thickness of the lens. (With two lenses of different thicknesses, it can be demonstrated to the children that the thicker lens focuses the light nearer the lens than does the thinner lens.) The thickness of the lens in the eye is controlled by muscles at the side of the lens that automatically keep the image focused on the light sensitive part of the eye.

In both the eye and the camera the image that is formed is upside down. In the camera it doesn't make any difference, because the picture can easily be turned. Similarly, the child learns early to interpret the image formed in the eye as being right side up. In fact, experimenters who have worn special glasses that inverted everything that they saw in a short time learned how to interpret the images that were formed. When the glasses were removed, the experimenters again adjusted without much difficulty.

In the camera the light sensitive material is on the film. In the eye it is the *retina*. There are two kinds of light sensitive receptors in the retina: *cones* and *rods*. The cones are most sensitive to bright light and are the mechanisms by which color is seen. The rods make it possible to see in dim light. However, the rods are not sensitive to color, and this is why in dim light everything appears to be gray. Also, the rods are mostly located around the periphery of the retina. Because of this, an object can be seen better at night through the edges of the eyes.

The light sensitive cones and rods are connected by the optic nerve to the brain. The interpretations of the varying electrical impulses that travel through the optic nerve probably take place in the brain.

The observance of a few simple precautions will help protect the eyes and avoid eyestrain:

1. Do not look directly at very bright sources of light such as the sun.
2. Read only in a well-lighted room.
3. Arrange the light to eliminate glare and shadows.
4. Rest the eyes occasionally by looking into the distance or by closing them.

The Ear

One of the best ways to explain the ear and its operation is to trace a sound as it moves through various parts of the ear. A model or a diagram such as the one shown in this book will help.

Sound waves are gathered in by the outer ear. The outer ear operates somewhat like a funnel through which sound waves are concentrated. To hear faint sounds the hands are sometimes cupped behind the ears. In a sense this enlarges the funnel that gathers in the sound waves.

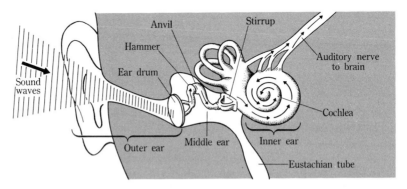

Fig. 16-4   A diagram of the ear.

A membrane called the *eardrum* is stretched across the auditory canal of the ear. Sound waves strike the eardrum and cause it to vibrate. In a similar way the membrane of a drum or a thin piece of rubber stretched across a container can be caused to vibrate by a nearby loud sound.

The movement of the membrane is transmitted through a set of three bones usually called the "hammer," "anvil," and "stirrup." These bones act something like a hydraulic press in that they increase the pressure that is exerted by a factor of about twenty-two. This pressure is exerted on fluid in the inner ear. This fluid, in turn, exerts pressure on another membrane. This membrane in the inner ear rubs against the auditory nerve endings. Electrical impulses are set up in the auditory nerve and are transmitted to the brain where they are interpreted.

Sounds are also transmitted through the bones in the skull. For example, the sounds made when chewing are transmitted to the ear through the bones. One of the factors involved in the distaste that most people have for the drilling of their teeth is the sound that is conducted to the ear by the bones. Some of the sounds of the voice are also conducted through the bones. These tend to be the lower frequency vibrations. Therefore, a person hears his speech as being deeper and richer than it is heard by his listeners. This is the reason that many people are disappointed when they hear a recording of their voices.

Behind the eardrum there is a tube that leads down into the mouth. It is through this *Eustachian* tube that the air pressure on the inside surface of the eardrum is equalized with that on the outside. By swallowing or yawning in an elevator or airplane, air is allowed to enter or leave the middle ear through the Eustachian tube.

It is important that children learn how to protect their ears from damage. The eardrum can be pierced by pins, pencils, and other objects. It has been said that "No object smaller than your elbow should be placed in your ear." The ears should also be protected from sudden loud sounds. When a person has a cold, it is important not to blow the nose hard because this may force phlegm up into the Eustachian tube.

Taste and Smell

The senses of smell and taste are interrelated. When a person holds his nose, or when his nose is constricted because of a cold, many substances seem to have no taste. A blindfolded person who holds his nose cannot taste whether he is biting into an apple or an onion. Some smells, however, such as the sweetish smell of chloroform, are actually due to the stimulation of the taste buds.

Both smell and taste are said to be chemical senses. To be tasted, the substance must already be in solution or become dissolved in saliva. For example, if the surface of the tongue is wiped dry, some substances, such as salt or sugar, cannot be tasted. They have to be dissolved before they can be tasted. Similarly, the materials in the air that are said to have an odor have to become dissolved in the fluid that covers the mucous membrane.

There are four basic sensations of taste: sweet, sour, bitter, and salty. Other tastes are due to various combinations of these four. The receptors sensitive to these various tastes tend to be located in different places. The taste buds for sweet and salty are mostly located near the tip of the tongue. The taste buds for sour tastes are found near the edges of the tongue, while those for bitter tastes are at the base of the tongue.

The sense of smell is a very sensitive one. As little as one part of certain chemicals in thirty billion parts of air can be detected. Dogs and other animals have an even more sensitive sense of smell. In fact, some animals depend largely on the sense of smell to learn of the environment about them.

Skin Sensations

There are five skin sensations: touch, pressure, pain, heat, and cold. An example of the touch sensation is the rubbing of the skin by some soft material, such as a soft cloth. When a rigid object, such as a pencil, is pressed against the skin, there is the sensation of pressure. The sensation of pain can be stimulated in a number of ways and serves as an indicator of danger to the body. Heat and cold sensations are due to the stimulus of different temperature conditions.

Children can study the ability of different parts of the skin to discriminate between two or more points of pressure. If the skin is touched with two pinpoints held close together, the points will probably be felt as one. As they are spread farther apart, a spacing is reached by which they will be detected as two sensations. The distances by which two points have to be separated before they are detected as two sensations varies with different parts of the skin surface. Through investigation children can determine the comparative sensitivities of various parts of the body.

APPROACHES TO TEACHING

The study of the human body can be used to develop further the concepts of systems and subsystems. For example, the children can be led to consider what structures can or cannot usefully be considered to be in the various systems within the body. Similarly, organs can be considered to be subsystems within larger systems. In addition to studying the structure and function of such organs as the heart and lungs, their relationships to the broader systems can also be considered.

An important approach to the teaching of the human body is to compare structures and functions within the human body to analogous physical devices. The eye is often compared to the camera, the heart to a pump, the nervous system to a telephone communication system, and the entire body to a machine such as an internal combustion engine. Such analogies are useful in developing understanding. However, the differences as well as the similarities between the body structures and these devices should also be noted.

What are cells like?

Human epithelial cells can be obtained for examination by scraping the inside of the mouth with a clean spoon or a tongue depressor. Dip the material that is obtained into a drop of iodine solution (iodine crystals dissolved in water) on a glass slide. Place a coverslip over the drop. The iodine solution will tend to stain the nucleus brown.

Have the children examine the material under a microscope. Have them note the nucleus and the cell membrane. A slide of a thin membrane from an onion may be prepared to permit the children to compare the human epithelial cells with the plant cells. A conspicuous part of the plant cell that is not found in human cells is the cell wall.

433

Although cells can be best examined under a microscope, the image of the cells can be projected onto a screen with a microprojector.

How does exercise affect the rate of heartbeat?

The rate at which the heart beats is affected by exercise. During vigorous exercise the body uses food and oxygen at a fast rate, and carbon dioxide and other wastes are produced rapidly. To provide the necessary food and oxygen and to remove wastes, blood has to be pumped to different parts of the body at an accelerated rate. This means that the heart has to work faster.

Have each child take his pulse, placing the middle and index fingers on the inside of the wrist below the thumb. Have the child count the number of beats for thirty seconds and multiply by two to get the rate per minute. Record this rate.

Obtain a bench or stool about fifteen inches high. Have each child step up onto the stool sixty times over a period of two minutes. Again, have him take his pulse. How much did each heartbeat rate increase?

How well do we hear?

Hold a watch near a child's ear. Then move the watch out from the ear until the point is reached where the sound no longer can be heard. Measure and record this distance. Do the same for the other ear. Have the children use this method to check each other's hearing. If there are children who have difficulty in hearing the watch, refer them to the school nurse or doctor.

How is air brought into and forced out of the lungs?

An improvised model of the chest cavity can be used to demonstrate how air is forced into and out of the lungs. To construct the model, cut the bottom from a gallon glass bottle. (The bottom can be removed from a glass bottle by tying a string that has been dipped in kerosene around the bottom of the bottle and igniting it. As the string burns, the bottle will usually crack. If not, a few drops of water dripped onto the part of the bottle that has been heated will cause the bottom to crack off. Be sure to burn the string in a place where there is nothing else that might be ignited.) Softly brush the edges of the glass with some wire screening to round off the sharp edges. Cover the edge of the glass with tape.

Stretch a rubber diaphragm across the open bottom end of the glass bottle. The rubber diaphragm may be a sheet of rubber especially designed for this purpose; if this is not available the rubber from a large balloon or a rubber shower cap may be used. In the model this rubber diaphragm will serve the same purpose as the diaphragm at the bottom of the human chest cavity.

Two balloons can serve as lungs in the model. With rubber bands fasten these to the two branches of a Y-tube. (If a Y-tube is not available, two separate pieces of glass tubing can be used.) The Y-tube can be connected with rubber tubing to a piece of glass tubing that is inserted through a one-hole rubber stopper that will fit the neck of the glass bottle. Fig. 16-5 shows how the model is assembled.

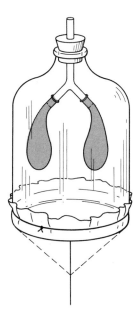

Fig. 16-5 *A model of the respiratory system.*

With this model the process of breathing can be demonstrated. Pull down on the rubber diaphragm. As this is done, the air pressure on the inside of the bottle is reduced and becomes somewhat less than the air pressure outside. Air from the outside is forced in through the glass tubing and into the rubber balloons. The rubber balloons become inflated. When the diaphragm is released, the pressure on the inside of the glass bottle is increased and air is forced out of the balloons. Have the children hold their fingers above the end of the glass tubing so that they can feel the air moving in and out. Air is forced into and out of the lungs in somewhat the same way as it is in this model.

How does this model differ from the human chest? It differs in many ways. One of the important differences is that the sides of the glass bottle are rigid, while the walls of the chest cavity are elastic. In breathing, the walls of the chest cavity move and help to change the air pressure within the chest cavity.

Mouth-to-mouth artificial respiration can be demonstrated with this model. Blow into the glass tubing as you would blow into the mouth of a victim of drowning. Air enters the balloons as air would enter the lungs. When you remove your lips from the glass tubing, air is again forced out of the balloons. Similarly, air will escape from the lungs.

How well do we see?

With a Snellen Chart the children's ability to distinguish objects at a distance can be determined. The chart consists of letters of different sizes. A child is asked to stand at a distance of about twenty feet from the chart and read the letters from the largest to the smallest. The smallest type that he can distinguish is determined. The child's visual acuity is then expressed as a fraction of what a person with normal vision can read at twenty feet. For example, if the child has normal vision, he is said to have 20/20 vision. However, if he can read at twenty feet what can be read at thirty feet with normal vision, he is said to have 20/30 vision.

If a child has some difficulty in distinguishing the appropriate line on the Snellen Chart, he should be referred to the school nurse or doctor.

How are the eye and the camera alike?

One of the best ways to gain an understanding of the eye and how it operates is to compare it to a camera. For this comparison obtain a camera in which the size of opening through which light enters can be controlled; if possible, use a camera that has a ground glass viewing screen (see page 341 for diagrams).

Help the children to examine the camera and make the following comparisons between the eye and the camera:

1. Compare the pupil of the eye and the opening through which light enters the camera.
2. Notice how the size of the pupil opening in the eye is controlled by the iris and how an iris is used to control the size of the opening in the camera.
3. In the eye, images are focused on the retina by controlling the thickness of the lens. The thickness of the lens in a camera cannot be changed. Instead, the image is focused on the film or ground glass screen by moving the lens back and forth.
4. In both the eye and the camera the image that is formed is upside down.
5. In the eye the image is formed on a retina, and there can be a continuing change of images transmitted to the brain. In the camera the image is formed on a film, and only one image can be developed. (The television camera which can transmit a continuing series of pictures is a better analogy for the eye.)

*How does the size of the pupil opening vary
with the brightness of the light?*

Arrange the children in pairs so that each of them can look into the eyes of another. Have them note the size of the pupil opening in their partner's eyes. Then darken the room as much as possible. Have the children note the size of the pupil. Then, quickly, switch on the lights to brighten the room. The children should be able to see a dramatic closing of the pupil as the room becomes brighter.

How can a lens be used to focus an image on a surface?

Darken the room. Then place some bright object, such as a lighted candle, a short distance from a wall or screen. Hold a convex lens between the candle and the screen and move it back and forth to find and note the position at which a clear image is formed on the screen. Focus the image with a second lens that is either thicker or thinner than the first. Note that this lens has to be placed in a different position to get a clear image. Point out that in the eye the thickness of the lens is changed in order to get a clear image on the retina.

How do we locate the direction of sounds?

Place one student in the center of the room and cover his eyes with a blindfold. Arrange a number of other children in a circle around the outside of the room. Provide them with some way of making a short, sharp sound. (One way is to give each child two small sticks or stones that he can strike together.)

Ask the child in the center of the room to close one ear by placing a hand over it. Have one youngster hit his sticks or stones together. Have the blindfolded child point in the direction of the sound. After having done this several times, have the blindfolded child uncover his ear and again point in the direction of the sound.

Was the child better able to locate the sounds in some directions than in others? Was he better able to locate sounds with two ears than with one?

Have several children try it. Are the results always the same?

How does the human hair appear under the microscope?

Place a human hair on a slide; cover it with a cover glass and examine it under a microscope. Is the color concentrated in any particular part of the hair? Are there scales in the hair? Comparison of a human hair with a wool fiber, which is a hair from sheep, will provide additional information.

Get a cross section of human hair by having a man shave close for a second time and then rinse the razor in clear water. Put a little of the water containing the hair on a slide and examine it under the microscope. What is the shape of the hair? Are there distinct features to be seen in the cross-sectional view of the hair?

What are the heart, lungs, and other organs like?

Animal hearts, lungs, and other organs can be obtained at most butcher shops. Have the children examine these organs and use the diagrams in this book to locate the various structures in the organs.

Have the children trace the flow of the blood through the heart as described on pages 425–426.

Have the children find the tubes through which air enters and leaves the lungs. Have them examine the tissues in the regions where air is absorbed into the bloodstream.

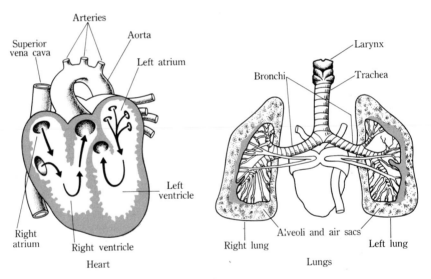

Fig. 16-6   Diagrams of the heart and lungs.

INVESTIGATION

What is the distance at which two points can be distinguished on different regions of the body?

If two points such as the points of two pins or of dividers are applied close together on the skin, they will be felt as being one point. As the distance between the points is increased, the sensations are eventually recognized as being made by two points. The distance required to distinguish the two sensations varies with different regions of the body.

Have the children work in pairs. With one member of each pair blindfolded, have the other child move the points of two toothpicks farther and farther apart in the palm of the blindfolded child's hand until he can detect the two points. Have the child doing the investigation measure the distance at which the two points can be detected and record it. Repeat for a finger tip, back of the hand, forearm, back of the neck, and leg.

Have the children in each pair exchange places and repeat the investigation. How much variation is there between the measurements taken on different parts of the body? How much do the measurements for the various body regions differ among the children?

Selected References

Asimov, Isaac, *The Human Body*. New York: New American Library, 1963.

Carlson, Anton J., and Johnson, Victor, *The Machinery of the Body*. Chicago, Ill.: University of Chicago Press,

Grollman, Sigmund, *The Human Body*. New York: The Macmillan Co., 1964.

Morrison, Thomas F., Cornett, Frederick D., Tether, J. Edward, and Gratz, Pauline, *Human Physiology*. New York: Holt, Rinehart & Winston, Inc., 1967.

READINGS FOR THE PRIMARY GRADES

Jacobson, Willard J., Lauby, Cecilia J., and Konicek, Richard D., *Living in Space*. New York: American Book Co., 1968.

Lauber, Patricia, *Your Body and How It Works*. New York: Random House, Inc., 1963.

Showers, Paul, *Your Skin and Mine*. New York: Thomas Y. Crowell Co., 1965.

READINGS FOR THE INTERMEDIATE GRADES

Beck, Lester F., *Human Growth*. New York: Harcourt, Brace & World, 1949.

deSchweinitz, Karl, *Growing Up*. New York: The Macmillan Co., 1953.

RAVIELLI, ANTHONY, *Wonders of the Human Body*. New York: Viking Press, 1954.

SCHNEIDER, HERMAN AND NINA, *How Your Body Works*. New York: William R. Scott, 1949.

SELECTED FILMS

Human and Animal Beginnings. Wexler Films. Contrasts a human baby's start in life with that of monkeys, ducks, rabbits, fish and guinea pigs.

Human Growth. Eddie Albert Productions. An introduction to the study of growth in an upper elementary grade classroom.

17 Science and Healthful Living

"Health is a state of complete physical, mental, and social well-being and not merely an absence of disease or infirmity." This positive definition of health is from the preamble of the constitution of the World Health Organization (WHO). According to this view health is more than just keeping well. It is a state of "complete physical, mental and social well-being." This is a lofty objective that defines the general aim in this broad area of elementary school science.

Children should learn how to care for themselves and nurture their bodies so as to achieve optimum growth and development. A healthy body is the basic prerequisite for a happy life. Just as sickness and sadness seem inevitably linked, there is often a relationship between health and happiness. Also, every individual is born with certain potentialities for growth and certain possibilities of development; to be deprived of the opportunity for such growth and development is a tragedy. Through their activities in this area, children can, perhaps, learn how to achieve optimum growth and development.

Children can learn how to prevent sickness and the spread of disease. Many diseases of man are spread from one human being to another. The viruses, microbes, or bacteria that are the bearers of disease may be transmitted by insects, drinking water, air, or by direct contact. Children can learn how various diseases are spread, some of the characteristics of the vector that is the bearer of the disease germs, and of greatest importance, how the spread of the disease can be prevented. As a result of such learnings, children can protect others from sickness as well as themselves.

Children should have an opportunity to study health in several areas of the curriculum. In science they should begin to learn some of the "whys" for some of the actions that are suggested to achieve health. Why is it im-

443

portant to eat a certain amount of food rich in proteins each day? Why is it important to remove garbage, trash, and other waste materials from the community? How does daily exercise contribute to health? Children need to know what should be done, but they also need to know why these acts are important. The explanations, of course, are scientific ones. Children learn the function of proteins in the body, that trash and waste materials are breeding grounds for flies and other insects, and that exercise helps build muscle tone and maintain a proper relationship between the energy taken into the body as food and the energy used in exercise. Instinctively children want to know "why." In elementary school science they should have a chance to "find out."

An objective for teaching in this area of the curriculum is to change habits or patterns of behavior. This is always difficult. However, there is considerable evidence to indicate that habits are more likely to be changed early in life. Therefore, it is especially important that there be some instruction in the health sciences in the early years of the elementary school.

Children's general health and well-being also affects their work in school. Some children always seem to be suffering from colds and other ailments and are often absent from school. Many children lack the vim and vitality usually associated with childhood. Their education suffers; they deserve a better deal.

The health sciences, such as nutrition and public health, should have an educational dimension. Pasteur developed the germ theory of disease, but if this theory is to have meaning in the lives of people, they must learn to live in ways that are consistent with the germ theory. Nutrition scientists have learned that certain nutrients are essential for healthy living. However, if people do not eat these nutrients, this knowledge has been of little benefit. While some sciences, such as chemistry and physics, need not necessarily be considered to have educational dimensions, education can be considered an integral and essential dimension of the health sciences. As examples, in this chapter the educational dimensions of two health sciences, nutrition and public health, are introduced.

FOOD AND NUTRITION

All living things ingest food of some kind and excrete wastes. Plants can use such raw materials from the environment as water, carbon dioxide, and minerals to manufacture food. All animals depend in some way or other upon the food that has been manufactured by green plants. However, the kinds of foods that can be utilized by different animals varies considerably. Termites, for example, with the help of microorganisms in their digestive tract, are able to digest cellulose. Most animals cannot. Some carnivores, such as wolves and tigers, depend almost entirely upon other animals for food. However, since the animals that the carnivores eat usually eat plants for food, even the carnivores depend upon green plants for food.

"The food we eat makes a difference." When enjoying the stories of gallant knights of yore, the reader may picture strapping six-footers subduing men of evil. In the Tower of London are displayed suits of armor once worn by these knights. The suits are very small; most men of today could not get into them. Since Civil War days, height and weight measurements of Harvard freshmen have been recorded. The freshmen of today are, on the average, three inches taller and two pounds heavier than the freshmen of a hundred years ago. These differences are due primarily to the foods that are eaten.

The life span of an individual will also be affected by his eating habits. The child who becomes obese in his early years and remains so throughout life usually will have a shorter life than if he had accumulated less body fat. The strain upon the heart and the increased chances that he will suffer from such diseases as diabetes and cirrhosis of the liver reduce the chances that the obese child will lead a long and healthy life. Then, too, man is a creature of habit, and such important habits as those that govern his patterns of eating are usually developed early in life; it is important that these be habits that can lead to healthy living.

The science of nutrition involves the study of the nutritional contributions of various kinds of foods. Nutrition is a relatively young science in which ideas and methods drawn from such older sciences as biology and chemistry are widely used. The laws of conservation of matter and energy are of special importance in the science of nutrition.

The Study of Nutrition

As in many other sciences, progress in the science of nutrition has been dependent upon the assumption that general physical and biological principles can be used to formulate hypotheses to be tested by observation and experimentation. An excellent example of the application of this approach is in the study of animal heat by the noted French scientists Antoine Lavoisier and Pierre Laplace.[1]

Before the work of Lavoisier and Laplace it was known that human beings and many animals maintained a fairly constant body temperature.

---

[1] An account of this work has been made generally available in Mordecai L. Gabriel and Seymour Fogel (Eds.), *Great Experiments in Biology* (Englewood Cliffs, N.J.: Prentice-Hall, Inc., 1955), pp. 85–93.

It was also known that animals could not survive without air. However, the ability of the body to maintain temperatures higher than those of its environment had been attributed to mysterious "vital forces." These were unsatisfactory explanations to such careful experimentalists as Lavoisier and Laplace, and they initiated a systematic study of energy relationships in the body.

Lavoisier and Laplace designed a three-chambered container. The inner chamber was for the experimental object. The outer two chambers were filled with ice. The amount of heat given off by the experimental object could be determined by measuring the amount of ice that melted. Lavoisier and Laplace determined the amount of "fixed air" (carbon-dioxide) formed by absorbing it in caustic alkali and measuring the increase in weight of the alkali. They used their apparatus to find out how much heat was generated when a certain amount of carbon dioxide was produced by the burning of carbon and by the body heat generated by a guinea pig.

When enough carbon was burned to form 224 grains of carbon dioxide, 10.38 ounces of ice had been melted. When a guinea pig placed in the experimental apparatus had produced 224 grains of carbon dioxide, it, too, had melted about 10.38 ounces of ice. The production of a given amount of carbon dioxide, therefore, through burning and through respiration yielded equal amounts of heat. Lavoisier and Laplace then concluded that respiration is a form of slow combustion and that it is the principal source of animal heat.

The very careful experimental work of Lavoisier and Laplace opened the door to a very successful approach to the study of nutrition. Their work and many subsequent studies are the result of assuming that the chemical and biological principles that are useful in explaining other phenomena can also be used in studying and explaining the functions of foods in the body.

The use of animals

The human race owes many debts to laboratory animals. For example, it is important to know the functions of various kinds of nutrients. However, for obvious reasons, experimenters hesitate to deprive human subjects of nutrients that may be critical for health. Fortunately, a number of animals, notably the laboratory white rat, have dietary requirements that are quite similar to those of humans. These experimental animals can be deprived of one or more nutrients for a period of time so that the effect of this deprivation can be studied. Through a study of the effects of dietary deprivation of animals it has become possible to recognize symptoms of dietary inadequacy among humans.

The laboratory white rat has been of special significance in the study of the effects of dietary deprivation. The dietary requirements of the white rat are essentially the same as those for humans. The only exception is that the white rat can synthesize vitamin C within its body, while humans are dependent on outside sources for this essential nutrient. The white rat has a considerably shorter life span than humans and therefore may be said to "live faster" than humans. This is important for nutritional studies, because the effects of dietary deprivation will be seen about thirty times as fast in rats as in humans. While the effects of a diet deprivation of calcium, may not be seen for sixty weeks in humans, the symptoms of calcium deprivation would be seen in two weeks in rats. Also, of course, the positive effects of a balanced diet are also seen thirty times as fast (see page 459).

How the body uses food

Food is both the fuel and the building material for the body. Foods provide the energy to operate the heart, lungs, and other essential organs. The energy used by muscles to lift a book or pedal a bicycle vigorously down the street is also produced by food. Food is the building material used in growth and repair. In eighteen years an eight-pound baby can become a two-hundred-pound fullback; the material that has gone into this growth has come from the food that has been eaten.

Food for energy

Energy is defined as the capacity for doing work. In an automobile engine the energy to turn the wheels and operate equipment ranging from power steering to windshield wipers comes from gasoline. Although the work to be done is somewhat different, the energy required by the human body comes from the food that is eaten.

In the study of foods and the energy requirements of the body, energy is usually stated in terms of *calories*. In nutrition the large calorie is the unit that is used. A large calorie is equal to the energy required to raise the temperature of a kilogram (1,000 grams) of water through one degree Celsius. (The Calorie should not be confused with the small calorie, which is the energy required to raise the temperature of one gram of water one degree Celsius.)

A certain amount of energy is needed for the essential processes that go on in the body: the heart beats, the blood courses through arteries and veins, the lungs expand and contract, the body maintains a constant temperature—all of these processes require some energy. The energy required for the essential processes of the body is called *basal metabolism*. If the energy expenditure of an individual is measured just after awakening and about 15 hours after eating, the energy that is expended is essentially that required to operate the body, If these measurements of energy expenditures are made over a period of days, it will be discovered that about the same amount of energy is always expended to keep the body operating. Among young adults the basal metabolism amounts to about one Calorie per kilogram per hour. To maintain the metabolic processes for 24 hours, a young adult weighing 70 kilograms (154 pounds) would require about 1,680 calories (1 $\times$ 70 $\times$ 24).

The energy requirements for basal metabolism in children are greater than for adults. The requirement for six-year-olds is about 1.7 Calories per kilogram per hour. As children grow older, the requirements are reduced, and a twelve-year-old child needs about 1.4 Calories per kilogram per hour.

Part of the energy that the body uses maintains the body temperature at about 98.6°F. The amount of energy required depends on several factors including the outside temperature. It has been a common experience of polar explorers that they have had to eat additional food while living under conditions of extreme cold. Even though they tend to eat more, explorers in polar regions usually lose weight, indicating that body tissue is being consumed to furnish some of the energy required to maintain a constant body temperature. Travelers to the tropics, however, will not need as much energy to maintain constant body temperature. They should reduce their food intake. Failing to do this, the excess food energy taken into the body is stored as fat.

Various physical activities, whether it is pushing a pencil or running up stairs, require energy, and the amount of food needed depends upon the amount of activity engaged in. The following table indicates the approximate number of Calories required by children and adults according to the amount of physical activity in which they engage.

Table 17–1: APPROXIMATE DAILY CALORIE REQUIREMENTS

Children	Calories	Women	Calories	Men	Calories
4–6 years	1600	Quiet, inactive	2000	Quiet, inactive	2400
7–9 years	2000	Moderately active	2400	Moderately active	3000
10–12 years	2500	Very active	3000	Very active	4500

The amount of energy given off by different kinds of foods as they are oxidized has been carefully determined. Lavoisier, Laplace, and scores of other scientists have shown that the energy given off by the oxidation of food in the body is equal to the energy given off when it is oxidized outside the body. Therefore, it is possible to determine the caloric values of foods by oxidizing them in such a way that the amount of energy given off can be measured. The caloric values of foods are often determined in a device called a bomb calorimeter. The food material is placed in a chamber called a "bomb." The food is surrounded by oxygen so that it will burn completely. Around the "bomb" there is a chamber filled with a known quantity of water. The amount of energy given off can be determined by using the measured rise in temperature of the water. The caloric values for some common foods are given in Table 17-2.[2]

The number of Calories of energy in a given amount of many foods varies. For example, the number of Calories in ice cream will depend upon the butterfat content. However, the table is sufficiently accurate for general determinations of Calorie intake. Of course, the daily Calorie intake can be compared with the Approximate Daily Calorie Requirements.

Food for growth and repair

Almost every living thing undergoes growth during some period of its life span. A newborn baby usually weighs about seven pounds. Under optimum diet conditions the newborn child will double its weight in six months and triple it in a year. By the age of ten, the child may be ten times as heavy as at birth. By the age of twenty he may tip the scales at two-hundred pounds. All of the material involved in this growth has come from the food that has been eaten.

There is a continual process of replacement of old protoplasm by new in the body. It has been estimated that over a period of seven years almost all the material of the body is replaced by new. The material that goes into the building of the new tissues comes from the food that is eaten. With growth and replacement both dependent on the foods that are eaten, it may not be a gross exaggeration to say, "We are what we eat."

When the body is injured, new tissue is formed to repair the injury. Most children will have suffered cuts or wounds of some kind and will have watched the cuts heal. Scar tissue is formed. The material for the repair of body tissue also comes from the food that is eaten.

Proteins are the basic food materials utilized in body building and repair. Proteins are very complex materials largely made up of the elements carbon, oxygen, nitrogen, hydrogen, and small amounts of such elements as phosphorus and sulfur. Nitrogen is of special importance, because of a continual demand for it on the part of every living cell. The chemical ele-

[2] A much more comprehensive list of the nutrients in common foods is to be found in U.S. Department of Agriculture, "Nutrients in Common Foods in Terms of Household Measures," *Food. The Yearbook of Agriculture. 1959* (Washington, D.C.: U.S. Government Printing Office, 1959), pp. 243–265.

Table 17–2: CALORIC VALUES FOR COMMON FOODS

Food	Calories	Food	Calories
Almonds, 12 plain	90	Grapes, seedless, 25	90
Apple, 1 large	115	Ham, fresh, 1 slice	340
Apple juice, 1 cup	120	Hamburger, 3 ounces	315
Apricot, 1 medium	18	Ice cream, 1 dish (1/7 quart)	165
Asparagus, 6 medium spears	22	Jam, 1 teaspoon	55
Bacon, cooked, 1 slice	95	Lamb chop, 1 medium	100
Banana, cooked, 1 slice	120	Lettuce, 2 large leaves	5
Beans, green, 1 cup	40	Liver, calf, 2 slices	120
Beans, lima, 1 cup	150	Lobster, 1/4 pound	100
Beef, 3 ounces	270	Maple syrup, 1 tablespoon	55
Beef, corned, 1 slice	100	Mayonnaise, 1 tablespoon	100
Beets, red, 1 cup	70	Milk, whole, 1 glass	165
Blueberries, 1 cup	90	Milk, skimmed, 1 glass	84
Bluefish, 1 serving	100	Oatmeal, 1 cup	150
Bologna, 1 slice	100	Orange, Florida, 1 large	105
Bread, 1 slice	65	Orange juice, 1 cup	130
Broccoli, 1 cup	40	Peanut butter, 1 tablespoon	90
Butter, 1 square	50	Peanuts, shelled, 1 cup	105
Cabbage, raw, 1 cup	25	Peas, green, 1 cup	110
Cake, layer, 1 slice	420	Pie, apple, 1 slice	330
Cake, plain, 1 slice	150	Pineapple, fresh, 1 slice	50
Candy, chocolate, 1 bar	150	Popcorn, popped, 1 cup	55
Candy, chocolates, 5 assorted	300	Pork loin, 1 piece	290
Carrot, 1 large	20	Potato, sweet, 1 medium	200
Celery, 1 large stalk	5	Potato, white, 1 boiled	105
Cheese, Cheddar, 1 ounce	115	Potato chips, 7 large	110
Cheese, pot, 1 cup	100	Pretzels, 6 small	90
Chicken, 3 slices (assorted)	200	Raisins, seeded, 1/4 cup	85
Clams, 6 medium	100	Roast, rib, 2 slices	275
Cola, 1 cup	105	Roll, 1 plain	100
Cookie, 1 plain	110	Sardines, canned, 7 small	70
Corn, 1 ear	85	Spaghetti or macaroni, 3/4 cup	100
Cornflakes, 1 bowl	95	Spinach, 1/2 cup	21
Crackers, 2 soda	35	Sugar, white, 1 tablespoon	50
Cream, 3 tablespoons	100	Tomato, raw, 1 medium	23
Doughnut, 1 plain	200	Tongue, beef, 4 slices	100
Egg, 1 boiled	75	Tunafish, drained, 1/2 cup	250
Egg yolk, 1 raw	60	Turkey, 1 slice	130
Farina, 1 cup	100	Veal, 1 chop	110
Fats and oils, cooking, 1 tablespoon	100	Watermelon, 1 slice	45
Frankfurter, 1 medium	80	Wheat, shredded, 1 biscuit	100
Grapefruit, one-half	105	Wheat flakes, 1 cup	125

ments that make up proteins are arranged in organic substances called *amino acids*. Eighteen different amino acids are commonly found in the foods that are eaten. The body must have eight of these amino acids because they cannot be synthesized from other materials. A diet deficient in certain essential amino acids may lead to such deficiency diseases as kwashiorkor.

Milk, meat, poultry, fish, and eggs are major sources of protein. These animal products contain all essential amino acids. Foods from plants such as corn, beans, and wheat also contain protein. However, these foods are often lacking in one or more amino acids. In some regions of the world, such as Central America, where plant products form the major portion of the diet, there is a danger of malnutrition if the diet is not supplemented with the amino acids that are lacking. Among certain groups of Central Americans about 680 out of every thousand children at the age of one die before they reach the age of five, many of the protein-deficiency disease kwashiorkor.

Corn is the basic staple food in Central America. While it is an excellent food, it is lacking in two essential amino acids. These amino acids are available in meat, eggs, fish, and poultry. As long as the babies are being nursed, they receive these essential amino acids from the mother's milk. When they are weaned, these infants are fed cornmeal gruel. Gradually they grow weaker and develop sores on their bodies; their hair sometimes changes to a reddish color, and they become susceptible to a variety of infectious diseases. Unless remedial action is taken, more than half of them will die before they reach the age of five. The addition to the diet of foods containing the essential amino acids can prevent kwashiorkor and bring about remarkable recovery in the children that are suffering from the disease.

Certain *mineral elements* are also essential for growth. About three pounds of the total weight of the body consists of minerals. Calcium and phosphorus are essential for the proper development of bones and teeth. It is especially important that growing children receive sufficient calcium and phosphorus. Milk and milk products are the most important sources of calcium. Phosphorus is found in so many foods that enough of this mineral is almost certain to be consumed.

Food for the control of essential processes

An old woman was sitting beside the produce from her garden: corn squash, potatoes, and yams. The produce was succulent and of the type that would contribute important nutrients to her diet. But she bore the grossly enlarged neck of one who suffers from goiter. Goiter is due to a deficiency of iodine in the diet. In the past, large numbers of people in the Midwest and other regions where there was a lack of iodine in the soil suffered from goiter. Now goiter is largely prevented through the addition of small amounts of iodine to table salt. Iodine is essential for the proper operation of the thyroid gland, which, in turn, is an important regulator of basal metabolism. Iodine is one of several minerals essential for the control of body processes.

The contraction of muscles is dependent upon the presence of com-

pounds containing calcium and phosphorus. Muscle tissue will not respond in solutions that do not contain these minerals. These compounds
remain fluid under acid conditions but swiftly congeal if conditions become slightly alkaline. When conditions become acid again, the compounds return to a fluid state. Because of the characteristics of these
compounds, the contraction and relaxation of muscles can be controlled
by slight changes in acidity and alkalinity.

The irritability of nervous tissue is also dependent upon the presence of
minerals. Nerve tissue placed in distilled water will not respond to a stimulus. In the body the operation of the nervous system is dependent upon
the presence of just the right proportions of such minerals as sodium,
calcium, and potassium.

Mineral elements help control the movement of substances within the
body. The element iron is essential for the transport of oxygen and carbon
dioxide in the blood. The movement of digestive foods into the bloodstream is partially controlled by the concentration of certain mineral
elements.

Vitamins

In the days of sailing vessels, sailors at sea for months would have very
little fresh fruit and vegetables. Sailors from England, France, Spain, and
other European nations would often suffer from the dreaded disease scurvy.
They would develop a sallow complexion, tire easily, feel generally depressed, begin to feel pain throughout their bodies, and often lose their
teeth. Japanese sailors, on the other hand, would suffer from beriberi. The
beriberi victims would develop great sensitivity to pressure on their limbs,
loss of muscle strength, increased heart rate, and a collection of fluids in
body tissues. Both scurvy and beriberi are nutrition-deficiency diseases.

In an extensive study of beriberi the Japanese scientist Kanehiro Tobaki
sent two similar ships on a 287-day trip around the Pacific Ocean. The
sailors on the first ship received the regular Japanese sailor fare which was
based largely on rice. The sailors on the second ship had a diet containing
more meat, fish, and vegetables. Among the 360 sailors on the first ship
there were 160 cases of beriberi with 75 deaths. On the second ship there
were 16 cases of beriberi and no deaths, and the 16 men who developed
beriberi had refused to eat the meat, fish, and vegetables. This study
showed that beriberi could be prevented by eating a proper diet.

A number of substances have been found to be needed in small quantities. At one time these substances were all thought to be of a family of
chemical compounds called amines. Since they were vital to health, they
were called "vitamines." It is now known that some of these compounds
are not amines, but the name *vitamin* has been retained.

Table 17-3: VITAMINS ESSENTIAL IN THE DIET

Vitamins	Important Sources	Functions	Symptoms of Deficiency
A	Liver, fish-liver oils, green and yellow vegetables, tomatoes, butter, milk, egg yolk	Important for healthy eyes, skin, mucous membranes, and for normal growth	Night blindness, dry skin and dry eyes, susceptibility to infection
B_1 (Thiamine)	Meat (especially liver), fish, fowl, milk, whole-grain cereals, peas, nuts	Promotes normal growth, good appetite, health of nerves, muscles, heart. Necessary for proper metabolism of sugar	Beriberi. Retarded growth, loss of weight, poor digestion, nervous disorders and fatigue
B_2 (Riboflavin)	Milk, lean meat, fresh vegetables, yeast, egg yolk	Important for growth, health of skin and mouth, sugar metabolism, functioning of eyes	Retarded growth, inflammation of tongue, cracks in lips, premature aging, dimness of vision, intolerance to light
Niacin	Meat, fish, fowl, nuts, tomatoes, potatoes, whole-grain cereals and breads, green leafy vegetables	Important for growth, metabolism of sugar, health of stomach and intestines, health of nervous system	Pellagra. Skin eruptions, digestive disturbances, mental disorders
B_{12} (Cobalamin)	Green vegetables, liver	Helps control pernicious anemia	Reduction in number of red blood cells.
C (Ascorbic Acid)	Fresh fruits (especially citrus) and green vegetables, tomatoes	Important for growth, strength of blood vessels, development of teeth, good skin, healing	Scurvy. Sore gums, hemorrhages around bones, tendency to bruise easily
D (Calciferol)	Liver, fish-liver oils, irradiated foods, fortified milk, eggs; also produced in body when sunlight strikes skin directly	Needed for building and maintaining bones and teeth, growth, regulation of body's use of calcium and phosphorus	Rickets. Soft bones and poor teeth
E (Tocopherol)	Wheat germ, green leafy vegetables, milk, butter	Prevents sterility in rats; effects in human uncertain	Undetermined
K (Phylloquinone)	Green vegetables, tomatoes	Important for clotting of blood and normal liver function	Hemorrhages

Water

While it is not a nutrient, water is essential for life. Man can go without food for several weeks, but he cannot go without water for more than a few days. A lack of water leads to fatigue. Complete deprivation of water leads to death.

More than half of body weight is water. Water is used to remove nitrogenous wastes through the kidneys. It is also essential for regulating body temperatures. The perspiration that is excreted through the skin is largely water. When this water evaporates, it cools the body.

How much water should a person drink? More water is needed in a warm dry climate than where it is cool and dry. In most cases thirst is a good guide to how much a person should drink.

Nutrition for Healthy Living

In picturing the class that she will be teaching when school opens in the fall, the beginning teacher sees in her "mind's eye" a group of healthy, husky, happy children. Their eyes are alight with excitement. Energy abounds, and minds are alert. The skin has a radiant glow, and the hair has a healthy luster. Teeth are sound, and the children have the height and weight that are associated with their age. This is a picture of healthy children, and good nutrition is essential for health.

But, look at a classroom of youngsters! Many would fit into this picture of health, but, alas, some would not. Some are lackadaisical and never seem to have enough energy for any activity. Some may be seriously overweight and probably already sentenced to a comparatively short life span. Some youngsters may have skin that is rough and dry; their gums may be red and swollen. Some of these characteristics may be due to malnutrition. Children with these characteristics certainly are not enjoying a state of "complete physical, mental, and social well-being."

It is possible for children to achieve better health and to improve the quality of their living through nutrition. The human body must get about fifty different substances from the foods that are eaten. Among these essentials are fats, proteins, and carbohydrates. These foods supply the energy, amino acids, and fatty acids that are needed by the body. In addition, the body needs a variety of minerals and vitamins. These essentials may be called the "Foundation of a Good Diet."

"Variety is the spice of life." It is also a key to good nutrition. However, the body does have essential requirements, and different foods vary in their nutritional contribution to a diet. It is advisable to have a guide to eating that can help a person achieve good nutrition. A plan based on four basic food groups has been suggested by the United States Department of Agriculture, and it can serve as the foundation of a good diet.

Milk

Milk, cheese, and ice cream; three to four cups of milk a day for children.

Without milk it is difficult for the body to receive the calcium that it needs. Therefore, it is especially important that children drink ample quantities of milk. Milk also provides other minerals, vitamins, and high quality protein that supply energy for active young bodies.

Meat

Beef, veal, pork, lamb, poultry, fish, and eggs; two or more servings a day.

The meat group of foods is the main source of high quality protein. It also supplies some minerals and vitamins.

Vegetables and fruit

Dark green and deep yellow vegetables, citrus fruit, and other fruits and vegetables; four or more servings a day.

These foods are the major sources of vitamins. Almost all vitamin C comes from fruits and vegetables. Since the body does not store vitamin C, it is important that some good source of vitamin C, such as citrus fruit, be eaten every day. American diets are most often weak in this group of foods, and a special attempt should be made to encourage children to eat vegetables and fruit.

Bread and cereals

Bread, breakfast cereals, wheat, rice, and oats; four or more servings a day.

The cereal foods, such as wheat, wheat germ, rice, and soybean products, are the most economical sources of energy. Wheat, corn, or rice serves as the base for diets in many parts of the world. The cereal foods are also important for protein, iron, and several of the B vitamins. In addition, most of the cereal foods sold in the United States have been enriched with vitamin supplements and other nutrients.

These four basic food groups provide a framework on which to plan diets. Additional food is needed, but if the suggested amounts from each of the food groups are eaten, sufficient quantities of the essential nutrients will be taken into the body.

It is believed that certain foods, called "protective foods," will help the body maintain vitality if they are eaten in generous quantities. These foods are rich in calcium and vitamins A and C. These nutrients are the ones that are most often lacking in the diets of American children. Milk, green and yellow vegetables, and citrus fruits are among the good sources of these nutrients.

APPROACHES TO TEACHING

As in other areas of elementary science, the activities suggested for the study of food and nutrition can be used to give children experience with different kinds of studies that are often carried out in the sciences. The methods that are used to conduct a survey or to compare experimental subjects with control subjects can be analyzed and discussed. Children should learn from the processes that are used in a study as well as from the results.

What foods do we eat?

Since one of the most effective ways of improving diets is to help children become aware of what they are and are not eating, a survey approach is used to find out what foods the children eat. As this study is carried out by the children, they should become aware of some of the pitfalls in this kind of research. "Are the records that are kept accurate?" "Are the records that are kept representative of the foods that are really eaten?" "What do the records mean?"

For the teacher, the results of a diet survey may be suggestive of matters that should be stressed in teaching. For example, if the survey shows that many youngsters in a class do not eat enough green and yellow vegetables, additional attention may be given to their contributions to the diet. The diet survey procedures that are described do not give an adequate picture of any individual child's pattern of eating, but they do give an indication of the general patterns of eating to be found within a group.

In the diet survey a record is kept of the foods eaten over a period of three or more days. If possible, the period should include at least one day that is a holiday.

In the upper elementary grades the children should keep their own records. In the morning, they can be asked to record the food that they ate after school the day before, at dinner, and for breakfast. In the afternoon they can record foods eaten at lunch and in daytime snacks.

If the study is carried out with early primary school children, the information will probably have to be obtained through interviews. One approach that has been used is to interview every third child listed on the class rolls.

To get information about the amount of food consumed, some orientation will have to be given to common measures. The children can be shown what is meant by one cup, one tablespoon or teaspoon, one slice, and other commonly used measures.

One effective way for the children to analyze the diet records is in terms of the four basic food groups. How many children ate sufficient amounts of each of the four basic food groups each day? In which food groups did the children tend to be deficient?

How can children learn to enjoy a variety of foods?

Variety is one of the keys to a balanced diet, and children who regularly eat a wide variety of foods are likely to receive a sufficient amount of essential nutrients. However, many children are willing to eat only a limited variety of foods. The teacher working in a school situation can help widen the range of foods that children can eat.

Children can be encouraged to taste new and sometimes unusual foods representing the four basic food groups. The children may wish to keep a record of how many foods in each of the food groups they have eaten. Through snacks and tasting parties children can gradually extend their lists of foods eaten.

Foods from different plants can be tasted. Children can be given the opportunity of tasting foods from different parts of many of the plants that are studied. In this way they will learn more about plants and their uses as well as extend the range of foods that they will eat.

When they study various countries and regions of the world, it is often effective to have them eat some of the foods from those places. Also, it is often helpful to investigate the ingredients of various prepared foods. For example, some children are more likely to eat a salad if they "know what goes into it."

What are the effects of different diets?

Adequate nutrition is essential for good health and optimum growth and development. "The food we eat makes a difference." Children can study the effects of different diets on laboratory animals that have nutritional requirements similar to those of humans.

This demonstration has many of the characteristics of a controlled experiment. The children will feed similar animals living under similar conditions different diets. The students should be helped to think through all of the conditions, such as temperature, environment, and initial state of health, that have to be controlled. (Sometimes an animal may become ill, or some other factor cannot be controlled. The children should gain experience in assessing the significance of this.)

Demonstrations of the effects of various diets can be carried out with animals such as laboratory rats, mice, and guinea pigs. Laboratory rats are often used. Since, in a sense, they live thirty times as fast as humans, the effects of diet are seen thirty times as soon in rats as in humans. These animals can be obtained from scientific supply companies, animal farms, or from agricultural experiment stations. At least four animals should be used, two of which are control animals and two experimental. The animals should be all of the same sex, or a male and a female should be put on each diet.

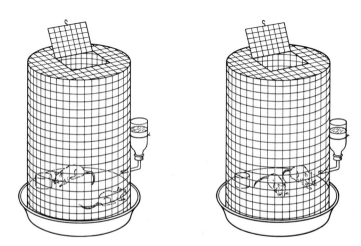

Fig. 17-1 *Animals can be kept in cages such as these with a watering bottle and a container for food.*

The experimental animals should be kept in one cage and the control animals in another. The cages should be kept clean throughout the demonstration. If there are considerable changes in the room temperature, small containers such as milk cartons can be put into the cage for the animals to burrow into. The animals will do best in a fairly quiet environment, with a fairly constant temperature.

Rats should be handled gently with slow, deliberate movement. Although it is not absolutely necessary, many teachers prefer that the children wear gloves when handling rats. To pick up a rat, place the thumb and forefinger around the neck of the rat and the other fingers around the rat's body. The rat can then be placed on the open palm of the other hand with the tail held between two middle fingers. The rat should be gently petted when held.

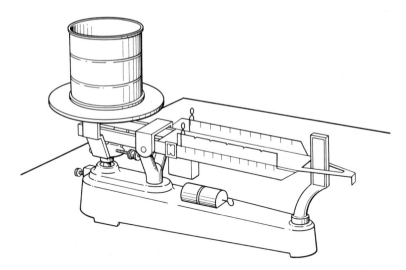

Fig. 17-2   *Animals can be weighed on a balance in a pre-weighed box.*

To weigh the rats, it is best to put them in a pre-weighed oatmeal box or coffee can. A triple beam balance with sliding weights that won't be lost is perhaps the most convenient scale to use.

The children should be involved in setting up the study of effects of different diets on rats. For example, they should help think through ways to make certain that all conditions for the rats are similar except for the diet. They should also help determine the nature of the experimental diet.

An interesting way to develop an experimental diet is to use the diet survey and to use the foods included in a typical poor breakfast. For example, one experimental diet that has been used consists of plain dough-nuts and instant coffee and water. The control diet should contain all essential nutrients. One effective control diet that has been used contains one part by weight of whole-wheat bread and two parts of powdered whole milk and water.

All such foods as bread should be ground into fine particles. The parts of a diet such as powdered milk and bread should be mixed. The bread and doughnuts should be heated in an oven for several hours to drive off the moisture and then ground into fine particles with a rolling pin or round bottle. The granulated foods should be mixed and stored in a large con-tainer. The children should begin to gain experience in weighing and measuring foods. The dry granulated foods are placed in dishes in the rat cages. The water is given to the animals in separate dishes. For the experi-mental animals the instant coffee can be mixed into the water.

The animals should be weighed at about the same time each day. The students should record the weights in laboratory notebooks. Such other possible changes as the following should also be observed and recorded:

1. Condition of fur
2. Condition of eyes
3. Condition of skin
4. Condition of tail
5. Colds and "runny noses"
6. Nervousness

One of the most effective ways to handle the data obtained from the weighings is to record the weights on a line graph. The graph below was made by a group of youngsters using the control and experimental diets that have been mentioned.

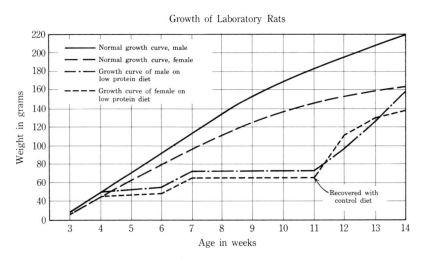

Growth of Laboratory Rats

——— Normal growth curve, male
— — Normal growth curve, female
—·— Growth curve of male on low protein diet
— — — Growth curve of female on low protein diet

Weight in grams

Recovered with control diet

Age in weeks

Fig. 17-3 *Weight can be graphed against time. The lower two lines are a record of an actual experiment carried out by children.*

When a definite difference appears in the experimental rats (usually after about six weeks), they should be "recovered." This can be done by feeding them the control diet. The children should continue their observations. The effects of the improved diet are often quite striking.

What opportunities for learning in nutrition do children have?[1]

The following are some of the kinds of activities that can be undertaken with children in the study of nutrition.

1. Have children taste new and unfamiliar foods.
2. Have children keep a record of all food eaten for a day.
3. Take field trips to learn more about foods in the community.
4. Invite resource persons to talk to children about foods.
5. Record weights and measurements of children.
6. Have children make surveys of the food they waste at lunch.
7. Use films and/or filmstrips relating to study on nutrition.
8. Have children prepare and serve nutritious snacks.
9. Have children conduct or observe small-animal feeding demonstrations.
10. Have children arrange bulletin boards illustrating some phase of their study of nutrition.
11. Have children check their daily milk consumption to see if they are drinking an adequate amount.
12. Review with each child his own food record.
13. Have each child develop a plan for improving his food practices.
14. Have children learn how different foods contribute to their growth and development.
15. Utilize children's questions to initiate a study of nutrition.
16. Have children identify a variety of foods through seeing and tasting foods.
17. Have children plan breakfast and dinner menus to supplement the school lunch menu.
18. Have children classify foods according to the basic food groups.
19. Have children collect evidences of progress in improving their food practices.
20. Have children plant vegetable seeds and watch them grow.
21. Review the health record of each child in the class.
22. Have children keep a record of their own height and weight.
23. Have children prepare exhibits of essential foods for health.
24. In cases where children are not getting an adequate diet, talk with the parents and child together about ways of improving food habits.
25. Have children wash hands before handling foods.
26. Discuss how much of the various foods are needed for growth and health.
27. Encourage each child to taste all foods served at lunch.

[1] This list is adapted from Fannie Lee Boyd, "An Appraisal Device for Teachers in the Elementary School to Determine Opportunities for Learning in Nutrition, Grades 1–6" (New York: *Nutrition Education Research Project*, Teachers College, Columbia University).

THE CONTROL OF DISEASE

In frontier America there were frequent absences from the classroom because of illness. One illness common in those days was diphtheria. When a child contracted diphtheria, all members of that family were quarantined. A sign was placed on the home; everyone stayed as far away as possible. Too often, all the children in a family succumbed to this dread disease. If children survived, they were shunned for weeks by neighbors who feared that they might also contract the disease if they came into contact with them. It was a long time before children from families that had had diphtheria returned to school.

Today many dread diseases have been controlled. Now almost all children are immunized against diphtheria, and the immunities that are built up last a lifetime. Because of programs of immunization, diphtheria has become a very rare disease. Antitoxins, antibiotics, and chemicals have been used to prevent or treat many other diseases.

Through proper sanitary practices and timely innoculations, many diseases can be prevented. Modern drugs can be used to cure quickly many diseases. But in most cases some action is required of the individual if the diseases are to be prevented or treated. By gaining a better understanding of the nature of diseases, disease transmission, and the scientific principles underlying the control and treatment of disease, children can learn to take action that will help them remain healthy.

Kinds of Disease

The diseases that inflict mankind can be classified as *noninfectious* and *infectious*. Noninfectious diseases are not transmitted from one person to another, while infectious diseases are spread from person to person.

Among the noninfectious diseases are nutritional-deficiency diseases, allergies, and inherited diseases. Kwashiorkor, rickets, and even obesity might be considered diseases due to nutritional deficiency. Allergies, such as those that cause hay fever, may lead to illnesses that are noninfectious. Inherited diseases such as hemophilia, the disease characterized by the inability of the blood to clot, are transmitted through the genes. There is no danger of contracting hemophilia through contact with someone who has the disease. Various mental diseases, such as schizophrenia and severe states of depression, are also noninfectious diseases.

The major role of the teacher in dealing with noninfectious diseases is to become sensitive to the symptoms of these diseases, to know how to secure competent assistance, and to help pupils to an understanding of the symptoms and how to secure help. In most cases the school health authorities are among the first to be turned to.

Infectious diseases are usually caused by very small organisms. *Bacteria* are one-celled plants. Disease-causing bacteria may be the round-shaped *streptococci*, the rod-shaped *bacilli*, or the spiral-shaped *spirochete*. Dysentery, typhoid, pneumonia, and boils are among the afflictions caused by bacteria. Diseases such as polio, influenza, smallpox, and probably some forms of cancer are caused by *viruses*. The viruses are smaller than bacteria, and some of them at times have more of the characteristics of crystals than of living organisms. Some *fungi* attack the skin and cause such conditions as ringworm and athlete's foot. *Protozoa* are one-celled animals, and such human diseases as amebic dysentery, sleeping sickness, and some kinds of malaria are caused by them. Such worms as the tapeworm, hookworm, and trichina also can invade the human body and cause harm.

The recognition that many human diseases are caused by small microorganisms is called the *germ theory* of disease. Louis Pasteur is generally credited as the originator of this theory. The germ theory superseded theories of disease causation that were almost mystical in nature, and it made possible a scientific approach to the study of disease. These studies have led to a clearer understanding of how these diseases can be controlled.

How infectious diseases are spread

Most infectious diseases are spread in some way from one human being to another. Sometimes skin diseases are spread through direct contact or through contact with towels and clothing. Some disease-causing germs are spread by sneezing, coughing, and spitting; these germs enter the nose or mouth of a healthy person as he breathes. The tetanus bacillus enters the body through open cuts in the skin. Some diseases, such as dysentery and cholera, are spread in this way and by food or water contaminated by persons who have the disease. Very often the microorganisms that cause diseases are carried onto food by insects such as the housefly. Malaria, of course, is transmitted by a mosquito from people that have the disease to those that do not. In their study in this area children should be helped to find out the ways that various diseases are spread from one human being to another.

Insects and other animals that help transmit disease-causing microorganisms are called *vectors*. One of the most common vectors is the ordinary housefly. The housefly usually lays its eggs in piles of garbage, manure, or wastes. The eggs change into white larva that can often be seen crawling around in piles of manure or wastes. The larva pupate, and from the pupal case emerges the adult fly. A complete metamorphosis has taken place. If the adult fly comes into contact with waste materials containing disease-causing microorganisms, these microorganisms may become attached to the hairy legs of the housefly and then deposited on foods with

Eggs   Larva   Pupa

Adult

Fig. 17-4 *Life stages of the fly.*

which it comes in contact. Diseases such as typhoid, tuberculosis, and dysentery can be transmitted in this way. In some cases flies may transfer disease-causing microorganisms directly to the eyes or skin. Other important insect vectors are mosquitoes, lice, and fleas. Animals such as rats, rabbits, cattle, and dogs can transmit such diseases as bubonic plague, tularemia, undulant fever, and rabies.

Diseases are also transmitted through food, water, and dirt. In a classic example, an unfortunate person who became known as "Typhoid Mary" was a carrier of typhoid. Many people contracted typhoid from the food that she handled. Some of the greatest epidemics in history have been caused by the contamination of drinking water. A large fraction of the population of Hamburg, Germany, succumbed to typhoid fever when the river water that they used became contaminated. Modern water treatment programs now make such epidemics highly unlikely.

How the body fights disease

The human body has a number of powerful defenses against disease. Many germs are prevented from entering the body by the *skin*. The outer layer of the skin, the epidermis, is made up of dead tissue that is a very effective protective layer. When the skin is cut in some way there is more chance for an infection. Within the body there are *mucous membranes* that provide an inner cover for the respiratory and digestive tracts. The membranes are covered with a thick liquid called mucous that is secreted by certain kinds of cells. The mucous traps germs and dirt particles that come into contact with it. Mucous containing such materials is discharged from the respiratory tract as phlegm.

Germs may enter the body in several ways. The tetanus bacilli may enter through a wound of some kind. The germs that cause boils may enter the skin alongside hair follicles. The germs that cause pneumonia, colds, and other respiratory diseases enter through the nose or mouth and manage to grow and multiply in the respiratory system. Other germs will grow and thrive in the digestive tract and cause a variety of gastrointestinal difficulties. While cleanliness, care in choice of food, and reduction of ex-

posure to others who have colds and other respiratory infections can reduce the incidence of disease, it is almost impossible to completely prevent
germs from entering the body.

The body has a variety of defenses against disease germs once they have
entered the body. In the skin there is connective tissue that serves to keep
the infection localized. *White corpuscles* in the blood tend to envelop germs.
In the process many of the white corpuscles are also killed and accumulate
as pus. If the disease germs enter the bloodstream and are not completely
controlled by the white corpuscles, *antibodies* are formed. Antibodies are
usually specific for a particular kind of germ. Some of the antibodies cause
the disease germs to clump together so that they can be more effectively
combated by the white corpuscles. Other antibodies, called *antitoxins*,
neutralize the poisonous substances called *toxins* that are produced by some
disease germs. One way to combat a disease is to introduce antibodies to a
specific disease from other individuals or from animals into the blood
stream. This immunity usually lasts for only a short time.

The body can develop *immunity* to certain kinds of diseases. An individual who has had chicken pox in childhood will be immune to it
throughout his lifetime. Because measles can be a very serious disease in
adulthood, especially for pregnant women, there are many who welcome
a mild case of measles in childhood. Acquired immunity is usually the
result of antibodies remaining in the blood after the body has had such a
disease. Sometimes dead or weakened germs can be injected into the body
through *vaccination* to stimulate the production of antibodies.

The prevention of disease

Individuals and communities can take a number of steps to reduce the
incidence of disease. However, to do this, it is essential that individuals
know what actions to take and how to carry out these actions. It also is
important to have some understanding of the scientific basis for these
steps. The following are some general kinds of actions that can be taken
by both children and adults to prevent disease and the scientific rationale
for them.

Some diseases can be prevented by destroying the vector that transmits
the disease. At one time there was a great deal of malaria in the United
States, transmitted by the anopheles mosquito. The eggs of the anopheles
mosquito hatch into larvae that live in water. The larvae are air breathers
and have to come to the surface to get the air they need. This is a vul-
nerable point in the life cycle of the mosquito. At this time it can be controlled. Marshes, ponds, and puddles have been drained to reduce the
number of breeding places for mosquitoes. In some reservoirs, the level of
the water is periodically raised and lowered to wash away the mosquito

Table 17–4: SOME CONTAGIOUS DISEASES

Disease	Cause	How transmitted	Symptoms	Prevention	Immunity
chicken pox	virus	contact, droplet	fever, rash, itching	none	permanent
German measles	virus	contact, droplet	fever, rash, slight respiratory difficulty, enlarged glands	none, gamma globulin used in pregnancy	permanent
measles	virus	contact, droplet	fever, cough, reddish spots, conjunctivitis	measles vaccine	permanent
mumps	virus	contact, droplet	fever, swelling of face and under jaws	none in children, serum for adults	permanent
poliomyelitis	virus	contact, droplet	fever, vomiting, diarrhea, sore throat, headache, stiff neck, muscle pain, paralysis	Salk and Sabin vaccines	permanent, but there are different types
scarlet fever	Streptococcus	contact, possibly milk and clothing	fever, scarlet rash on body, sore throat, headache, vomiting	penicillin or sulfa drugs if contact is suspected	permanent
whooping cough	Bacillus	contact and coughing	like a cold; coughing may become difficult to control	vaccine plus booster shots	permanent

eggs or to prevent the mosquito larvae from having access to water. Stagnant pools have been covered with thin films of oil to make it impossible for the mosquito larvae to get air. With these and other measures malaria has been practically eliminated from North America and many other regions of the world.

Systematic attempts can be made to prevent the spread of disease germs. In many diseases that are spread from one human being to another, as the chart on page 467 shows, droplet infection is the mode of transmission. In observing someone sneeze in a beam of sunlight, where the spray of drops is visible, the way disease germs are spread throughout a room by this means becomes clear. People with colds and other diseases should stay away from gatherings where they are likely to infect others. A handkerchief placed over the mouth and nose while sneezing will reduce the amount of droplet spray. In some cultures, people with colds wear cloth masks somewhat like those worn by doctors and nurses during operations to reduce the amount of droplet spray.

It is important to prevent the contamination of food and water. To cause harm, disease germs must, in some way, penetrate the body. Since both food and water are taken into the body, germs can enter with them. To prevent this, a food such as milk is pasteurized in order to kill bacteria and other microorganisms, and other foods are grown, handled, and inspected to reduce the possibility of disease transmission through foods. Modern water supply systems are designed to prevent the water from being contaminated with germs from human wastes. To destroy any germs that may enter the water, it is usually treated with chlorine, which effectively kills most of these microorganisms.

Certain practices are known to increase the likelihood of contracting certain diseases. Heavy cigarette smokers, for example, are nine to ten times as likely to contract lung cancer as non-smokers. An obvious step that the individual can take to reduce his chances of lung cancer is to never start smoking or to reduce or stop smoking if he has once started. Since the incidence of lung cancer increases with years of smoking, and the smoking habit is often formed early in life, it is especially important that children become aware of the dangers of smoking and carefully consider the consequences before beginning practices that may endanger their health.

The nature of the environment influences the health of individuals. It is known that severe air pollution is associated with increases in the incidence of respiratory diseases. Accumulations of garbage and filth are conditions under which the incidence of intestinal diseases increases. As is described in Chapter 18, these factors in ecosystems can be controlled to produce a healthier environment.

APPROACHES TO TEACHING

A number of very fine films and other audio-visual materials are available for use in teaching this area of science. The following are some of the kinds of observations, projects, and investigations in which children can become engaged and through which they can get a better understanding of how diseases are spread and can be controlled.

How do microorganisms multiply?

Bacteria and other microorganisms can be cultured and their growth studied. Biological supply houses offer prepared culture media in test tubes or Petri dishes that are ready for inoculation. If these cannot be obtained, a suitable medium can be prepared in the following way:

Dissolve a beef bouillon cube in eight ounces of boiling water. By following the directions on the box, prepare some unflavored gelatin. Substitute the beef broth for the boiling water called for in the recipe.

Sterilize five Petri dishes or other flat-bottomed dishes by placing them in boiling water for ten minutes. Pour a layer of beef enriched gelatin into the dishes.

Allow the culture medium to cool. Cover one of the dishes immediately. It will serve as a control. Then, cough into one; touch another with a finger; place a dead fly in the third Petri dish; and leave the fourth exposed to the atmosphere for about twenty minutes. Cover the Petri dishes and place them in a warm, dark place.

Periodically examine the dishes. What happens? Do colonies of bacteria form? If so, what are they like? How have they grown? Does it seem that different kinds of colonies have appeared in the different dishes?

After the study is completed, the dishes should be placed in boiling water or heated in a pressure cooker for thirty minutes or more and the water and dishes discarded.

469

How do chemicals and antibiotics affect microorganisms?

Prepare six Petri dishes with culture media as described in the previous experiment. Inoculate these dishes by transferring microorganisms from colonies that have already been grown or by coughing onto them or touching them. Place the dishes in a warm, dark place until substantial colonies of microorganisms are seen in the Petri dishes. Now number the Petri dishes with a wax pencil and treat them in the following manner:

No. 1 Leave covered as a control.
No. 2 Place a few drops of tincture of iodine in the center of a colony.
No. 3 Place a few drops of soapy water in the center of a colony.
No. 4 Place a few drops of rubbing alcohol in the center of a colony.
No. 5 Place a few drops of hydrogen peroxide in the center of a colony.
No. 6 Soak a small piece of filter paper in water containing a dissolved penicillin tablet. Place the piece of filter paper in the center of a colony.

Again place the Petri dishes in a warm, dark place. Observe what happens to the colonies in each of the Petri dishes. Suggest possible explanations for what is observed.

After the study is completed, the dishes should be placed in boiling water or heated in a pressure cooker for thirty minutes or more and the water and dishes discarded.

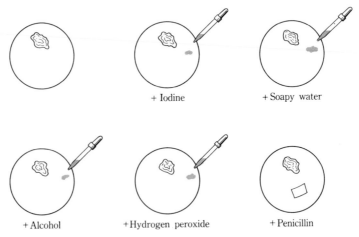

+ Iodine   + Soapy water

+ Alcohol   + Hydrogen peroxide   + Penicillin

Fig. 17-5   *Test the effect of chemicals and antibiotics on microorganisms.*

How can the housefly carry disease germs?

Examine the leg of a dead housefly through a magnifying glass. Describe the appearance of the leg. Does it seem possible that filth and other materials would be likely to adhere to the leg of the housefly?

Place a housefly leg on a glass slide and examine under low power of the microscope or with a binocular microscope.

How do mosquito larvae behave? How can they be controlled?

Collect water that contains mosquito larvae from a rain barrel or a stagnant pool. Observe and describe the behavior of the larvae. What is a possible explanation for this behavior?

Pour a little oil onto the surface of the water. What happens to the mosquito larvae? Does this observation suggest a way of controlling mosquitoes?

INVESTIGATION

Under what conditions do insects thrive?

Interconnecting terrariums can be made using two gallon pickle jars. Conditions in the two terrariums can be varied to try to find out conditions that seem to be preferred by houseflies and other insects.

The interconnecting terrariums can be made by laying two gallon pickle jars with their open ends toward each other as shown in the sketch. The junction between the two jars can be sealed with masking tape. Some soil and grass can be placed in each of the jars, and some houseflies or mos-

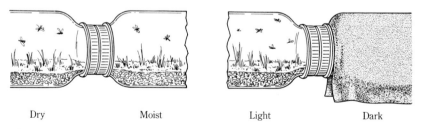

| Dry | Moist | Light | Dark |

Fig. 17-6 *Where do the insects tend to stay?*

quitoes can be put into the jars. Such experiments as the following can be carried out:

1. Cover one of the jars with black paper or cloth. Do the insects tend to stay in one of the jars? If so, which one?
2. Put moist soil and some water in one jar and keep the other jar dry. How does this affect the movement of the insects? Repeat this experiment when both jars are darkened.
3. Devise other experiments.

Selected References

JACOBSON, WILLARD J., BOYD, FANNIE LEE, AND HILL, MARY M., *Promising Practices in Nutrition Education in the Elementary School*. New York: Teachers College Press, 1959.

JACOBSON, WILLARD J., KLEINMAN, GLADYS S., HIACK, PAUL, SUGARBAKER, JOHN, AND CARR, ALBERT, *The Human Organism: Application of Science to Living*. New York: American Book Co., 1968.

JOHNSON, ROBERT A., *Microbes*. Ithaca, N.Y.: Cornell Science Leaflet, Vol. 58, No. 1, October 1964.

MICKELSEN, OLAF, *Nutrition Science and You*. New York: Scholastic Book Services, 1964.

ROTHENBURG, ROBERT E. (Ed.), *The New Illustrated Medical Encyclopedia for Home Use*, 4 vols. New York: Abradale Press, 1963.

TANNENBAUM, BEULAH, AND STILLMAN, MYRA, *Understanding Food*. New York: McGraw-Hill Book Co., Inc., 1962.

TAYLER, CLARA MAE, AND PYE, OREA F., *Foundations of Nutrition*. New York: The Macmillan Co., 1966.

UNITED STATES DEPARTMENT OF AGRICULTURE, *Food*. U.S. Department of Agriculture Yearbook 1959. Washington, D.C.: U.S. Government Printing Office, 1959.

READINGS FOR THE PRIMARY GRADES

JACOBSON, WILLARD J. AND COWE, EILEEN, "Food" in *Beginning Science*. New York: American Book Co., 1966.

JACOBSON, WILLARD J., LAUBY, CECILIA J., AND KONICEK, RICHARD D., *Food.* New York: American Book Co., 1968.

READINGS FOR THE INTERMEDIATE GRADES

DIETZ, DAVID, *All About Great Medical Discoveries.* New York: Random House, Inc., 1960.
EBERLE, IRMENGARDE. *Modern Medical Discoveries.* New York: Thomas Y. Crowell Co., 1960.
GEORGIOU, CONSTANTINE, *Whitey and Whiskers and Food.* Irvington-on-Hudson, N.Y.: Harvey House, Inc., Publishers, 1964.
HYDE, MARGARET O., *Medicine in Action.* New York: Whittlesey House, 1956.
JACOBSON, WILLARD J., LAUBY, CECILIA J., AND KONICEK, RICHARD D., *Food.* New York: American Book Co., 1968.

SELECTED FILM

Hungry Angels. Institute for Nutrition for Central America and Panama. Shows how three children in Central America are affected by different kinds of nutrition. Very powerful.

18 Man and His Environment

Man has made many changes in his environment. The plow that broke the plains and the ax that felled the trees transformed the land for good and ill. Today, flying across North America, millions of acres of cultivated lands and thousands of miles of hard surfaced highways can be seen. Many large cities are masked in a smokish haze. The air above may be crystal clear, but the inhabitants below are sheathed in an envelope of dust and smoke. Around the cities are beautiful reservoirs of fresh, clear water. But almost all the water that enters a city will be discharged as sewage, and it will carry with it many of the wastes of home and industry to pollute nearby rivers, lakes, and oceans. Yes, man is a changer; more than any other kind of organism he changes the environment in which he lives—for good and ill.

Man must change his environment in order to survive. It would be impossible to support present-day populations by picking berries, hunting wild game, and generally living off the food that grows naturally. In order to survive, soil must be tilled and the water and atmosphere harnessed. Often, there is a yearning for the wild and unspoiled environment. Sections of the environment should be kept wild and unspoiled, but it also should be recognized that much of the environment must be changed drastically in order to support the large human population that now inhabits planet earth. It is no longer a question of whether the environment should be changed. It is now a question of how it should be done.

It is important that changes in the environment lead to beneficial results. Before changes are made an attempt should be made to predict the possible consequences of the changes. To make these predictions, it is essential to understand the basic physical and biological principles that are germane. An important function of elementary school science is to help chil-

dren gain an operational understanding of some of these scientific principles and how they can be used to predict the consequences of changes that
are contemplated in the environment.

In considering changes in the environment, it is important to consider
them from an ecological point of view.[1] In this chapter consideration will
be given to the scientific principles involved in changes in land and water
environments, the atmosphere, and among wildlife.

CHANGES IN A LAND ENVIRONMENT

A great variety of organisms live in land environments. This is partially
due to the wide range of conditions that exist on land, from the cold, dry
Antarctic to the tropical forests, from the arid desert regions to the lush
rain forests. Since organisms that live in a land environment are of great
importance to man, an understanding of this environment and how organisms live in it is essential.

The Soil and Living Things

Most plants obtain the minerals that they need from the soil. These minerals become dissolved in the water to be found in the soil and are taken
into the plant through the roots. The kinds of plants that will grow in a
soil will depend on the kinds of nutrients that are available. In some soils,
such as saline soils, there may be too much of certain kinds of minerals for
many plants to grow. Saline soils are usually found in desert areas, and
there are only certain kinds of plants that can grow under the conditions
that exist in these areas.

The soil also provides support for plants. Think of the support that must
be provided for the giant redwood trees along the Pacific Coast. When the
winds blow, these trees may sway back and forth. But unless there are
tremendous winds of hurricane force, the trees will not fall. The roots
penetrate the soil and rocks, providing support for trees and other plants.

Many microorganisms live in the soil. The soil is the environment of
many of the bacteria and fungi that help to decompose organic matter
and change it into a form that can be used by plants. These microorganisms help to build up the very valuable topsoil that is so needed by plants.
Other microorganisms, the nitrogen fixing bacteria, are able to take nitrogen from the air and make the nitrates that can be used by plants.

Worms, insects, rodents, and larger animals live in the soil in great numbers. As many as a million earthworms have been found under an acre of

---

[1] For further discussion of ecology and the nature of ecosystems see Chapter 10.

land surface. These animals help to digest organic matter in the soil, thus making it easier for the microorganisms to change it into a form that can be used by plants. The small holes and burrows that these animals dig make it possible for more air to enter the soil. Although important for the decomposition of organic matter, the large holes that such animals as gophers, badgers, and woodchucks make harm the farmer's crops and threaten carefully tended lawns.

How Soils Are Formed

Most soils are formed from the underlying rocks. A number of processes lead to the breaking up of rocks and the formation of soil.

Large rocks may be broken into smaller rocks by temperature changes. For example, a glass will break when very hot water is poured into it. Similarly, a hot glass may break when it is put into cold water. Materials such as those in glass and in rocks expand when heated and contract when cooled. However, if all parts of a rock or glass are not heated or cooled to the same extent, strong stresses are set up inside the glass or rock. These stresses may cause the glass or rocks to break. Large rocks are broken up into smaller rocks in this way.

The freezing of water can help break up rocks. Water expands when it freezes. Water pipes are sometimes split if the water inside them freezes. Water will seep down into cracks in rocks. When the water freezes, it expands, and the great pressure may split rocks apart.

One of the most important ways that soil is formed from rocks is through chemical action. If a drop of hydrochloric acid is placed on a piece of limestone or marble, a little bubbling and fizzing will be observed. A little of the rock will be broken down by this chemical action. Although hydrochloric acid is a strong acid, there also are weak acids that can, over a long period of time, help form soil from rock. The lichens that grow on bare rock help form a weak acid that aids in breaking up the rock. This process of soil formation is especially important in warm climates where chemical action takes place relatively fast.

Plants can also help to break down rocks. Trees often grow out of cracks in rocks. The pressure of the growing roots of plants sometimes will split rocks apart.

Sometimes the soil has been transported from somewhere else. In many places in northern North America, the soil has been transported there by the huge glaciers that once covered the area. On the other hand, much of the soil in such river valleys as the Mississippi River Valley has been carried there by water. In many parts of the world, including some regions in the Middle West, the soil has been deposited by the winds. Glaciers, water, and winds are the three important ways that soils are transported into a region.

The Layers of Soil

A cross section of a fresh road cut, a stream bank, or the sides of a hole, illustrates a *soil profile*. From an examination of the soil profile, a great deal can be learned about the soil and its history.

A soil is often divided into layers called *horizons*. There are usually three main horizons in a soil profile. The upper horizon is called the *A horizon;* the middle horizon is the *B horizon;* and the parent material formed from

A - horizon

B - horizon

C - horizon

Fig. 18-1   A soil profile.

the underlying rocks is called the *C horizon.* Many soils do not have all three horizons. Often, there are thinner layers within each of the horizons. To complicate the study of soil profiles, the dividing lines between the horizons are often not clear or definite.

In its development a soil goes through stages somewhat like the succession of plants. The bedrock is the parent material for soil. By the various processes that have been described, some of the bedrock is broken up into the small particles that make up soil. This process has been going on for a long time, and most of the earth is now covered with a mantle of soil that has been formed from the bedrock. In most soil profiles, the material formed from bedrock makes up the C horizon.

Various plants begin to grow in the new soil. In fact, plants such as the lichens can begin to grow in the parent rock and contribute to the soil-forming process. When the plants die, they fall to the ground and are decomposed by microorganisms in the soil. The microorganisms also die and become part of the upper layer of soil. The dark material in the upper layer of soil is called *humus.* It may be that humus is composed largely of the dead bodies of microorganisms. A soil that contains a great deal of humus is usually a very fertile soil.

Over a long period of time, organic matter and other materials may be moved down from the A horizon to form a B horizon. Since this usually takes a long time, a definite B horizon usually indicates an old soil.

How are soil materials moved up and down in the soil? Water is one of the most important agents for transporting soil materials. Rain water passing down through the soil will carry soil materials with it and in especially dry regions, water in the soil can also move upward carrying soil minerals with it. Earthworms, insects, and burrowing animals also help carry soil particles up and down. The roots of large trees that are blown over by the wind may carry with them to the surface soil particles from all of the horizons of the soil profile.

The rate at which soil development takes place depends upon the climate, the amount and kind of plant and animal life in a region, and the nature of the parent rock. To make a chemical reaction go faster, heat is often supplied. Similarly, the chemical reaction on rocks to form soil takes place faster in warm climates. In places where there are many living organisms, the horizons in the soil will be formed faster. Some very hard and resistant rocks, such as quartz, change to soil only very, very slowly.

How long does it take for soil to be formed? In most cases it takes a very long time for the bedrock to be broken down to the parent soil material. However, in the millions and billions of years since many of the earth's surface rocks were formed, there has been time for soil to be formed. The upper horizons of the soil are formed much faster. Thirty years after a glacier melted away, an A horizon was formed in soil in Alaska. Both A and B horizons have been formed in soils formed on top of 2,000-year-old Roman ruins in Europe.

The soil profile is somewhat like a history book. By examining it a great deal can be learned about what has happened to form the soil under man's feet.

Characteristics of Soil

Take a handful of soil. Look at it. Feel it. Crumble it. What are its physical characteristics?

Color is one of the best indicators of the nature of the soil. Decayed organic material usually has a dark color. The A horizon, usually darker than the lower layers, is often a rich soil. The deep agricultural soils of the Middle West usually have thick layers of dark soil. The rich "black belt" in Alabama has long been a center for the growing of cotton.

Red usually indicates iron in the soil. The red soil of the Mesabi Range in Minnesota has been one of the richest sources of iron in the world. Water usually sinks quickly through red soils, and, therefore, they are well drained.

Blue and gray soils contain a great deal of clay. Clay particles are very small, and there is very little space through which water can move. These soils, therefore, usually have poor drainage. After a rain, puddles of water may remain for days without sinking into the ground. When clay soils dry, they form a very hard surface almost like brick.

Light-colored soils may contain a great deal of sand. Since sand particles are large, water can sink through sandy soils quickly. These soils have good drainage but dry quickly if there is little rain. In desert regions the light color of soils may be due to the presence of salt.

Soil texture refers to the different sizes of particles that make up the soil. Aside from pebbles and gravel, the largest particles in soil are sand. Sand in soil makes it possible for air and water to enter easily. Silt particles are smaller than sand but larger than clay. Clay particles are very small. Soils that contain large amounts of clay are able to hold a great deal of water.

Another physical characteristic of soil is *structure*. Soil structure refers to the way that particles of soil stick together. The best soils have a crumbly structure. The clumps of soil should be about the size of an acorn and soft enough to be easily crumbled in one's hand.

Compare handfuls of soil from a garden, roadbed, and from the bottom of a pond or puddle. How do they compare as to color? Texture? Structure?

Water in Soil

Water is an important raw material that plants use for the production of food. Green plants combine water with carbon dioxide from the air to make food. Most of the water that plants use, essential for plant growth, comes from the soil. Most land plants also get the minerals that they need from water in the soil. These minerals, dissolved in water in the soil, are taken into the plants as the water enters the roots.

Almost all the water in the soil comes from rain. When rain falls, some of the water flows off as surface runoff into rivers and streams. However, some of it sinks into the soil to become *groundwater*. The amount of rainwater that enters the ground is increased if the ground is covered with grass, leaves, and other rain-absorbing substances.

When water enters the soil it will usually move downward through the soil. This downward movement of water in soil is called *percolation*. Percolation takes place fastest in soils, such as sandy soils, that have fairly large spaces between the soil particles.

Groundwater will also flow downhill. However, this downhill flow of groundwater is often very slow. In some cases, it may be at a rate of only a few feet a year.

If a hole is dug deep enough into the ground, water will appear in the hole. This is groundwater that has seeped in from the sides. The level to which water will rise in a hole or open well is called the *water table*. The underground water table usually follows very closely the contours of the ground. Lakes, ponds, and some springs indicate places where the water table is above the surface of the ground. The water table will rise after a great deal of rain and sink during dry periods. When a well goes dry, it usually means that the water table has sunk below the lowest level of the well.

In addition to percolating down through the soil after a rain, water will move upward through the soil by *capillary action*. If a piece of narrow glass tubing is placed in water, the level of the water inside the tube will rise higher than that on the outside. The force of attraction between water and glass leads to capillary action, and water is pulled up in the tube. In the same way capillary action leads to water rising in the spaces between soil particles.

Even though it may not have rained for a long time, the soil will be moist just a few inches below the surface. Through capillary action the water has moved up from the water table. This is the groundwater that plants use.

Many soil minerals will dissolve in water. As groundwater percolates downward, the minerals are carried farther down into the soil, very often resulting, in areas where there is heavy rainfall, in poor soils. The minerals that may have been in the soil have been leached out by the water that has percolated downward. On the other hand, in areas where there is little rainfall, groundwater may carry minerals upward through capillary action. When some of this water evaporates, the minerals will be left at the surface of the soil. The white deposits to be found in many deserts are made up of such minerals. Unfortunately, many of these minerals, such as salt and gypsum, are harmful to many crops.

Acids and Alkalis in the Soil

In chemistry two chemical compounds that are often used are *acids* and *bases*. Sulfuric acid and hydrochloric acid are two acids often found in laboratories. Sodium hydroxide (lye) and ammonium hydroxide (ammonia water) are common bases. Acids and bases are also found in the soil.

Soils may be alkaline, acid, or neutral. *Alkaline soils* have more compounds that can form bases than acids. Soils that contain large amounts of such compounds as salt (NaCl) and gypsum ($CaSO_4 \cdot 2H_2O$) are usually alkaline soils. Soils that contain more acid than basic substances are *acid soils.* Organic materials in the soil, such as humus, will form acids when water flows through them. *Neutral soils* have a balance between alkaline and acid materials.

The relative acidity or alkalinity of the soil is expressed in terms of *pH*. The following table shows the pH values of various kinds of soils:

Table 18–1: pH VALUES OF SOILS

pH	Type of soil
below 4.5	Extremely acid
4.5–5.0	Very strongly acid
5.1–5.5	Strongly acid
5.6–6	Medium acid
6.1–6.5	Slightly acid
6.6–7.3	Practically neutral
7.4–7.8	Mildly alkaline
7.9–8.4	Medium alkaline
8.5–9.0	Strongly alkaline
9.1 and above	Very strongly alkaline

In practice pH indicators used to determine the relative acidity or alkalinity of the soil are either in the form of indicator paper or liquids. Small samples of the upper five to eight inches of soil are taken. The indicators are applied to a very small sample of the soil following the directions given. Usually the indicator changes color. The acidity or alkalinity of the soil can be determined by comparing the color with that of a color chart that is provided.

Most plants grow best in soils that are neutral or only slightly acid or mildly alkaline. Table 18–2 shows the best pH ranges for a few common plants.

Table 18–2: pH VALUES FOR PLANTS

peas	6.0–7.0
carrots	5.5–7.0
strawberries	5.0–6.5
geranium	6.0–7.5
clover	6.0–7.0
grasses	5.5–7.0
tomatoes	5.0–6.0

Since alkaline materials are more soluble in water than acidic materials, where there is heavy rainfall alkaline materials will have dissolved out of the upper layers of the soil, leaving acidic materials. This is what has happened in most of eastern North America. In many parts of the western United States, the soluble alkaline materials have been carried upward by capillary action. Here the soils tend to be alkaline.

An early Virginia farmer, Edmund Ruffin, found that he could get better crops by adding lime to the soil. It is now known that lime is an alkaline material. The lime that is used is powdered limestone. When it is added, the soil becomes less acid. Crops such as clover and many vegetables will grow better in this less acid soil.

Soils can be made less alkaline by *leaching* the alkaline materials from the soil. This can be done by pouring a great deal of water onto the soil. As the water percolates through the soil it carries much of the alkaline material with it. This alkaline groundwater can then be carried away in drainage ditches or through tile drains. In this way, very alkaline soils can be prepared to grow a variety of crops.

Soil Erosion

Wind, running water, and in some places the ice of glaciers wear down the hills and mountains on the earth's surface. This wearing down process is called *gradation*. Over very long periods of time even high mountains can be worn down to become plains. This process of gradation affects the soil and the plants that live in it.

Both wind and water may be considered fluids. If they come into contact with unprotected soil, they can move it from one place to another. The faster that wind blows or water runs off the more soil will be carried away.

An old farmer said, "My fields seem to grow stones." Actually, stones were not growing in his field. Instead, soil was being eroded away, uncovering the stones underneath. This is an example of *sheet erosion*. In sheet erosion thin "sheets" of soil are removed from the top surface of fields. In *gully erosion* the running water opens up deep ditches and great gullies in the land. If the gullies grow large enough, trees and buildings may actually fall into them as a result of a hard rain.

In the dust bowl in some of the Plains States, so much soil is sometimes blown into the air that the sky is darkened, and lights have to be turned on. Strong winds pick up exposed soil and carry it away. Precious topsoil may be removed from some farms. Great drifts of sand and soil may be deposited in other places. Sometimes these deposits of dust may be almost high enough to cover buildings. Crops can be ruined if they become covered with such piles of wind-blown dust.

Farmers, foresters, and park managers try to control soil erosion. One general way is to reduce the amount of direct contact between wind and running water and the soil. Sometimes a cloth or straw is spread across fresh road cuts to prevent erosion until grass can begin to grow. Many farmers try to keep their soils from being directly exposed to rain and wind any more than necessary by growing "cover crops" of grass to prevent the running water and wind from coming into contact with soil. A second general way to control erosion is to reduce the speed of the running water and wind. Contour farming, strip-cropping, and check dams are procedures that are used to reduce the speed of running water. Trees are planted to form windbreaks to slow down the winds. When the flow of wind and water is slowed, they will not pick up as much soil, and they will release some of that which is being carried.

Both wind and water tend to lay down their deposits in layers. Sedimentary rocks, and the soils that have been formed from such materials, often have these layers. Soils that are formed from deposits by wind and running water are often very fertile. The Nile River Delta has very fertile soils that have been carried there from various parts of eastern Africa by the Nile River. Many of the rich farm lands of North Central United States have soils that were carried there long ago by winds.

Ice is another important agent that moves soil. Most of northern North America has been covered four or five times by great glaciers. These glaciers scratched and gouged out grooves in hard rocks. They also picked up soil and rocks and transported them from one place to another. High in the mountains glaciers still move rocks and soil. Greenland and the continent of Antarctica are almost completely covered with glaciers.

Unlike wind and water, glaciers do not deposit soil in layers. Instead, soil, rocks, and even huge boulders may be all mixed up together. In the northern parts of North America it is common to see soil, rocks and boulders all mixed together in a soil profile, indicating that these soils have been deposited by glaciers.

CHANGES IN A WATER ENVIRONMENT

Rivers and streams, lakes and oceans are also an important part of man's environment. The wastes from home and industry are poured into nearby rivers, and the shad and trout disappear. Pollution of the Great Lakes has destroyed large numbers of certain kinds of fish, endangered the water supplies of large cities, and disrupted the ecological balance in the lakes. The accidental breaking up of a large oil tanker can threaten aquatic life in the oceans and foul hundreds of miles of beaches. To understand the possible consequences of changes in the water environment it is important to understand some of the physical and biological principles that operate in aquatic ecosystems.

Changes That Take Place in a Lake

A number of changes take place in a lake during the course of a year. Lakes, and the kinds of plants and animals that live in them, also change as the lakes "grow older." Although there are many variations in these changes, those that will be described are typical of many of the lakes in northern North America.

In the summer, lakes often have three layers of water at different temperatures. The surface layer, which is usually quite warm, contains oxygen, carbon dioxide, and nutrients that make rich plant growth possible. In the second layer the temperature drops with depth. This change in temperature can often be felt when diving into a lake for a swim. Usually,

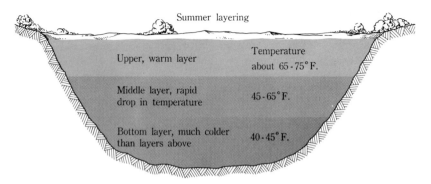

Summer layering

Upper, warm layer — Temperature about 65-75° F.

Middle layer, rapid drop in temperature — 45-65° F.

Bottom layer, much colder than layers above — 40-45° F.

Fig. 18-2   In the summer lakes often have three layers that are at different temperatures.

there is also a great deal of oxygen and nutrient material for use by living organisms in this layer. The lowest layer has cold water which is at about the same temperature throughout. Because it is deep, there is little or no light. Organic matter sinks down from above and decays. Since most of the available oxygen is used up by the decay process, there is little available for fish. During the summer there is very little mixing between these layers.

In the fall when the surface layer begins to cool, the water contracts and becomes more dense, causing it to sink. Also in the fall there usually are strong winds that churn up the water. In this mixing of the waters in the lake, water with dissolved oxygen reaches the bottom, and minerals and other nutrients move from the bottom to the top.

When the water is cooled to 4° C., it begins to expand and rises to the top where it may freeze to form a covering of ice. During the winter, the coldest water, which is below 4° C., is just below the ice; the warmer water is near the bottom. The ice covering prevents churning of the water by the winds. All of this leads to very little mixing of the waters in the lake during the winter.

In the spring, as the ice melts and strong winds blow, the lake is again churned up. Air and nutrients dissolve in water and usually spread throughout the lake. As the surface of the water is heated again by the spring and summer sun, the water again becomes arranged in layers.

Although living organisms may be found throughout a lake, plants such as algae and duckweed are found near the surface. This is where there is light needed for photosynthesis. As a product of photosynthesis, these plants give off oxygen that is needed by both plants and animals. The cooler layer of water beneath the surface may contain a great deal of dissolved oxygen. Often, it also contains a large number of the insects that are food for fish. These regions, just beyond the places where cattails and bulrushes grow, are favored spots for fishermen.

Succession in Lakes and Ponds

Other changes also take place in lakes and ponds. The streams and rivers that empty into lakes carry with them soil and silt, and the plants that grow along the shores of lakes and ponds also build up soil around the water. These processes tend to fill lakes, many of which have been completely filled and are now dry land.

As was the case with the barren rock, as the open water gradually becomes dry land, a succession of plants will grow in the changing environment. Algae, duckweed, and other plants that have no attachments to the bottom of the lake grow in open water. Sometimes the growth of plants can be so thick that it is difficult to push a boat through the water. As the remains of these plants sink, the bottom of the lake is built up.

When the lake or pond becomes shallow enough, plants that have roots begin to grow. Water lilies, lotus, and pondweeds have broad leaves that float on the top of the water, cutting off much of the light from underwater plants. Many frogs, turtles, snakes, and small fishes are found during this stage of succession.

As the soil is built up, cattails and various rushes are able to grow in the shallower parts of the lake. These plants have their roots under water, but their leaves, flowers, and most of their stems are out of the water. Since these tall plants tend to shade the floating plants, the floating plants will remain in the deeper parts of the lake but stop growing in the areas where the cattails and rushes grow.

During some parts of the year, the area at the edge of the lake may be above the water of the lake. This is not the environment in which cattails and rushes grow. Sedges and other short grass-like plants with solid stems begin to grow in these areas.

When a section of a lake has been filled in, grasses and shrubs begin to grow. These are followed by other stages of dry-land successions until the climax community is achieved. Sometimes it is possible to see the various stages of succession, from the plants of the open water to the climax community, in one area along the boundaries of a lake.

Changes That Take Place in Running Water

In streams and rivers the currents are of special importance to life. Where there is a swift current, a large amount of sediment may be carried along. There is also a churning action which usually causes a great deal of air to become dissolved in the water.

Another important difference between streams and lakes is that contact between water and land is more important in a stream. If there are swift currents, there will be few green plants to manufacture food. Instead, the animals that live in streams depend to a large extent upon food that is washed into streams from nearby land.

Streams also tend to be shallower than lakes, so that all of the water will be heated by the sun. Also, water in the stream will cool faster. This leads to much greater fluctuations of temperatures in streams than in lakes. Because of the stream currents, layers of water at different temperatures are not usually present.

The churning action of stream flow causes a great deal of air to become dissolved in the water, thus creating an environment in which animals that require more oxygen can live. However, when streams become polluted with organic materials, decay organisms use up some of the oxygen as they attack the organic material, and thus reduce the amount of oxygen left for certain fish and other animals.

Plants and animals that live in swiftly moving streams have interesting adaptations that help keep them from being swept away by the swiftly flowing water. Long green algae and mosses are sometimes attached to rocks and boulders in the stream. Some insects have hooks or suckers that make it possible for them to cling even to very smooth surfaces. Most of the animals that swim in streams are streamlined. Many of them continue to swim against the stream currents all their lives.

The Pollution of Streams and Rivers

Cities and industries pour out tremendous quantities of waste. Cities usually have to dispose of about as many gallons of sewage as the amount of water that they use. Since water is used in some cities at a rate of more than 1,000 gallons per person, there is a great deal of sewage to be dumped. In addition to the liquid sewage, there is also a great deal of garbage.

Since rivers flow away from our cities and empty into lakes or oceans, they have been used to carry away the sewage and sometimes the garbage. However, other people living downstream are affected by the sewage poured in upstream. When there are great quantities of sewage, the lakes and the ocean waters along the shore may also become polluted.

When waters become polluted, perhaps the greater harm is done to the living things in the water. There were once great runs of shad up the Hudson and other rivers along the East Coast. Great beds of oysters were found in Chesapeake Bay. Great quantities of shellfish were obtained from the Mississippi River. All of these sources of food from the water have suffered from pollution. In addition, many a pleasant brook now reeks with wastes from farms, cities, and industries.

Streams and lakes are polluted with various chemicals, soil and silt, and waste organic matter. Certain chemicals, such as acids and various chemical salts, may kill most living things in a stream or lake. In addition to filling in lakes and reservoirs, soil and silt in the water keep light from penetrating the water, thus hindering or preventing the growth of plants beneath the surface. Beds of vegetation in lakes which have served as places for fish to spawn have sometimes been covered and destroyed by silt and soil. The waste organic matter that comes largely from the sewage poured into streams has a very important effect on life in the water.

When organic matter enters a stream or lake, it is attacked by decay organisms. In the process of decay much of the oxygen that is dissolved in the water may be removed, lowering the oxygen content of the water. Many game fish and other organisms that live in the water are sensitive to the lowered oxygen levels. When the amount of oxygen in a stream is reduced, such fish as trout and bass may no longer be able to live there. "Rough" fish such as carp and catfish that can live in waters that contain relatively little dissolved oxygen move into this water. Many streams and rivers are now populated with such fish.

Sewage and fertilizer washed off farmer's fields can serve as fertilizer for algae and other plants that grow in the water, sometimes leading to excessive growth of these plants. A lake in Wisconsin has become so filled with algae that swimming and boating is difficult. The shores of a lake in New York have rotting algae and other water plants piled upon it. The odors are quite unpleasant.

Water is also used for cooling in electric generator plants, in steelmaking, and in other industries. Although no materials are added to the water to pollute it, the temperature may be raised several degrees. Since some fish and other animals that live in the water are very sensitive to temperature, the heating of the water will affect the population of a river or lake.

Purifying Water

Homes and communities obtain water from reservoirs, rivers, and wells. The water, brought into homes and factories through pipes, is used and then flows out again through a sewage system. The sewage is dumped into rivers, lakes, and oceans.

Sewage is mostly water. However, when water is used, chemicals and organic materials are added to it. As much of this as possible should be removed from the sewage before it is dumped into streams, lakes, or the ocean.

Certain basic scientific principles are used in the procedures by which sewage is treated. Similar principles and procedures are used in water purification plants to treat water before it is brought into homes and cities.

One method of sewage treatment is called screening. As sewage is passed through various kinds of screens many solids can be removed.

Since some solids suspended in liquids will settle out when the liquid is allowed to stand, another method of sewage treatment allows sewage to be held in sedimentation tanks where soil and other fine particles will settle to the bottom.

Organic material can also be changed in form. By oxidation, carried out by bacteria and other biological organisms, a process similar to the decay process that goes on in soil is achieved. The sewage may be trickled through stones that are covered with the organisms that form a slime on the stones. These organisms oxidize much of the organic matter in the sewage. Or, the sewage may be put into large tanks along with a sludge that contains many organisms. As air is bubbled through the sewage, the organisms oxidize the organic material, and the sludge that is formed settles out of the sewage as sediment.

Heat and chemicals are also used to kill harmful organisms. The oxidized solids can be heated and stored for a period of time to kill harmful organisms. The solids can then be used safely as fertilizer. A little chlorine can be added to the remaining liquids to remove microorganisms. This liquid that has passed through a sewage treatment plant is now almost entirely water and can be released into a stream or lake.

Cities that take water out of a nearby river use water that has been used before by cities upstream. However, if the upstream cities have passed their sewage through a sewage treatment plant and the downstream city passes water through a water purification plant, the water will be perfectly safe to use. In cases of serious water shortage, small cities have pumped the water coming out of their sewage treatment plant into their water purification plant. After the water has been purified it has been used again. In places where there is a serious shortage of water, the water can be recycled for reuse.

CHANGES IN THE ATMOSPHERE

As the fog rolls in from the Pacific and blankets the valleys of northern California, the atmosphere drips with moisture in this land of the giant redwood. From the dripping atmosphere comes abundant rain, while the thick fog limits the amount of evaporation. The redwoods are found only along the coast where this atmosphere exists. Man and other organisms also depend on the atmosphere.

The atmosphere is so much a part of the ecosystems that it is usually taken for granted. Yet, it is sometimes well to be reminded of its importance. Each day each person will breathe in about as much air as there is in a box 10 feet high, 10 feet long, and 5 feet wide (500 cubic feet). Of course, this amount of air is also breathed out. An automobile may use up as much air as in a box 10 feet long, 10 feet wide, and 10 feet high in order to travel only 15 or 20 miles. This air is greatly changed by the burning of fuel which runs the auto.

The Pollution of the Atmosphere

The atmosphere is both a source of raw material and a place for the disposal of wastes. Living organisms get the oxygen that they need from the atmosphere. The carbon dioxide used by plants to manufacture food also comes from the atmosphere. Every time a person exhales, body wastes are added *to* the atmosphere. The wastes from furnaces, incinerators, industries, and automobiles are also discharged into the atmosphere.

Almost all mechanisms that use fuels discharge wastes into the atmosphere. Living things discharge air that contains a great deal of carbon dioxide. The gases that enter the atmosphere from smokestacks and the exhaust pipes of automobiles also contain carbon dioxide. But they also may contain more harmful substances. It is these more harmful substances that are of greatest concern in air pollution control.

There are two different kinds of materials that pollute the atmosphere: particles and gases. The soot of a thick, black smoke coming out of a chimney contains small particles. If an evaporating dish is held over a candle flame, particles of black soot will collect on the surface. Most of these particles will settle out of the atmosphere. They can often be seen and felt on window ledges. Very small particles, sometimes called aerosols, may stay in the atmosphere almost indefinitely.

Among the gases that are spewed into the atmosphere are carbon monoxide, sulfur dioxide, and hydrogen sulfide. Carbon monoxide is a very poisonous gas given off in automobile exhaust. Fortunately, it tends to rise and mix with the atmosphere. However, if an automobile engine is run indoors in a closed garage enough carbon monoxide may accumulate to be fatal to a human organism. Sulfur dioxide, often formed when coal is burned, has a very sharp smell. When sulfur dioxide combines with water, an acid is formed. It can irritate the eyes and corrode metal and other surfaces. In some industrial processes hydrogen sulfide is given off. It has the smell of rotten eggs and is quite unpleasant.

In most cases exhaust gases are warmer than the surrounding air and therefore rise. However, there are *temperature inversions*. Usually, the atmosphere at an altitude of a thousand feet is cooler than it is near the earth's surface. The warm exhaust gases will rise through this cooler air. When there is a temperature inversion, however, the temperature above a certain height in the atmosphere is higher than that below. Then the warm exhaust gases will be trapped below the upper layer of warm air. If a city has a temperature inversion for several days, a great deal of exhaust gas may be trapped. The air may become smelly, the eyes irritated, and the general conditions will be quite unpleasant.

Air pollution is usually a big problem in regions where there is a great deal of fog. In the combination of smoke and fog, commonly called smog, it is believed that particles and gases that are found are changed by the action of sunlight. As the sun shines down on the smog, new chemical compounds are formed. Some of these compounds irritate the eyes and harm plants.

Some Effects of Air Pollution

At one level, air pollution is unpleasant. No one likes to breathe bad-smelling air. The housewife dislikes having to continually clean away soot. A white shirt and clean suit will soon become dirty in sooty, smoky air. Smarting, runny eyes are not enjoyed by anyone.

Air pollution can affect the health and well-being of people. If more people suffer from colds, bronchitis, and pneumonia during a temperature inversion, the obvious cause is air pollution. But how much ill health is due to air pollution at other times is difficult to say. It cannot be ascertained that the people who get these illnesses would not have become ill even if the atmosphere were perfectly clean. However, it is suspected that unclean air may have something to do with these illnesses.

There have been some very serious cases of air pollution in which many people have died. In 1948 in Donora, Pennsylvania, a thick smog was trapped within a valley. More than 1,000 people became ill and 20 died. During a very serious smog in London, 4,000 more deaths were recorded than were normal for that period. Large cities, such as Los Angeles and New York, also have had serious smog conditions in which more deaths have been recorded than usual.

Air pollution also affects plants. In one famous case, sulfur dioxide from a copper smelting plant killed all the plants for miles around. More often, air pollution causes injuries to the leaves of plants. In cities where air pollution is especially bad, some kinds of trees will not grow, and there is little doubt that garden plants and fruit trees are also harmed by air pollution.

The large amounts of carbon dioxide being released into the atmosphere may be affecting climate. In trapping solar energy, the atmosphere works something like a greenhouse. The solar radiation passes through the atmosphere and strikes the surface of the earth. Some of it is re-radiated as longer wavelength radiation and absorbed by gases in the atmosphere. One of the gases in the atmosphere that absorbs a great deal of radiation is carbon dioxide. If the amount of carbon dioxide in the atmosphere is increased, then more of the re-radiated solar energy will be trapped in the atmosphere. This might lead to warmer climates. If the climates were to be warmed over a long period of time, it might lead to a melting of much of the ice now in glaciers. This in turn would lead to a rise in the level of the oceans.

Controlling Air Pollution

Many waste materials need not pollute the atmosphere. Some of the larger particles can be removed by simply placing screens over smokestacks. Many of the smaller particles can be removed with electrostatic precipitators. One of the basic principles of electricity is that objects having like charges repel each other, and those having unlike charges are attracted. Many of the very small particles that make up smoke are electrically charged. When smoke is forced between two surfaces having opposite electrical charges, the electrically charged smoke particles will be attracted to the surface that has the opposite electrical charge. Electrical precipitators are used in many industries to reduce the amount of smoke particles poured into the atmosphere.

The amount of air pollution can be reduced by improving the combustion of fuels. Automobiles, trucks, and buses, for example, are sources of a great deal of air pollution. Through proper adjustments, the amount of smoke given off can be greatly reduced. Air can also be mixed with the exhaust to oxidize additional materials before they escape into the atmosphere. In a somewhat similar way, air pollution can be reduced by improving combustion in furnaces, incinerators, and thermoelectric generating plants.

A very important approach to air pollution control is to shift to sources of energy that do not give off smoke. Large cities such as London and Pittsburgh have greatly reduced pollution by forbidding the use of fuels that give off great quantities of smoke. Nuclear energy is a very clean source of energy. If electric powered automobiles come into general use, there will be much less pollution of the atmosphere.

CHANGES THAT AFFECT WILDLIFE

Floating quietly in a rowboat well out from the shore of a lake, something that looks like an old broken stem of a small tree might be noticed near the shore. But, look more carefully! It is the majestic blue heron marvelously camouflaged in its natural setting. If the heron becomes suspicious, it will fly off with gigantic sweeps of its huge wings.

Sit quietly in the woods near the edge of a forest clearing as dusk begins to settle. A white-tailed deer may come to browse on the meadow grass. Don't move! At the slightest disturbance, the magnificent animal will bound off into the protecting woods.

Watch a Baltimore Oriole build its nest. Observe the cliff swallows as they dart into their small holes in cliffs or stream banks. Search the night for an owl sitting on an old abandoned shed. Scan the sky for a hawk soaring as it rides on rising air currents—these are some of the ways that wildlife can be enjoyed.

Changes that take place in man's environment also affect the wildlife in his environment. It is important to understand what these creatures need so that they can continue to live in man's environment.

Needs of Wildlife

In the broadest sense, wildlife includes all living organisms except man and the plants and animals that have been domesticated by man. Usually, however, the term wildlife is restricted to the animals that are observed, studied, and hunted in the "wild" environment. This definition of wildlife includes birds, mammals, reptiles, amphibians, and possibly some smaller animals.

Wildlife has basically the same requirements for life as other living organisms. However, these animals usually must obtain these requirements from the natural habitats in which they live. Since man changes these habitats, wildlife is affected. Some animals, such as the passenger pigeons that once darkened the sky in their flights, have been completely destroyed by the actions of man. Other wildlife, such as pheasants that feed on the farmer's grains, are helped by man.

Food

Like all other living organisms, animals in the wild need food for energy, growth, and repair. Lack of food may be the most important limiting factor for most wildlife. It has been suggested that the populations of various living organisms tend to grow to the point where there is not enough food. The lack of food tends to limit the population. It may very well be that lack of food will finally limit the growth of human population. It has certainly limited the growth of wildlife populations, for the destruction of the food supply has led to starvation and death for some forms of wildlife.

At one time the prairies of central North America may have supported as many as sixty million bison, some herds stretching as far as the eye could see. These bison grazed on the grass that grows on these prairies. Now there are only a few thousand bison living in protected areas. Although many were killed by hunters, the bison population was also affected by the plowing of the grasslands. Today wheat fields are found where the bison once grazed. The lack of grazing land became a limiting factor for the bison.

The population of many kinds of animals seem to change periodically. The Hudson's Bay Company has kept a record of skins of the snowshoe hare that it has purchased. Every ten years there is a sharp increase in the number of skins. This is followed by a sharp decline. The sharp decline may be due to the snowshoe hare population outstripping its food supply. The lemming is another animal living in the north whose numbers seem to change periodically. Every three or four years the population of lemmings increases sharply. In Norway, hordes of lemmings actually tumble to their death over the steep cliffs beside the sea. The reasons for this behavior are not definitely known. However, it has been suggested that it may be due to the lack of food.

In some cases the actions of man provide more food for wildlife. Deer, for example, eat grass in much the same way that cows do. In areas where fields have been abandoned, the resulting grass is ideal food for deer. In places where the deer are also protected, such as in some national parks, the abandoned clearings support large deer populations. In a similar way, grains, grasses, and fruit trees planted by man provide food for birds and other wildlife.

Cover

Animals need protection from their natural enemies and from the weather. Cover is the natural shelter for animals. Many small animals, hunted by hawks, owls, and other large birds, escape in a cover of grass, brush, or trees. For many animals, man is an enemy. They need cover in which they can hide from the hunter. Where there are extremes of weather, many animals need some place in which they can find protection. The lemmings, for example, burrow in the snow to protect themselves from the extreme cold of the north. Snakes, gophers, and many other animals of the sun-baked desert will seek protection from the high temperatures in holes in the ground or under rocks.

Additional cover can be provided for many kinds of wildlife. Farmers grow rosebushes and grasses along fence rows to provide cover for birds and rabbits. Trees along the edges of clearings serve as cover for deer. The rushes and sedges along the edges of lakes and ponds are favorite hiding places for birds and amphibians.

Breeding habitat

Many animals need special conditions under which to breed and rear their young. Many birds, for example, need special conditions for the building of their nests and the incubation of their eggs. When the young birds hatch, they are often very weak and need a great deal of protection. Because so many animals need special protection during the breeding season, it is especially important they they have good cover at that time.

Many game refuges are set up to provide cover for animals during the breeding season. Special refuges have been set up, for example, to provide a place for the whooping crane to breed and grow. It is hoped that this may prevent this bird from becoming extinct like the dodo and the passenger pigeon. Farmers put flushing bars on their mowers to prevent injury to birds that are nesting in meadows. Farm ponds and protected lakes have also become important breeding habitats for some kinds of wildlife.

The Web of Life

"Big fish eat little fish who eat littler fish." Similarly, wildlife eats and is eaten. The number of field mice or the number of deer depends upon how many of these animals are born and how many are killed by other animals before they are old enough to breed more of their kind. All living things are parts of such a web of life.

In many regions a balance is reached between numbers of various kinds of animals and the amount of food and cover that is available. Animals that feed on other animals, such as hawks and mountain lions, help to maintain this balance. Man, however, through his actions may upset this balance.

One clear example of how man upset the balance of the web of life occurred when an attempt was made to increase the number of deer on the Kaibab Plateau on the northern rim of the Grand Canyon in Arizona. At one time, it was estimated that there were about 7,000 deer on the plateau. For about 15 years the wolves, coyotes, and pumas that fed on the deer were hunted and large numbers were killed. It is estimated that the deer population jumped to about 100,000. There was not enough food, however, to feed this increased deer population. Grass, shrubs, trees—everything that could be eaten was devoured. Many of the deer starved; a herd of about 10,000 survived. The vegetation in the area was harmed for a long time to come. Before man's intervention there had been a balance on the Kaibab Plateau. But the deer population, as man learned, could not be increased greatly by reducing the numbers of the animals that preyed on it, because the land itself could not supply sufficient food for the increased numbers of deer.

Man has also tried to introduce new animals into ecosystems where they were not found before. Some of these animals survive. Sometimes they multiply to the point where they become pests. When the jackrabbit was introduced to Australia, for example, it quickly multiplied to the point where it seriously harmed grasslands and crops. Similarly, the mongoose, introduced into the Hawaiian Islands to control the rats that harmed the sugar cane, also multiplied and became a pest. Starlings, introduced into Eastern North America from Europe, have multiplied and now reach the West Coast. Since both starlings and bluebirds nest in holes in trees and poles, it may be that the starlings have reduced the number of bluebirds.

Changes in the environment can also seriously affect wildlife. The wild turkey, for example, needs large areas of undisturbed forest. At one time it was feared that the wild turkey might disappear because so much of the eastern and southern forests in which it roamed had been changed by lumbering, grazing, and fire. The bald eagle and golden eagle also need large relatively undisturbed areas. Because there are so few such areas left, eagles are now seldom seen in the West outside of the state of Alaska. Squirrels, which thrive in hardwood forests, are diminishing. This reduction is probably due partly to the cutting away of some of these forests.

The web of life is complicated, and any attempts to interfere with the web should only be done after a great deal of research and planning. The hunting and trapping of animals that kill and eat other animals may upset a balance in nature. This was what happened when the animals that hunt the Kaibab deer were killed. In this case the entire environment was harmed. The introduction of new species must also be done with great care. Many other organisms were affected by the introduction of jack-rabbits into Australia. A drastic change in the environment can also have tragic effects on the wildlife that live in a region.

Wildlife Conservation

Students of nature, bird watchers, nature photographers, hikers, hunt-ers, and people in general are interested in wildlife. Principles of the science of ecology are used to try to maintain populations of various kinds of wildlife. Often these attempts are hampered by lack of knowledge of the niche of various animals in their ecosystems and of the life histories of the animals. Research into the habits of various animals and their inter-actions with their environment can lead to better wildlife conservation.

Three general approaches to wildlife conservation are often used:

1. Habitat improvement
2. Artificial stocking
3. Protecting breeding stock

Habitat improvement is probably the most effective approach to wild-life conservation. The planting of grasses along fence rows has improved the habitat for quail and other birds. Large game refuges around lakes and ponds in both the north and the south help such birds as ducks and geese. Since these birds migrate with the season, they need the necessary habitats along the way. The draining of many swamps and marshes has destroyed some of the areas where ducks and geese could rest and feed as they migrate. The habitat for rabbits can be improved by leaving brush along the edges of fields and along the borders of forests. When the require-ments of various kinds of wildlife are understood, the proper habitats in which these animals can live can be provided.

In some cases animals are raised on game farms and then introduced into various habitats. This is called *artificial stocking*. Attempts have been made to increase the number of quail in a region. However, in almost all cases where the quail were already present there was very little increase in quail population as a result of artificial stocking. Probably there was just greater competition for the available food and cover. Artificial stocking has helped, however, when some form of wildlife was about to disappear from a region. The beautiful trumpeter swam was introduced again into some regions in the West and can now be seen proudly gliding on the surfaces of lakes in such places as Yellowstone National Park.

To protect breeding stock, hunters are often forbidden to shoot the females of a particular animal. In many places, for example, deer hunters can shoot bucks but not does. Many animals are least able to protect themselves during the breeding season, and steps have been taken to protect them and provide them with a suitable habitat. Game laws are designed to protect animals during the time they are giving birth to and caring for their young. Sometimes people are prevented from entering the natural rookeries where the nests of such birds as the blue heron are located.

With an understanding of the needs of wildlife, man can help these other members of his environment to survive.

APPROACHES TO TEACHING

The emphasis in the study of this area should be placed on investigation of conditions in the local community and region. Whenever possible the children should be taken on field trips to see local soil profiles, examine evidence of soil erosion, and find animal tracks. In other cases they can collect samples of soil, river water, and particles that settle out of the atmosphere. These materials can be examined and studied in the classroom. This is an area of science that has direct relevance to the local community and region. Children can carry out studies such as those that are suggested, and they should be encouraged to suggest ways that conditions in the local community and region can be improved.

Is soil being eroded away?

The following are some indications of soil erosion. Check a field, hillside, or neighborhood park for these indications. Which of them do you find?
Gullies and ditches
Stones that seem to "grow" in fields
Uncovered roots of trees
Soil on sidewalks and roads
Pebbles that seem to be on pedestals of soil
Sand and soil piled up behind fences
Uncovered sewer pipes
Silted-in ponds and lakes

What is the nature of the soil profile?

Examine a soil profile in a new road cut, stream bank, or a newly dug hole. If this is not possible, a soil auger can be used to obtain samples of soil at various levels.

Examine the soil profile and answer the following questions:

1. Are there three soil horizons?
2. How many centimeters thick is the A horizon?
3. How many centimeters thick is the B horizon?
4. How many centimeters thick is the C horizon?
5. Are there thinner layers within the horizons?
6. What is the color of each horizon?
7. What kind of rock forms the bedrock? What color is it?
8. Is the C horizon formed of the same material as the bedrock?

The upper layer of soil will often contain considerable organic matter. Much of this organic matter can be separated from the soil by floating it in water. Fill a 1,000 ml. beaker with water, then pour the soil into it. Stir the soil in the water, then allow it to stand for a few minutes. Much of the organic matter will float to the top of the water. Estimate what fraction of this soil is composed of organic matter.

It may be useful to make a profile of the soil that can be studied indoors. Obtain a piece of plywood or cardboard about six inches wide. Cover it with a coating of glue. Fix particles of soil from the profile onto the board exactly as it is in the actual profile.

What are some of the physical characteristics of local soils?

Obtain a sample from the top eight inches of soil in a garden or field. Feel the soil between your fingers. How can the texture of the soil be described? Do the particles feel small or large?

Separate the soil particles on the basis of their size. This can be done with a soil sieve. If none is available, sift the soil through various sizes of wire screening. What size particles does the sample contain?

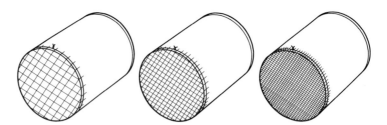

Fig. 18-3 *Homemade soil sieves for the study of the particles that make up soil.*

Examine the soil particles with a magnifying glass and, if possible, a binocular microscope. Are the small soil particles round or angular? If they are round, they may have been worn smooth by the action of water or wind. If possible compare the soil particles with sand and soil from a beach.

Examine cultivated or plowed soil in a garden or field. Are there small clumps of soil? If there are, do they crumble easily? Soil that has clumps about the size of acorns that crumble easily between the fingers has good soil structure.

What is the acidity of the soil?

A soil testing kit will be necessary for this experiment. Such kits can be obtained at garden supply stores and many hardware stores.

Obtain a small sample of soil from a garden, field, or lawn. It is desirable that this sample of soil be representative of the type of soil to be found in the garden, lawn, or part of a field.

Following the instructions on the soil testing kit, find the pH of the soil? What kinds of plants would grow well in this soil? What could be done to improve the soil?

What materials are in river water?

Fasten a strong string to a glass jar or jug and dangle it in a stream or river. (The most striking results for this experiment will be obtained if the sample of water is taken when the stream is in flood.)

Place the sample of water on a table to allow some materials to float to the top and the sediment to settle to the bottom.

Skim off whatever material is floating at the top and examine it with the aid of a magnifying glass. What kind of material does it seem to be?

Inspect the material that has settled to the bottom. Compare the amount of sediment at the bottom with the amount of water.

Pour off the water into another container and examine the sediment with the aid of a magnifying glass. What color is the sediment? Are all the particles the same size? Do the particles appear to be sand, clay, or silt? Pour a little of the river water through a paper filter. Are there small particles of soil to be found on the filter?

Pour a little of the river water into a clean evaporating dish. Place the dish on a hot plate and heat until all the water disappears. Is there any material left at the bottom of the evaporating dish? What is its color? These are the minerals that were dissolved in the water. You may wish to compare the amount of mineral matter in the river water with that in an equal amount of tap water.

What is the level of the water table?

Find a well or hole that has water at the bottom. The level of the water in such a well or hole indicates the height of the water table. Using a string and a weight, measure the distance down to the water from a fixed point at the surface. Repeat this measurement once a week for several weeks. Does the distance down to the surface of the water vary? How can the variations be accounted for? Measure the well or hole at some other season. What has happened to the level of the water table?

What is a temperature inversion?

A temperature inversion can be simulated in a system containing cold and warm water.

Fill one glass milk bottle, or similar glass container, with cold water and a second such container with warm water. Put some food coloring (or ink) into the warm water. (It is best to do this experiment in a sink or a shallow tray. There is almost always a little water spilled.)

Place a 3 × 5 card over the mouth of the bottle containing the warm water. While holding the card over the mouth of the bottle, tip it upside down and place it on top of the bottle containing the cold water. Gently pull the 3 × 5 card from between the bottles. What happens to the water in the two bottles?

Warm

Cold

Fig. 18-4 A way to study what happens when waters at different temperatures meet.

For comparison, repeat the experiment, but this time place the bottle with cold water on top of the one with warm water. What happens? How does this compare with the usual conditions in the atmosphere?

For a more striking demonstration of this effect, grasp the two bottles. While pressing them together, tip the bottles over on their sides. What happens? In what ways is the behavior of the warm and cold water like a temperature inversion?

What animal tracks can be found in the community?

One of the ways to discover what kinds of animals may be living in the community is to find and identify animal tracks. The tracks shown are those of mammals that are often found in many parts of the country. The tracks of birds can also be studied.[1]

One of the best places to find tracks is around a small pond or lake that serves as a watering hole for animals. Late in the afternoon, smooth out the mud or sand near the water so that animals that come near the water will make fresh tracks. In the morning, look for tracks. What animals came for a drink during the night?

[1] For a description of additional animal tracks see O. V. Murie, *A Field Guide to Animal Tracks* (Boston, Mass.: Houghton Mifflin Co., 1954).

A local museum or zoo may have publications showing the tracks of animals often found in the surrounding region.

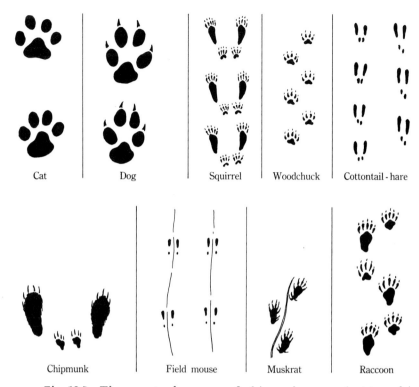

Cat   Dog   Squirrel   Woodchuck   Cottontail-hare

Chipmunk   Field mouse   Muskrat   Raccoon

Fig. 18-5 These are tracks you may find in mud or snow (not to scale).

A salt lick, grain, and other animal food placed out in the open will attract some animals. As with the pond, smooth out the area around the salt or food so that the animals will make fresh tracks.

One of the best times to look for animal tracks is when there is newly fallen snow.

Make a list of the various kinds of animal tracks, the dates, and the place and conditions under which they were found. How many different kinds of animal tracks have been found? Are different kinds of tracks found in different places? What kinds of tracks are found at different times of the year?

INVESTIGATION

How do various wildlife conservation measures work?

The following are some steps that have been taken for wildlife conservation. Try to discover and explain how each of these steps might help conserve wildlife.

1. Seed-bearing grasses are planted along fence rows.
2. Hunters are prevented from shooting deer in the spring.
3. Stream bank erosion control projects are undertaken.
4. Farmers do not cut the grass near the edge of lakes and ponds.
5. Large tracks of land have been set aside as wilderness areas.
6. The grazing of cattle and sheep in clearings near the forest is controlled.
7. Marshes and swamps are not drained.
8. Hunting is limited to the hours between sunrise and sunset.
9. South American countries prevent the destruction of habitats for birds.

Selected References

BARNETT, LINCOLN, *The World We Live In*. New York: Time, Inc., 1956.

BATES, MARSTON, *The Forest and the Sea*. New York: New American Library, 1960.

JACOBSON, WILLARD J., KLEINMAN, GLADYS, HIACK, PAUL S., SUGARBAKER, JOHN, AND CARR, ALBERT, *The Organism and the Environment: Field Research and Models* and *Ecology: Field Research in Science*, New York: American Book Co., 1968.

NATIONAL GEOGRAPHIC SOCIETY, *Wild Animals of North America*. Washington, D.C.: National Geographic Society,

STORER, JOHN H., *The Web of Life*. New York: New American Library, 1956.

READINGS FOR THE PRIMARY GRADES

BARTLETT, MARGARET FARRINGTON, *Down the Mountain*. New York: Young Scott Books, 1963.

CASTLE, JANE, *Whose Tree House?* New York: Holiday House, Inc., 1963.

CROMER, RICHARD, *Soil*. Chicago: Follett Publishing Co., 1967

GOINGHUIS, DIRK, *From Tall Timber*. Chicago: Albert Whitman & Co. 1964.

HOFMANN, MELITA, *A Trip to the Pond*. Garden City, N.Y.: Doubleday & Co., 1966.

JACOBSON, WILLARD J., LAUBY, CECILIA J., AND KONICEK, RICHARD D., *Soil*. New York: American Book Co., 1968.

MANNHEIM, GRETE, *Touch Me, Touch Me Not*. New York: Alfred A. Knopf, Inc., 1965.

505

SELSAM, MILLICENT, *You and the World Around You*. Garden City, N.Y.: Doubleday & Co., Inc., 1963.

READINGS FOR THE INTERMEDIATE GRADES

KANE, HENRY B., *The Tale of a Meadow*. New York: Alfred A. Knopf, Inc., 1959.

KANE, HENRY B., *The Tale of a Pond*. New York: Alfred A. Knopf, Inc., 1960.

McCARTHY, J. D., *Animals and Their Ways*. Garden City, N.Y.: Natural History Press, 1956.

NEWMARK, JOHN AND GEORGE, *To the Zoo in a Plastic Box*. New York: Random House, Inc., 1965.

SELSAM, MILLICENT E., *Birth of a Forest*. New York: Harper & Row, 1964.

SUTTON, ANN AND MYRON, *Animals on the Move*. New York: Rand McNally & Co., 1965.

SELECTED FILM

Plant Succession. McGraw-Hill. Shows the succession of plants from bare rock to hardwood forest. Also shows the nature of the climate conditions in forest, prairie, tundra and desert.

VI
Building
Science Programs
in the Elementary School

A science program is a plan for developing science experiences with children. Careful planning makes it possible to have readily available the science materials and equipment, films and filmstrips, and other science resources and facilities so that the teacher can take optimum advantage of those precious "teachable moments." A well-designed program will provide an environment in which children's interests in science will be generated. Imaginative planning will make it possible to utilize the physical and intellectual resources of the entire community. With this kind of planning teachers will be able to use the biological and geological features of their region and make the optimum use of such cultural resources as museums, parks, gardens, and planetariums. Effective science programs are not detailed, minute-by-minute plans for teaching that enchain the creative teacher. Instead, flexible science programs open up opportunities that would not be available without planning and make it possible for the teacher to be ready for the eventualities that arise in the classroom. "To plan or not to plan is not the question." It is only through careful planning that high quality science programs can be built.

Who should do the planning? The teacher, the science consultant or supervisor, and other members of the local school and community must take primary responsibility. They are the people who know the children, community, and the nature of local scientific and cultural resources. The responsibility for planning programs cannot be abrogated or delegated if the children in the classroom are to have the best possible science experiences. However, all possible resources—local, state, and national—should be utilized in the planning.

Optimum use should be made of policy statements, science materials and equipment, and other resources for teaching that have been developed elsewhere. Professional organizations and other groups periodically make suggestions for program planning; these suggestions are usually based on expert opinion and science education research and should be considered in planning the local program. The development of high quality text, library, and laboratory materials requires resources that are usually not available to local school systems; these kinds of materials are being developed by a number of groups, and teachers and schools should use their products to build effective programs. Films, filmstrips, transparencies, videotapes, and other audio-visual materials are also made available and should be used to optimum advantage. While the teacher and his associates have the primary responsibility for planning the science program, they should take advantage of the wide range of high quality materials that are being produced by groups that have resources that no individual teacher or school system can possibly have at its command.

Program planning involves development of the science facilities needed for a wide range of experiences. What kinds of facilities and equipment should be in the classroom? What kinds of special facilities such as darkrooms, greenhouses, gardens, nature trails, and project areas should and can be made available? What community resources are available? These are some of the questions related to equipment and facilities that should be considered in program planning and eventually can be dealt with only by teachers, consultants, and administrators who know the children, school, and local community.

An essential feature of a science program is a systematic procedure for evaluating science materials, activities, units, and the over-all program. The eventual test of effectiveness is an empirical one: "How effective is the science program in making it possible for children to learn science?" With constructive planning, teachers and others can gather information related to this question that will help them to make the judgments that are central in evaluation.

19 Science Programs in the Elementary School

Science programs are plans for experiences in science. These experiences should help children grow and develop in the direction of the goals that have been set for elementary school science. Some of the plans are long range and make it possible for the teacher and the school to provide the time, materials, and facilities needed for high quality science experiences. In addition, short range plans, often growing out of children's questions and interests or current events in science, make the science program spontaneous and lively. All of these plans are developed to help children move in the direction of the goals that have been set for science instruction.

Every teacher should plan a program for a year's work in science. First, there should be a broad outline of science areas that will be considered during the year. This is the skeleton outline that helps the teacher decide what kinds of science facilities are needed, what materials and equipment must be procured, and the field trips, science films, and interviews with experts that should be arranged. Second, there should be specific plans for the study of particular topics. For example, if a class is to study the various adaptations of plants and animals, plans may be made to study various plants in their natural habitats and to visit a zoo to see the adaptations of exotic animals from all over the world. In addition, the teacher may wish to plan the science program so that it is related to the experiences that children are having in other subjects.

The teacher's plan should be consistent with the school's over-all science program. During a pupil's sojourn in school he should have some contact with all of the most significant areas of science. This can be done only if there is an over-all school science program. Specific broad science topics can be assigned to various grades. Each teacher can then plan to cover each of these areas to considerable depth. A carefully planned school science program can help eliminate deadening repetition and ensure that each child has the kinds of science experiences that are judged to be most suitable for his stage of development.

PLANNING SCIENCE PROGRAMS

Effective planning is essential to creative teaching in science as in all other areas of the curriculum. The following factors[1] should be considered in planning:

The nature of the learner

The supreme test of a science program is: Do the children actually grow in their ability to understand and interpret the phenomena that occur in the surrounding physical environment and within their bodies? To be effective, teachers must have a general understanding of how children learn. For example, they should be aware of the general characteristics of the stage of intellectual development through which their children are passing. It is also important to be aware of the peculiar interests and concerns of the individual children they teach. To a certain extent, the science program should deal with these interests and concerns. Children are more likely to learn that which they consider to be interesting and important.

Learning is an individual matter. In the final analysis we are concerned that the individual children whom we teach change their patterns of behavior in the direction of the goals of our instruction. To accomplish this, we must relate our teaching to the characteristics of the learners.

The nature of the subject matter

The internal logic of arithmetic dictates that we teach addition before we teach multiplication. Similarly, there is logical dimension to the teaching of science. The basic elements of science are its assumptions, methods, and broad generalizations. These provide a framework around which we can build a well-organized science program. Through science children should become aware of the basic assumption of science that all events and all phenomena can be explained in a rational, logical way; gain some understanding of the methods that are characteristic of investigations in science; and learn the meaning of the broad generalizations of the sciences. In other words, children's experiences in science should be consistent with the nature of science.

---

[1] These factors are considered in some detail in the various chapters of Part I.

The nature of the society

An educational program, including the science program, should help prepare children for effective citizenship in the society in which they live. For example, a democratic society makes unusual demands upon its citizens; an educational program that may be adequate for a totalitarian society will in all likelihood be completely inadequate for a democratic society. In a democracy, the basic policy decisions are made by citizens and their representatives in government. More and more of the critical issues that we must resolve are directly related to science and technology, and some literacy in these fields is essential if we are to deal with these issues intelligently and democratically. Our science programs should include experiences that will help our children become effective citizens in a democracy.

The history of elementary school science

Many kinds of programs have been developed in elementary school science. There have been failures and successes. In planning school science programs it is essential that the lessons of the past be learned so that we shall have greater success in the future. The study of the history of elementary science can help us to avoid the mistakes and profit from the successes of the past.

Research in science education

Through research we try to obtain data that will help us to find better operational answers to the problems that perplex us. Through status studies we try to find out what are current practices in elementary school science. Experimental studies test various approaches to teaching and compare them to other approaches. Synthetic or analytical studies analyze various areas of elementary school science and suggest new approaches to teaching and learning. In planning elementary science programs we need to be cognizant of the important, although meager, research that has been carried out in this area.

The K-12 science program

The elementary school science program should be the basis for the entire K-12 science program. However, this requires careful planning to avoid deadening repetition and to make certain that various areas of science are studied when the children are ready for them. The classroom teacher correlates science with the other areas that are studied during a school year. However, these science experiences must also be fitted into a thirteen-year science program. This requires planning on a school-wide basis.

A TWO-DIMENSIONAL SCIENCE PROGRAM

A successful science program may be considered to have two dimensions: a flexible dimension and a planned dimension.[2] Through the flexible dimension the teacher can take advantage of timely events in science and plan special science activities to meet the needs and interests of individual pupils. The planned dimension involves the planned sequence of science topics that are studied from year to year. If a science program is to be more than a series of accidental incidents, there must be careful planning for the study of specific areas of science. However, a plan is a design or outline for action. It is not a procrustean maze to be negotiated slavishly. A plan is an outline for action with sufficient flexibility to allow for fascinating side excursions. Planning and flexibility are two keys to effective elementary school science programs.

The Flexible Dimension of Elementary School Science

In the flexible dimension of the elementary science program, the interests and needs, related to science, of individual children are dealt with. Some children may raise and wish to pursue unusual science questions that may be of little interest to the rest of the class; usually, they should be encouraged to carry out these investigations. Other children may wish to construct apparatus, charts, dioramas, or undertake an individual project. For the children who have special aptitude or proclivity for science, a teacher may wish to plan special activities to help these youngsters go as far as they can. Other youngsters may not have had an opportunity to develop certain essential skills or consider certain text materials, or they may find that they have to travel the path of science a bit slower than others. They, too, will benefit from specially planned science activities.

Since the major goal of elementary education is to help children achieve optimum intellectual, physical, and emotional growth and development, it will always be important to develop science experiences that meet the needs and interests of children. This requires that teachers have a pro-

---

[2] For a further discussion of these dimensions of the elementary school science program see Willard J. Jacobson and Harold E. Tannenbaum, *Modern Elementary School Science* (New York: Teachers College Press, 1961).

found knowledge of children in general, a deep understanding of the individual children they teach, and the intellectual resources to know many of the possible kinds of science activities that can be undertaken with children. The flexible dimension demands resourceful, imaginative teaching. The following are some of the kinds of science experiences that can be developed within the flexible dimension of the science program.

Developing science experiences related to the questions raised by children

Most children raise a myriad of questions ranging from the simple and superficial to the penetrating and profound. Some questions are asked on the spur of the moment, stimulated by some chance happening in the classroom, and can be dealt with swiftly and expeditiously. Other questions are expressions of deep concern and are important in terms of the child's development. To distinguish between the superficial and the significant in children's questions is a critical facet of the art of teaching. In some cases, a question may be of such concern to a child that he cannot deal with other matters until the problem is in some way resolved. The science subject matter to deal with such questions is of intrinsic value and should be an important part of the elementary science curriculum.

"What happens when something burns?" The children had seen paper, wood, and other fuels burn and change form. Billy, a quiet, slow-to-speak child, after considerable pondering, raised that question and thereby stimulated some very fruitful investigation on the part of the entire class. First, the teacher had the children clarify the basic question by raising such other questions as: "What happens if one of the requirements for burning is taken away?" "What is formed when something burns?" "What happens to the material that is burned?" Next, the children suggested a reasonable hypothesis to each of the questions that could be tested by experimentation, and the class carried out many of these experiments using a burning candle. The final experiment was to find out whether or not the material that was burned actually was destroyed—in a sense, a check of the law of conservation of matter. In this classroom, a question raised by one pupil led to a series of very important science experiences related to some very important areas of science.

The study of questions and problems gives children a chance to learn fruitful approaches to dealing with problems. They are encouraged to state their questions as precisely as possible and to clarify for themselves and for others the meaning of the questions that they ask. They suggest possible answers to their questions and learn how to use these hypotheses as tools in their investigations. They gain practice in setting up experiments and in searching for and evaluating sources of information. They find the best possible answers to their questions and learn how to relate their experiences to the broad generalizations of science. Obviously, many of the approaches to problem-solving used by the children are similar to those used in scientific investigations.

Developing science experiences to meet the diverse needs of individual children

In most classrooms there is a wide range of interests and abilities. Some children are so interested that they will devote a great deal of time and energy to their science activities. Obviously, they should be encouraged and helped to do so. Some children have more ability than others. As in all education, each child should be encouraged to pursue worthwhile interests and helped to move ahead as far as he can.

Among the most effective approaches to individual differences in elementary school science are individual or small group investigations. A pupil or a group of pupils identifies some question or topic that it wishes to study further. In their studies, the children may undertake various kinds of experimentation, use books and pamphlets that are available at home or at school, or visit public libraries and consult with people in the community who may know a great deal about the topic under investigation. Often, reports of the investigations are made in "seminars" to their fellow pupils or through various kinds of construction projects. In some schools, special periods are set aside each week for these activities. Children who are deeply interested often continue their investigations after school and on weekends.

In some communities, interested adults with special competencies have been enlisted to work with keenly interested youngsters. Scientists have helped children plan their investigations; engineers have worked with children to overcome various difficulties they encounter in their projects; farmers have made it possible to carry out studies of soil, plants, and animals; mechanics have assisted in the construction of equipment and projects; many professional people, at one time or another, have provided essential information and advice. Often, many of the intellectual resources of a community have to be tapped so that our children can have optimum achievement.

Various kinds of programmed instruction are available for use by children who wish to master certain areas of science subject matter or skills or for children who may have weaknesses in certain areas of science. Carefully constructed programs are designed to be consistent with the logic of any particular area of subject matter. Most programs help the student to check the correctness of the concepts that he develops. More and more programs are becoming available for use in elementary school science, and they should be a great help to the teacher in individualizing instruction.

Various kinds of science kits have been developed in such areas as chemistry, electricity, microbiology, plant physiology, and mineralogy which can be used by children who wish to undertake laboratory studies in such areas. A variety of such kits should be available for use by interested youngsters. The teacher should become familiar with the kinds of activities that are suggested in order to help children overcome various difficulties that may be anticipated. Of perhaps greater importance, after a child has completed various activities, the teacher should help the child ascertain the meanings that can be arrived at from the activities. A child may use a chemistry kit to prepare oxygen. The teacher should help him to gain educational profit from this experience by learning more about chemical reactions in general as well as the specific characteristics of oxygen gas.

The science club is one of the most widely used and highly successful approaches to providing a variety of science experiences for children especially interested in science. Children from several grades usually participate in the club. The principal prerequisite to membership is a keen interest in science. Individual children may undertake special projects and report on them at a club meeting. Science field trips may be planned. There may be showings of science films, and speakers may be invited to discuss various science topics. Science clubs have proved to be an effective way to stimulate and nurture interest and achievement in science.

Science experiences related to other areas of study are developed

Science is closely related to such other elementary school subjects as reading, arithmetic, writing, social studies, and art.

Many a child has learned to read from experience charts developed from a science experience or from some of the excellent science trade books and textbooks that are available. One of the essentials in a good reading program is that there be available reading material on subjects that are of interest to children. There are many such subjects in science, ranging from aardvarks to zoos. Also, an important aspect of learning to read is to associate symbols in the form of the written word with concrete objects and direct experiences. The direct experiences with materials and equipment that are characteristic of elementary school science provide the subject matter to which children can relate words and phrases as they learn to read. Undoubtedly, the development of elementary school science has helped in the building of more effective reading programs.

Mathematics and science are always closely related. In fact, mathematics is sometimes called "The Handmaiden of the Sciences." In elementary school science, many experiments involve counting and recording the results in numbers. Almost all aspects of arithmetic are used at one time or another in tabulating the results of experiments. There is a great deal of measurement, and older children can begin to use elementary geometry as they make measurements of inaccessible objects and astronomical distances. As in the case of reading, the work in science shows children the importance of mathematics and how it can be put to practical use.

As in almost all other elementary school subjects, writing plays an important part in science. The keeping of a journal is an excellent practice in science, and, as children keep a record of their science experiences, they should be encouraged to preserve these experiences in the best possible literary form. Written records should be kept of experiments performed. Some science clubs occasionally "publish" articles by its members in a science journal.

Conservation is an example of an area of study that bridges science and social studies. The conservation of our natural resources is important for social and economic reasons, but to understand how various conservation measures can be carried out and how they work requires a knowledge of the physical principles on which they are based. Many other social problems that children study require a knowledge of the scientific principles involved if there is to be a genuine understanding of the social problem.

Often in the elementary school the work in various areas of the curriculum is correlated as the children study a broad topic. In the early years of the elementary school, for example, children often make a study of the local community. This study should include some consideration of the natural resources of the community, the kinds of plants and animals to be found there, the major local industries, and how the people obtain the necessities for life. In all such topics science has a role, and it should be considered and studied along with all other subjects that are pertinent to the broad, encompassing topic.

The Planned Dimension of Elementary School Science

The planned dimension is the program or scope and sequence of science topics that are planned for study in each year of the elementary school. Through the planned program of elementary school science, each child should have some contact with the major areas of science. The planned program is a framework within which each teacher can plan for a year's work in science. It makes it possible for a school system to plan for the science facilities that are needed in each school and classroom, provide the types of trade books and textbooks that are needed in the classroom and library, order needed equipment and science materials, plan radio and television programs, and recruit the kind of staff that is needed to implement the program. Community agencies, such as museums, planetariums, parks, television stations, and local offices of state and federal agencies, can relate their educational programs to the planned dimension of the local elementary school science program.

An effective planned elementary school science program should have the following characteristics:

1. The science program should provide opportunities for children to have some contact with all of the major areas of science. In many elementary school science programs, including the sample program offered in this text, children have some contact with each of the broad, general areas of science each year. Children will have the opportunity to deal with all or most of the significant topics in science only if their study is planned for in a comprehensive K-12 science program.

2. The newer sciences should be represented in the elementary science program. Such relatively new sciences as oceanography, nutrition, genetics, and electronics are of great interest to most youngsters; and since they deal with important scientific generalizations and methods of inquiry, they should be included in the elementary school science program.

3. Children should have opportunities for experiences in depth in the different areas planned for study each year. If we decide to do something, it should be done well. Of particular importance, children should have some opportunity to become acquainted with methods of investigation that are used in the science being studied. The chief limitations that the teacher must keep in mind are the limited skills and previous experiences of the children.

4. There should be no unnecessary deadening repetition in the science program. If various science topics are studied in depth, there is no need to deal with them each year. Instead, new science topics should be introduced. When a science topic similar to one that has been studied earlier is considered again, it should be approached in a new and fresh way. To avoid deadening repetition the elementary science program should be planned as a part of the over-all K-12 science sequence.

5. The topics covered in other subjects during a school year should be

considered in planning the science program. For example, if conservation is considered in a particular year in the social studies program, it might be well to plan to study soil and water resources in the same year in the science program.

6. The science program should be planned so that children have an opportunity to become acquainted with various methods of investigation in the sciences. In some sciences, the controlled experiment is the chief tool, while in other sciences dissection and the analysis of structure and function are of critical importance. Children should have some contact with all of these methods.

During recent years there has been more effort devoted to science curriculum development than during any other period in the history of elementary school science.[3] But how can the products of these efforts be utilized in the elementary school curriculum? In this book a synthesis is suggested. The key to this synthesis is the simple, but profound, question, "What should children gain from a study of science?" In answer to this question it is suggested that children should benefit in the following ways:

1. Build a world view that takes into account the world view that is being developed in the sciences.
2. Gain an understanding of the conceptual structure of science.
3. Develop skill in the use of some of the processes of science.
4. Gain an understanding of man and of how science affects man and his society.

Science programs, such as the two sample programs that follow, will give children opportunities to grow in these directions.

---

[3] Much of this development work has been done in such course content improvement projects as the following:

American Association for the Advancement of Science (AAAS), *Science—A Process Approach* (Washington, D.C.: American Association for the Advancement of Science). Emphasizes the processes of science.

Elementary School Science Project, *Six Units on Astronomy* (Urbana, Ill.: University of Illinois). An upper elementary school program in astronomy.

Elementary Science Study (ESS), Printed Material and Kits for Scientific Study, (EDC) McGraw-Hill, (Webster Division) Manchester, Mo.

Minnesota Mathematics and Science Teaching Project (MINNEMAST) (Minneapolis, Minn.: University of Minnesota). A coordinated science and mathematics program.

Science Curriculum Improvement Study (SCIS) (Berkeley, Calif.: University of California). A science program based on an analysis of the conceptual structure of science and developmental psychology.

Science Manpower Project (SMP) (New York: Teachers College, Columbia University). A guide to program planning in elementary school science.

Sample Program I[4]

A synthesis based on the goals of elementary school science

I. Building a World View
   A. The Universe and Solar System
   B. The Earth on Which We Live
   C. The Air and the Atmosphere
   D. Water and Oceans
   E. The World of Living Organisms

II. Building a Conceptual Structure of Science
   A. The Study of Objects and Systems
      1. Relativity
      2. Operational Definitions
   B. The Study of Interactions
      1. Biological
      2. Chemical
      3. Magnetic
      4. Electrical
      5. Heat and Temperature
      6. Light
      7. Sound

III. Processes of Science
   A. Observation, Classification, Measurement
   B. Experimentation
   C. Model Formation

IV. Science and Man
   A. The Human Body and How It Functions
   B. Science and Healthful Living
   C. Man and His Environment

Sample Program II[5]

A program dealing with broad areas of science

One of the effective and widely used approaches to elementary science program planning is to categorize the science topics into broad science areas. The following six areas are used in the program that follows:

[4] Unit texts, lab-texts, equipment, and materials for the implementation of Sample Program I are available from the American Book Co. Units developed by the course content improvement projects listed on page 522 can also be used to implement the program.

[5] The Thinking Ahead in Science Series by Willard J. Jacobson, Cecilia J. Lauby, and Richard D. Konicek is based on this program. This series along with lab-texts, material, equipment, and audio-visual materials, organized in a systems approach, are available from the American Book Co.

Table 19–1: SAMPLE PROGRAM USING SPIRAL APPROACH

Grade Area	The Universe and Solar System	The World of Living Organisms	Matter and Energy	The Earth on Which We Live	The Physical World	Space Science
K	A variety of experiences in science emphasizing the flexible dimension. Planned experiences related to plants, weather, aquarium, objects, food, light, sound, magnets, water, and seeds.					
1	Day and Night	Animals	Fire and Temperature	Rocks	Machines	Rockets
2	The Moon	Plants	Food	Soil	Forces and Magnets	Exploring Space
3	Sun, Seasons, and Climate	Living Things on Earth	The Air Around You	Weather	Sound	Earth Satellites
4	Exploring the Solar System	Prehistoric Plants and Animals	Materials of the Earth	The Earth and Its History	Energy to Do Work	Living in Space
5	The Milky Way and the Universe	Living Things in Their Environment	Changes in Matter	The Earth and Its Changing Surface	Electricity	Distances in Space
6	Energy From the Sun	Insects and Senses	The Atom and Nuclear Energy	The Ocean	Light and Heat	Exploring the Universe

> The Universe and Solar System
> The World of Living Organisms
> Matter and Energy
> The Earth on Which We Live
> The Physical World
> Space Science

The units within each of these broad science areas can be developed to help children to grow in the direction of such goals as gaining an understanding of the conceptual structure of science and developing science process skills. One of the advantages of this kind of program is that work toward these goals is carried on within the context of an important area of science content.

The broad science area approach to program planning makes possible a spiral development in the curriculum. In a spiral development children consider similar areas of science more than once in the program. In a "tight spiral" similar areas are considered each year or every two years. In a "broad spiral" children will have experiences in similar areas two or three times in the program—often once in the primary grades and once in the intermediate grades. The sample program described utilizes a broad spiral approach. The broad spiral makes possible a "depth" approach to each unit so that considerable attention can be given to process as well as content.

Selected References

Hopman, Anne B., ed. *Helping Children Learn Science*. Washington, D.C.: National Science Teachers Association, 1966.

Karplus, Robert, and Thier, Herbert D. *A New Look at Elementary School Science*. Chicago, Ill.: Rand McNally & Co., 1967.

Jacobson, Willard J., and Tannenbaum, Harold E. *Modern Elementary School Science*. New York: Teachers College Press, 1961.

National Science Teachers Association. *Theory Into Action In Science Curriculum Development*. Washington, D.C.: National Science Teachers Association, 1964.

National Society for the Study of Education. *Rethinking Science Education*, Fifty-ninth Yearbook, Part I. Chicago, Ill.: University of Chicago Press, 1960. Chapters VII and VIII.

Renner, John, and Ragan, William B. *Teaching Science in the Elementary School*. New York: Harper & Row, Inc., 1968.

Victor, Edward, and Lerner, Marjorie S. *Readings in Science Education for the Elementary School*. New York: The Macmillan Co., 1967. Sections 2 and 8.

20 Science Materials and Facilities in the Elementary School

"What materials, equipment, and facilities should we have and use?" The best answer is: *the materials, equipment, and facilities that will best facilitate learning.* The old questions of which are best—textbooks or tradebooks, films or filmstrips, television or a teacher demonstration—are really not adequate. It is much more productive to ask "What materials, equipment and facilities will best help our children learn?" and, "Under what conditions and for what purposes can various kinds of materials and equipment best be used?"

ORGANIZING THE CLASSROOM FOR SCIENCE

There are two general kinds of classroom organizations for science: the *self-contained classroom* and the *science* room. The self-contained classroom in which the teacher works with children in most areas of the curriculum is by far the most common type of organization. However, a significant number of schools provide a special science room in which science is taught by either the general classroom teacher or a science consultant or teacher. The major emphasis in this chapter is the organization of self-contained classrooms for experiences in science. An example of a science room is offered. Some suggestions for community science facilities and how they can be used are also given.

Science in the Self-contained Classroom

The self-contained classroom serves as a place where children study and the teacher works in almost all areas of the elementary school curriculum. Fortunately, the facilities used in many of the other areas of the curriculum can also be used in science. The following are some of the arrangements that can be made for science instruction in a self-contained classroom.

The classroom as a laboratory

Many experiences that children should have in science are of the laboratory type in which each child participates in the activities. Children's desks can serve as laboratory tables. For some kinds of experiments, three or four desks may be pushed together to provide a larger work space.

Most of the activities that are carried on in elementary school science do not require running water, gas or electricity. However, it is highly desirable if these can be provided at one or more stations in the classroom. Usually, these utilities can be located along the periphery of the room. Experiments requiring these utilities can then be set up at stations along the walls of the classroom.

To protect the surface of desks during experiments, many teachers have found it helpful to use cafeteria-type trays. These may be either the regular cafeteria trays or cardboard trays that can be obtained inexpensively.

Children should help organize the classroom as a laboratory. Through careful planning, they can help distribute the materials, collect them, and clean up after the laboratory activities. To have a part in the management of the classroom as a laboratory is, in itself, an important learning experience.

A science activity center

One section of the classroom can be set aside as a science activity center. This may be an area where various utilities are available and workspace can be freed where projects and experiments taking a long period of time can be stored. Sometimes, a portable demonstration table can serve as a science activity center. Usually, it is desirable to have science books and reference materials easily available to the children in the activity center.

It is highly desirable that there be a workbench with some basic tools readily available to the children. These tools and workbench can be used for industrial art activities as well as for science.

Life science activities

Every classroom should have some facilities for life science activities. As a basic minimum, the classroom should have one or more aquariums and terrariums with sufficient shelf space. Usually, it is desirable to place aquariums out of direct light. In many classrooms, aquariums are placed on shelves on the wall opposite the windows. The terrariums may be placed at various places throughout the room, depending on the type of terrarium that is developed.

A plant-growing area is also desirable. This may be a place to grow potted plants or a larger growing area. In any case, a place for soil is needed and preferably some provision for drainage. Usually, the plant-growing facilities will be near the window where there is ample sunlight. Although it is not absolutely necessary, it is also helpful to have a source of running water nearby.

Facilities for maintaining animals such as rats, hamsters and gerbils are also useful. Cages are needed and a place to keep them. Also, some storage space is needed for the animal food.

Work-storage area

It is highly desirable that there be a work-storage area where a teacher can prepare demonstrations and laboratory materials and store the various kinds of science material and equipment that is to be kept in or near the classroom. The work-storage area may be part of the regular storage area used by the teacher. Some schools have provided portable science demonstration desks. The drawers and spaces in these desks provide some room for the storage of science materials and equipment. Specially designed kits can also be used to store the materials and equipment that are needed. The tools, equipment and space used for the science activity center may also double as a teacher work-storage area.

For convenience and economy some science materials and equipment should be stored in a central storage facility in the school. Some kinds of materials and equipment can be used by more than one teacher. Also, some kinds of equipment are bulky and take up a great deal of room in the classroom. Since they may be used only a few times during the year, it is not an economical use of precious classroom space to store the equipment permanently in the classroom. However, experience indicates that it is highly desirable that someone be responsible for the central storage room. If there is a science consultant, he obviously is the person who should have this responsibility.

In order to make the optimum use of materials and equipment kept in a central storage area, it is important to have some system for keeping track of the location of material and equipment. One such system that has been used successfully is to have each teacher place a card with his name and room in the slot allotted for the equipment or material that he is removing for use in his room. Then, if another teacher needs to use this equipment, he can quickly locate it by referring to the card.

The science library

While many of the science books should be kept in the school library, it is important to have a number of the most frequently used science books available in the classroom. Many teachers use multiple texts. These texts should be stored in the classroom where they are easily available for use. Tradebooks related to the topic that is currently being studied may also be kept in the classroom. Laboratory manuals, lab text, and other source materials for activities and experiments should also be readily available in the classroom.

A science resource file

A wide variety of suggested teaching procedures and science resource materials pass across a teacher's desk. It is important to have some systematic way of storing these materials so that they are easily available for use. Many teachers have found it helpful to keep a science resource file. This can be a useful resource to turn to for suggestions for children who wish to do additional work, develop special interests, or need extra help.

Light-tight shades

Films, filmstrips, transparencies and other audio-visual materials are important for science instruction. Also, the study of light is often an important area of elementary school science. For these kinds of experiences, it is important to be able to darken the classroom with light-tight shades.

Clock with second hand

Many experiments in science require some way of recording time. A wall clock with a sweep second hand is usually adequate.

The Science Room

Many schools have found it desirable to provide a special room for instruction in science. These rooms are usually used by science consultants or by teachers who have special responsibilities for the teaching of science.

The following are some considerations that should be kept in mind in planning for an effective science room:

There should be ready access from the room to the out-of-doors.
Maximum possible natural light.
Storage facilities for books, maps and charts.
A locked storage facility for chemicals.

A refrigerator and a stove.
One or more woodworking benches.
A demonstration unit.
Work areas for laboratory experimentation by students.
At least two outlets for hot and cold water and sinks.
Chalkboards, pegboards and tackboards.
Electrical outlets at the demonstration area and around the room.
Light-tight blinds.
Clock with sweep second hand.
Television antenna connection.
At least two outlets for gas.
Space for animal cages.
A life science center.
Shelf space for storage of aquariums.
A large aquarium which can be used for breeding aquarium organisms
       for use in other classrooms.
Locked microscope storage.
Locked storage for audio-visual equipment.
A darkroom area.
A greenhouse.

Fig. 20-1 shows a well-planned elementary school science room.

Outdoor Laboratories

An outdoor laboratory enables studies to be made in the natural environment. Preferably, the outdoor laboratories show a variety of conditions. For example, one school developed an outdoor laboratory on donated land containing a small pond, marsh, a formerly cultivated field, and a stand of trees. In this outdoor laboratory, children were able to study various kinds of organisms in their natural setting. The cultivated land was allowed to revert back to its original state. Children over a period of years studied the succession of plants that were found to grow on this land. During the year, children studied changes that took place with the seasons. Around the pond, animal tracks were studied. The changes that take place in a pond were observed in the small pond near one corner of the outdoor laboratory. Almost any kind of land can be used for an outdoor laboratory. However, it is desirable to have a variety of organisms included.

Nature trails can be developed in local parks or on land to which students can have access. Resource people from the community can be asked to help identify various kinds of plants and animals that may be seen along the nature trail.

Small *science museums* can be developed by children. Obviously, these science museums cannot rival professionally developed museums. However, the experience of collecting, classifying, and exhibiting various kinds of specimens is an enlightening activity in itself.

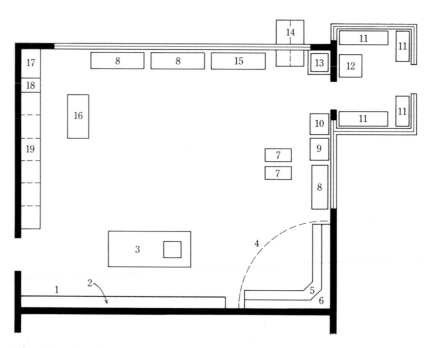

Fig. 20-1 *An elementary science room.*[1]

1. *Chalk Board*
2. *Book Shelves Above and Below Chalk Board*
3. *Teacher's Demonstration Area*
4. *Darkroom Curtain*
5. *Counter Top Work Area with Sink and Cabinets Below, with Tack Boards Against Wall*
6. *Additional Storage Above Tack Board Units (Above Sink)*
7. *Portable Book Carts*
8. *Student Work Tables (Movable)*
9. *Oven and Range Unit*
10. *Refrigerator*
11. *Planting Tables with Storage Below*
12. *Preparation Table*
13. *Recessed Tub*
14. *Indoor-Outdoor Cages*
15. *Storage Unit with Ceramic Tile Work Surface*
16. *Shop Table*
17. *Double-Door Storage Cabinet with Adjustable Shelves*
18. *Map and Chart Storage Closet*
19. *Student Coat Storage with Tack Board on Doors*

[1] Design suggested by Dr. Lawrence J. Heldman.

Community Science Facilities

An outstanding science program utilizes facilities outside the school. Many communities have developed museums, parks, planetariums, aquariums, wild life refuges, conservation tracts, and other facilities. These should be considered in planning the school science program. Often, the people responsible for these facilities are delighted to plan their programs so that the schools can make optimum use of their resources.

MATERIALS FOR SCIENCE INSTRUCTION

A variety of materials is used in good science instruction. "How can these materials be judged?" "Under what conditions and for what purposes can they best be used?"

Textbooks

Science textbooks should be available in sufficient quantities so that they can be used and read by all children in any class. The text should be used as a basic reference source for information to supplement class activities and discussion. It can never take the place of laboratory experimentation, field trips, class discussion, and other kinds of activities in which children should take part. However, it can enrich these activities by providing a convenient source of information and ideas for use by children.

Most textbooks provide a rich variety of possible activities in which children can participate. Many of these are experiments. With the descriptions of these laboratory activities, children can engage in a variety of science experiences.

A textbook series provides a possible science program. The outline of a textbook series usually has been planned to provide a step-by-step development of a science program. Some school systems choose to accept these outlines as their science program.

When a school system has developed its own science program, it is often desirable to have multiple texts available. For example, it may be desirable to have several copies of one text that can be used by children who are good readers and are particularly interested in science, and other texts that can be used by children who may have reading difficulties. The use of multiple texts in a classroom makes it possible to provide reading materials for the wide range of children's abilities and interests. Of course, it also broadens the range of activities and reference materials that are available to the children.

A major consideration in the selection of the textbook is the extent to which it corresponds to the science program that a school system wishes to develop. Most textbooks are carefully checked for scientific accuracy and reading difficulty. However, teachers may wish to make judgments on the basis of their knowledge of the children's interests and reading abilities.

Tradebooks

Tradebooks are usually available in limited quantities in the school library or in the classroom. Through the reading of tradebooks, children can delve more deeply into science topics in which they are interested. A rich assortment of tradebooks is essential for a good elementary science program. There are lists of tradebooks following each of the chapters in Parts II–V.

Programmed Instruction

Units of programmed instruction are designed to help students explore specific areas of science or to develop needed skills. Good programmed instruction is organized in a logical sequence so that the student starts with the most basic initial steps and proceeds to the logical conclusion.

Programmed instruction is especially valuable for youngsters who wish to explore areas in which they have become particularly interested. With programmed units they should be able to explore these areas with minimal assistance from adults. Obviously, programmed instruction is limited to youngsters who are able to read fairly well.

Also, the most effective programmed instruction deals with limited areas of subject matter. For example, the program on "Flower Parts" is organized so that the student gains a thorough knowledge of the relationships between the various parts of a flower. A program such as one on "How to Use a Microscope" takes a youngster systematically through the steps that are required to learn how to use the microscope effectively. Programmed instruction units can be very helpful in making it possible for children to explore areas in which they may be interested and highly motivated.

Films

The motion picture film contributes uniquely to science instruction. Through the use of motion, children can see how objects are related in a system. For example, the operation of the various parts of a gasoline engine can best be shown when the parts are shown in motion. Also, through time-lapse photography it is possible to show changes that take place over a considerable period of time. For example, a classic motion picture shows the various events that take place in the growth of a plant. Changes that take place over a period of weeks are telescoped into a few minutes on film. Through animation, processes that are invisible to our eyes can be shown. For example, one of the best ways to show how current is generated in an electric generator is with an animated film.

In some cases, it is desirable to give youngsters a general picture of the content of the film before it is shown. However, it is usually not desirable to give the detailed account of the film before showing it. This will rob the film of much of the excitement.

Many films should be shown more than once. Before the second showing, it may be desirable to give more detailed direction as to what to look for.

In general, films should be discussed. It has been said, "A film worth showing is worth discussing." On the second showing it is sometimes desirable to stop the film at appropriate places to discuss certain aspects.

Cartridge films which can be used by one or more children in the classroom are also effective. These cartridge films provide the teacher with another tool for special experiences. For example, films showing adaptations of different kinds of animals provide excellent supplementary materials for the study of the adaptation of the organisms.

Filmstrips

Filmstrips are an organized sequence of pictures in combination with a script. The script is used as running commentary for each corresponding picture. The sequence of pictures can be stopped at any frame for discussion or explanation. In some respects, this feature is an advantage over the motion picture film because it gives the teacher an opportunity to relate the subject matter of the filmstrip to the children's experiences.

Transparencies and slides

Transparencies and slides can be made both by the children and the teacher. Since both the overhead projector and the slide projector are very easy to use, they provide the teacher with a simple means of showing a diagram or picture to the entire class for discussion and explanation. These audio-visual materials make it possible for pictures and diagrams to be flashed onto a screen where all the children can view them, ask questions about them, and take part in discussions.

Television

Television makes it possible to bring current events in science to the classroom. Television enables children to take part in the space program and other important science events that are taking place at great distances from their classroom.

Magazines

Science magazines such as *Nature and Science* and *Current Science and Aviation* make it possible for children to be up to date in science.

SCIENCE EQUIPMENT

Since a critical characteristic of good elementary science programs is that children have a chance to experiment and carry out investigations, science equipment is essential. It is needed by children as they experiment, investigate and carry out science projects; it is needed by the teacher as he demonstrates and undertakes cooperative investigations.

Some science equipment can be improvised from cheap and inexpensive materials available locally:[2] Basements, shops, garages, 5 & 10 cent stores, and garbage dumps are often rich sources of materials for constructing equipment. Children can often be helpful in securing such material. An important advantage in the use of improvised materials is that children's participation in the actual construction of equipment gives them some knowledge of how it works. The science equipment is not a "black box that works in mysterious ways." Instead, the children have constructed the equipment and know how it operates.

While it is desirable to use some improvised equipment, there are certain difficulties and handicaps in relying entirely upon it. Often, it is difficult to obtain enough equipment for all children to undertake experiments; considerable effort is required to obtain enough to do a demonstration or to carry out a single project, and even more effort is needed to provide for individual instruction. More know-how and certainly more

---

[2] The following are excellent sources of ideas for the use of improvised materials:

Glen O. Blough and Marjorie H. Campbell, *Making and Using Classroom Science Materials in the Elementary School.* (New York: Holt, Reinhart & Winston, 1954.)

David E. Hennessy, *Elementary Teacher's Classroom Science Demonstrations and Activities.* (Englewood Cliffs, N.J.: Prentice-Hall, Inc., 1964.)

Elizabeth Hone et al., *A Sourcebook for Elementary Science.* (New York: Harcourt, Brace & World, Inc., 1962.)

UNESCO. *Source Book for Science Teaching.* (New York: Unesco Publications Center, 1956.)

time and energy are required to provide the equipment that is needed. Also, children should have some experiences in working with equipment somewhat like that used in the sciences.

It is probably desirable that children have experiences with both improvised equipment and with equipment available from commercial sources. For example, children can learn how masses can be compared and how objects can be compared with standard masses or weights with an equal arm balance. They learn how balances are constructed and used and possibly how systems of measurement for mass and weight are developed. However, it is also important to learn how to make more precise measurements than can be made with most improvised balances. With these tools the limits to precision and significant numbers take on more meaning.

Three Approaches to Equipment

There are three general approaches to planning and providing equipment for Elementary School Science:

1. Science kits are available that provide all, or almost all, the materials and equipment needed for teaching lessons in a science program. This approach is used in most of the science programs developed under the auspices of the National Science Foundation.[3]

These kits have an important advantage in that they provide everything that is needed for a laboratory approach to science. Usually, the materials and equipment are organized in a very convenient way so that they are readily accessible to children and teachers. The kits have a disadvantage of being relatively high in cost and are geared specifically to a particular program. It is difficult to use the kits with other programs.

2. Science kits of a generalized nature can be provided. Usually, these generalized science kits provide the materials and equipment that can be used in a wide variety of science lessons and programs. For example, such kits usually include balances, magnets, and electrical equipment that can be used in a wide variety of lessons and units. These generalized science kits have greater flexibility, are less expensive, and are not as closely meshed with a particular kind of science program. Possible disadvantages are that these kits require more planning on the part of the

---

[3] Three programs that have developed such science kits are:

American Association for Advancement of Science. *Science — A Process Approach.* (Washington, D.C.: The American Association for the Advancement of Science.)

Elementary Science Study. *Science Units.* (Newton, Mass.: Educational Development Corporation.)

Science Curriculum Improvement Study. *Science Curriculum Improvement Study Elementary Science Program.* (Berkeley, Calif.: Univ. of Calif.)

teacher or science consultant, and all of the materials and equipment needed for programs may not be present in the kit.

3. Most often, equipment and materials for elementary school science are provided by the local school system. Ideally, the purchase and distribution of materials and equipment is planned in relation to the local science program. The advantage of this is that the equipment and materials are closely coordinated with the science program that is to be developed in the schools. Also, there can be direct and quick feedback from the teachers to the science consultant or administrator who has the responsibility for the purchase and distribution of equipment. The disadvantage is that considerable time and energy have to be expended by teachers, consultants, and administrators to develop a list of the needed equipment and to purchase and distribute this equipment.

To help in the planning of such equipment lists, the following is a checklist of equipment that is often included in locally prepared equipment lists. Not all of this equipment may be needed. However, the list will help you to recall necessary items that are easily forgotten.

Equipment

Fire extinguishers
Sand buckets
Blankets
First aid kits
Ant houses
Terrariums
Aquariums
Electroscopes
Glass rods
Rubber rods
Dissecting kits
Medicine droppers
Blowpipes
Animal cages
Rain gauge
Crucibles
Mortars and pestles
Pneumatic troughs
Electric hot plates
Bunsen burners (use burners with attached bottle gas if piped gas is not available in school)

Radiometers
Pulleys, assorted
St. Louis motors
Compasses
Magnets
Head phones
Radio equipment
Magneto or generator model
Doorbells
Telephones
Telegraph sets
Spark coils
Rheostats
Galvanometers, student
Tuning forks (assorted frequencies)
Microprojectors
Convection box
Compound bar
Chimneys, lamp
Ball-and-ring apparatus
Mirrors
Magnifying glasses

Ring stands
Soil testing kit
Insect collections (including
  cocoons and egg cases)
Seed collections
Shell collections
Rock and mineral collections
Polaroid camera
Pin-hole camera
Photography equipment
Thermostats

Old eyeglasses
Convex lenses
Concave lenses
Prisms
Color wheels
Bell jars
Graduated cylinders, Plastic
Battery jars
Air pumps (compression and
  vacuum)
Watering cans

Instruments

Telescope and tripod
Binocular microscope
Compound microscopes
Standard weights and measures
Bathroom scales
Kitchen scales
Spring balances

Two-pan balances
Triple beam balances
Hydrometers, heavy and light
  liquid
Aneroid barometers
Thermometers

Models

Models of the solar system
Star charts
Geodetic survey and three-dimen-
  sional maps (especially of local
  area)
Globes

Pump models (lift and force)
Model steam engine
Human skeleton model
Human torso model
Human eye model
Anatomic models

Supplies

Sand
Vaseline
Steel wool
Lima beans
Rice, white and brown
Kidney beans
Rubber gloves
Enameled pans
Pieces of metal

Glue
Paste
Bags, plastic
Bags, paper
Clothesline
Sealing wax
String
Needles (both darning and metal
  knitting needles)

Pieces of wood
Rubber balls (various sizes)
Gravel
Soil
Sandpaper
Screws
Hydroponic materials for plants
Flower pots
Wire netting
Wooden boxes (assorted sizes)
Tin cans (assorted sizes)
Cardboard milk containers
    (half-pint and quart size)
Absorbent cotton
Pith balls
Wool
Fur
Silk
Marbles
Matches
Petri dishes
Glass squares
Thin rubber sheeting
Glass tubing
    Y tubes
    T tubes
Glass tubing (assorted sizes)
Rubber hosing (assorted sizes)
Corks
Rubber stoppers (one- and two-
    hole in assorted sizes)
Funnels
Pinch cocks
Clamps (assorted)
Asbestos pads
Wire gauze
Tumblers
Pans
Jars
Filter paper
Evaporating dishes
Beakers (assorted sizes)

Thread (strong sewing thread)
Labels
Rubber bands
Thumb tacks
Paper clips and fasteners
Pins
Aluminum foil
Masking tape
Adhesive tape (both cellophane
    and cloth)
Colored chalk and crayons
Wood splints (tongue depressors
    and swab sticks can be used)
Food dyes
Colored inks
Water colors
Straws
Colored paper and cellophane
Modeling clay
Balloons
Photography equipment
    Photography developers and
    fixatives
Blue print paper
Daylight photographic paper
Iron filings
Crystals and ticklers
Old radio parts (including tubes,
    speakers)
Fahnestock clips
Variable condensers (365 mmf)
Antenna wire
Antenna coil (standard broad-
    cast band)
Solder
Extension cords
Friction tape
Electric wall plugs
Sockets, standard base sockets
Sockets (for flashlight bulbs)
Switches
Fuses, assorted

Flasks (assorted sizes and shapes)
Test tube racks
Test tube brushes
Test tubes (assorted sizes, both
   pyrex and soft glass)
Old household appliances
Clocks (for the children to take
   apart and examine)
Photographic trays

Flashlight bulbs
   (for use with 1, 2, and 3 cells)
Wire, assorted; including:
   Bell wire #18 and #20
Dry cells
Lens paper
Cover slips
Microscope slides
Candles

Tools

Files, triangular and flat
Cork borers
Can openers
Strainers
Trowels
Spades
Razor blades, single edge
Flashlights
Meter sticks
Yardsticks
Rulers
Drawing compasses
Protractors
Glass marking pencils
Pencils and pens
Knives (particularly penknives)
Scissors

Brushes (both water color and
    larger paint brushes)
Nails and screws (assorted)
Wire cutters
Files
Tin snips
Wire strippers
Mallets
Saws
Chisels
Pliers
Hammers
Screw drivers
Spoons
Tongs
Test tube holders
Soldering irons

Chemicals

Fehling's solution
Concentrated and dilute nitric acid
Concentrated and dilute
   sulfuric acid
Concentrated and dilute
   hydrochloric acid
Calcium carbonate (Marble chips)
Chromium oxide
Cobalt chloride
Copper (metal strips)

Iodine solution
Hydrogen peroxide
Glycerine
Formaldehyde
Ferric chloride
Carbon tetrachloride
Bromthymol blue
Boric acid
Benzine
Benedict's solution

Copper sulfate
Iron chloride
Iron sulfate
Iron oxide
Iodine crystals
Lead
Lead nitrate
Manganese dioxide
Mercury
Nickel sulfate
Potassium chlorate
Sodium hydroxide
Strontium nitrate
Sulfur
Vinegar
Tin
Zinc
Sodium thiosulfate (hypo)
Ammonia water
Potassium permanganate
Phenolphthalein solution
Lime water
Lead nitrate

Acetic acid
Alcohol
Machine oil
Gasoline
Turpentine
Vinegar
Kerosene
Litmus paper
Lamp black
Charcoal
Corn oil
Paraffin
Flour
Gum arabic
Corn starch
Baking powder
Baking soda (sodium bicarbonate)
Cane sugar
Grape sugar
Salt
Cement
Plaster of Paris

Selected References

AAAS. *Science Book List for Children*. Washington, D.C.: American Association for the Advancement of Science.

ACEI. *A Bibliography of Books for Children*. Washington, D.C.: Association for Childhood Education International.

ACEI. *Equipment and Supplies Tested and Approved for Preschool, School and Home*. Washington, D.C.: Association for Childhood Education International, 1964.

BLOUGH, GLENN O., AND CAMPBELL, MARJORIE H. *Making and Using Classroom Science Materials*. New York: The Dryden Press, 1954.

Educator's Guide to Free Science Materials. Randolph, Wisc.: Educators' Progress Service.

Educator's Guide to Free Filmstrips. Randolph, Wisc.: Educators' Progress Service.

Educator's Guide to Free Films. Randolph, Wisc.: Educators' Progress Service.

Growing Up With Science Books. New York: Library Journal.

PILTZ, ALBERT. *Science Equipment and Materials for Elementary Schools*. Washington, D.C.: U.S. Government Printing Office, 1961.

PILTZ, ALBERT, AND GRUVER, WILLIAM J. *Science Equipment and Materials: Science Kits*. Washington, D.C.: U.S. Government Printing Office, 1963.

ROCKCASTLE, VERNE N. *Science Equipment in the Elementary School*. Ithaca, New York: Cornell University Press, 1962. (A Cornell Science Leaflet.)

SCHMIDT, VICTOR E., AND ROCKCASTLE, VERNE E. *Teaching Science With Everyday Things*. New York: McGraw-Hill Book Co., 1968.

545

21 Evaluation in Elementary School Science

Evaluation may be thought of as "placing a value on something." In education the major concern in evaluation is first "the placing of value" on the efforts of children, and, secondly, the evaluation of all or part of the educational program. Usually, the teacher has the responsibility to evaluate the child's growth in science. Teachers, consultants, supervisors, and parents have a responsibility to evaluate the elementary science program. A third important dimension of evaluation is a diagnostic one in which teachers and educational personnel attempt to evaluate their strengths and weaknesses, and find ways in which to improve their ability to work in elementary school science.

Teachers require information concerning the growth of children in science if they are to evaluate that growth. Those who are concerned with the evaluation of elementary science programs also need information concerning the general growth of children. In addition, they need information about teacher difficulties with segments of an elementary science program, feedback on strengths and weaknesses of various materials and equipment, and suggestions for the improvement of the program. A major emphasis in this chapter is on various procedures that can be used to obtain information needed to make evaluational judgments and suggested questions that can be used to evaluate science programs and to suggest ways that teaching can be made more effective.

EVALUATION FOR GOALS AND OBJECTIVES

Goals are broad, general statements of directions toward which we hope children will grow.[1] However, statements of goals may have considerably

[1] For a more extended discussion of goals and their operational meanings see chapter 1.

547

different meaning for different people. For example, almost everyone would probably agree that the development of a world view is a desirable goal in elementary school science. But what should be the nature of that world view? What aspects should be emphasized? On such questions there are often considerable differences of opinion among those who plan elementary science programs and experiences.

Statements of goals benefit from being given an *operational* meaning, such as descriptions of teaching operations that might lead youngsters in the direction of the general goal. Operational definitions are consistent with the concern for the actual experiences that children have and the empirical test of ideas stressed in "What happens when you try it?" In this book an attempt has been made to define operationally meanings of broad goals for science instruction.

Objectives are statements of specific directions toward which we wish to have children grow as a result of their experiences in science. For example, as an objective for growth in the directions of the broad goal of "Building a World View," we might want to have our children gain an understanding of the vastness of the solar system. This might take the form of a comparison of the time it would take to travel to one of the planets as compared to the time it takes to travel around the earth.

To be useful for evaluation, objectives are often stated in relation to what children should be able to do as a result of the science experiences. Through observation or planned evaluational tasks the extent to which children achieve these objectives can be determined.

The following are sample objectives, stated in behavioral terms, for each of the broad goals of elementary school science with examples of how information can be obtained for evaluation.

GOAL: Building a world view.

OBJECTIVE: 1. As a result of their science experiences, children should be able to compare the time it would take to travel to the sun at the speed of a modern jet plane with the time it would take to fly around the earth.
Evaluational activity:
Pose this problem: If it takes about two days to fly around the earth in a jet plane, about how many times longer would it take to travel from the earth to the sun?

OBJECTIVE: 2. Children should be able to state or demonstrate specific ways that man is similar to other organisms.
Evaluational activity:
Show the children two animals such as a cat and a goldfish. Ask them to state at least two ways in which the bodies of the cat and the goldfish are like their own bodies.

GOAL: Developing an understanding of the conceptual structure of science.

OBJECTIVE: 1. Children should be able to describe objects by their physical properties.
Evaluational activity:
Give the children several objects whose functions they know, such as scissors and forks, and ask them to describe them. Note whether the children describe the objects by physical properties or functions.

OBJECTIVE: 2. Children should be able to give operational definitions of terms with which they have had experience.
Evaluational activity:
Ask children to give an operational definition for such terms as "down" and "up." A possible definition of "down" is the rest position of a plumb bob free to swing from a string. "Up" can be operationally defined as the opposite of "down."

OBJECTIVE: 3. Children should be able to define a system of objects that should be included in the study of a phenomenon.
Evaluational activity:
Carry out a demonstration for the children, such as placing a large jar over a burning candle until it flickers and goes out, and ask the children to state the objects that should be included in the study of this phenomenon. Have them suggest reasons why they include each of the objects.

GOAL: Developing the ability to use processes of science.

OBJECTIVE: 1. As a result of a series of experiences in comparing masses of objects, children should be able to arrange objects in serial order according to their masses.
Evaluational activity:
Give the children a series of objects that differ considerably in mass. Have them compare the masses of the objects by lifting and arrange them in order from least mass to greatest mass.

OBJECTIVE: 2. Children should be able to use an equal arm balance to compare objects that have only slight differences in mass.
Evaluational activity:
Give the children an equal arm balance and two objects that differ only slightly in mass. Let them use the equal arm balance to indicate which of the objects has the greater mass.

OBJECTIVE: 3. Children should be able to suggest improvised units that can be used to measure the length of an object.
Evaluational activity:
Give the children a variety of objects, such as dowel rods and toy blocks, and ask them to suggest a way that the length of a table can be measured using only materials that are available. Ask the children to use this unit to measure the length of the table and to report it to you.

GOAL: Developing an understanding of the human body and the relationships between man and his environment.

OBJECTIVE: 1. Children should be able to locate and identify in a manikin the major organs that make up the respiratory system.
Evaluational activity:
Have the children find and point to the major organs of the respiratory system in a manikin.

OBJECTIVE: 2. Children should select foods that will make a nutritional diet for a day.
Evaluational activity:
Have the children keep a record of the kinds and amounts of foods eaten during a day. Have them analyze this record into the Basic Four Food Groups.

OBJECTIVE: 3. Children should be able to predict some of the possible consequences of making various alterations in an ecosystem.
Evaluational activity:
Show the children a picture of some nature setting such as a forest or take them to some spot such as a hillside and ask them to predict the possible consequences of such changes as cutting trees or planting more trees, removing the grass or planting more grass, digging drainage ditches or building a pond.

KEEPING RECORDS OF GROWTH IN SCIENCE

Growth takes place over time. Therefore, it becomes important to keep records of children's behavior. These records can then be compared to the behavioral objectives that we have set for ourselves. For example, a teacher may see a child destroying a plant or other living organism. If at a later time, this same child expresses concern for the welfare of certain organisms and uses what he has learned to help maintain the living organisms, this would be evidence that this child has grown in the direction of a commonly accepted behavioral objective for science instruction.

In order to accumulate information for evaluation of growth, a systematic attempt must be made to keep records. A number of procedures and technological devices are available for use.

Anecdotal records

Anecdotal records are records of discussions and other kinds of behaviors. Anecdotal records can be kept by teachers. However, it is more desirable to have observers in the classroom who can record the behavior as it occurs. It is essential that the records be kept objectively. It is desirable that there be occasional comparison of anecdotes written by two or more observers of the same scene.

Since it is nearly impossible to keep anecdotal records of all behavior, it is desirable to focus attention on certain kinds of behavior. In elementary science, attention may be focused on behavior related to certain concepts. For example, if a teacher were concerned with the children's concepts of the sources of the materials that we use in our daily lives, a record would be kept of comments and overt behavior that indicates children's conceptions of the sources of the materials we use.

Observational checklists

For some purposes, record keeping can be simplified through the use of observational checklists. Each time certain behaviors are observed they can be checked. For example, we can observe and check children's handling of science materials in relation to specific safety behaviors. Or, children's verbalizations concerning conservation can be related to actual conservation behavior that they practice in the classroom or laboratory.

Children's writings

With older children, a great deal can be learned through an analysis of their writings. In fact, some children feel free and can express themselves better in writing than in verbal class discussion. Children's writings can be analyzed to determine the extent to which they are conscious of various aspects of their environment and how they apply scientific information to social issues.

Reactions to demonstrations or experiments

Demonstrations or experiments can be carried out that are closely related to scientific concepts with which we are dealing. Children's reactions to these demonstrations can tell us a great deal about the nature of their concepts and the stage of their intellectual development. Demonstrations related to the conservation laws are among those that have been especially useful.[2]

Tape recordings

Tape recorders are useful for making records of classroom discussions. Tapes can be transcribed for further analysis. Tapes and transcriptions are especially valuable for analyzing the effectiveness of teaching methods. Some essential questions are:

"What percentage of time is devoted to 'teacher talk'?"

"To what extent are there discussions between students?"

"How are questions phrased? How can the phrasing be improved?"

Tape recordings fail to pick up many of the essentials of interactions in science experiences such as facial expressions, adjustments made in demonstration apparatus, and writings on the blackboard. However, with videotape these forms of interaction can also be recorded.

Time sampling studies

In time sampling studies, observations for certain kinds of behavior are made for limited, but specific, periods of time. For example, one teacher kept a record of all significant comments and behavior during the second five minutes of each of a series of science lessons. Different kinds of behavior can be codified, and the number of times certain kinds of behavior are exhibited can be determined. For example, it is possible to note the number of times that children try to obtain more precise information by insisting on counting or measuring rather than merely making general qualitative statements. Such information, of course, would indicate these children are moving in the direction of a generally accepted objective of elementary science instruction.

Tests

Written and verbal tests can have some significance for evaluation in elementary school science. However, their primary function is a diagnostic one. We can use tests to help us find out what children know or do not know, can or cannot do. This information can be used to plan new experiences based upon the children's achievements and designed to move on to other accomplishments.

[2] For descriptions of demonstrations that elicit valuable information related to children's ability to "conserve" see pp. 170–177.

Several limitations of tests should be noted. There is little point to using tests in elementary school science in the old traditional way to rate or rank children for the purpose of assigning arbitrary grades. In science instruction a primary goal is to help children learn and grow in the direction of our goals and objectives for science instruction. Tests can help us make this kind of instruction more effective. Also, it is important to recognize that children's responses to tests are limited by their ability to express themselves. Essay-type tests, for example, cannot be used until children have learned to express themselves in writing.

The following are kinds of questions, with a few examples, that can be used in elementary school science:

I. *Essay.* For the elementary school, essay questions usually call for short answers. They call for children to organize and express their ideas. It is important in constructing questions that it be made clear to students what is being asked for. In evaluating responses it is important to focus on the quality of the ideas expressed and mode of organization, it is important to guard against being unduly influenced by such factors as penmanship.

EXAMPLES:

1. Why is it difficult to make a model of the solar system in a classroom?
2. We can collect a tremendous amount of information about the atmosphere. Yet, we cannot predict the weather with 100% accuracy. Suggest some reasons for this.

II. *Multiple choice.* Tests using multiple choice questions are widely used. Most standardized tests use this form of question. They can be written so that only one response among several can be considered correct. It has been argued, however, that answers to many questions are much more complicated than the possible choices indicated, and that this tends to penalize the student who is more knowledgeable about a subject and can see complications associated with various responses. Multiple choice items can be responded to correctly by youngsters who may not be able to express themselves well. Multiple choice tests are easy to score, and the results can be handled without much difficulty.

However, good multiple choice questions are difficult to write. Here are some guides to the writing of questions:

a. Try to write the questions so that they are easy to read. There is a danger that questions will become tests of reading rather than of science.
b. Try not to use trick questions. It is best to use straightforward questions. We learn very little if the students are confused by the questions.

c. Try not to give the answer away by the way a question is asked. Sometimes there is a tendency in writing questions to make the correct response longer than the others.

d. Write the questions so that the problems are given in the stem of the question. All possible responses should fit the stem.

EXAMPLE:

1. A farmer reported that rocks "seemed to grow in his fields." The rocks probably appeared as a result of

   a. meteorites that exploded as they entered the atmosphere.

   b. frost heaving the rocks up from below.

   c. the rocks being washed down from above by running water.

   d. the soil that once covered the rocks being washed away.

   e. the rocks being blown there by strong winds.

Laboratory practicums

An important goal of science instruction is to develop certain skills. For example, we may wish to have children learn how to use a camera or to bend glass. In practicums, children are given set tasks. The degree to which they can perform these tasks can be assessed, and, more importantly, the particular weaknesses in a pupil's procedure can be ascertained and steps can be taken to correct it.

Often, a certain amount of scientific knowledge is also required to carry out routine tasks. For example, it was noted that one student did not recognize the relationship between the size of the lens opening in his camera and the extent to which his film would be overexposed or underexposed. Once this was recognized it could be quickly corrected. In laboratory practicums, children are given the necessary tools and equipment and asked to carry out certain operations. The teacher may wish to observe the operations to see what parts of the task the child can and cannot do.

EXAMPLE:

1. The children are given dry cells, wire pliers, screwdriver, flashlight bulbs and sockets. The children are asked to connect the bulbs in series and then in parallel. Each time they are asked to connect their circuits to a dry cell and demonstrate some of the characteristics of each of the circuits.

2. The children are asked to make a slide of a human hair and to arrange it so that it can be viewed under a microscope.

EVALUATING SCIENCE PROGRAMS

One of the primary functions of evaluation is to find ways to improve the program. The following checklist has been developed to give teachers, principals, and other instructional leaders a basis on which to make suggestions for the improvement of the program. A "no" or "maybe" answer to any of the following questions indicates a direction for improvement.

1. Is there a planned program for elementary school science?
2. Is there sufficient flexibility in the planned program so that interests and concerns of children can be explored? Can you give an example of how such an interest has been used as a basis for a science activity?
3. Are there specific behavioral objectives for instruction?
4. Are testing procedures or instruments available to help teachers ascertain the extent to which behavioral objectives have been achieved?
5. Is consultant help available to teachers to advise on the development of elementary science experiences and to provide assistance when difficulties are encountered?
6. Is it possible for teachers to obtain needed equipment and materials quickly?
7. Are there enough materials and equipment available so that each youngster can take part in laboratory experiments?
8. Are such audio-visual resources as films, filmstrips, recordings, slides, overhead projections, and television easily available to the teacher?
9. Are there enough textual materials, preferably of several kinds, available so that all youngsters in the classroom can have a common reading experience?
10. Are there a variety of science books at different reading levels available in the classroom which children can consult in their studies in science?
11. Are there a variety of science books available in the school library?
12. Is there at least one set of children's encyclopedia available in the school library?
13. Does the school have a systematic arrangement for the utilization of such community educational resources as museums, planetariums, zoos, botanical gardens, nature centers and aquariums?
14. Can the teacher easily and quickly arrange for transportation for field trips?

15. Does the school system have a system for monitoring the ongoing science program to identify problems and difficulties and to suggest ways to improve the program?
16. Is there sufficient time provided in the program for science? Many elementary school educators have suggested that about one-fifth of the time in the elementary school program should be devoted to science.
17. Are there professional books and curriculum materials in elementary school science available for use by teachers?
18. Is there a planned program of in-service education to help teachers develop their proficiency in science?

SELF EVALUATION IN ELEMENTARY SCHOOL SCIENCE

It is important for all teachers to continue to improve their teaching in all areas of the curriculum. One of the best ways for anyone to improve his work is through self evaluation. While everyone may agree with these general statements, it is often difficult for a teacher to identify specific ways in which his teaching can be improved. The following checklist is intended to help you analyze your work with children in science. If you answer "no" to any of the following questions, you may wish to consider that aspect of your teaching and in some cases seek ways to implement the ideas suggested by your self evaluation.[3]

1. Do all the children in your class have frequent opportunities to handle and manipulate science materials and equipment?
2. Are the children asked to assume some of the responsibility for the distribution, collection, care and storage of the science equipment and materials?
3. Have your children had the opportunity to have some experience with each of the following kinds of approaches to science learning?
    a. laboratory experimentation
    b. individual or small group investigations
    c. cooperative investigations
    d. demonstrations
    e. science projects
    f. field trips
    g. reading to obtain needed information
    h. use of community resources such as museums and nature centers

[3] For discussions of many of these questions see chapter 4.

4. Do the children have an opportunity to report the results of their investigations and projects to their class?
5. Do you ask some divergent questions, i.e., questions to which you do not know the answer and which may lead children to consider and explore further implications of the science that they are studying?
6. Do you consider a child's response to questions, even though they may seem to be implausible or unrelated to the question, before turning to some other child for his response?
7. Do you help children try to derive meaning from the activities in which they engage?
8. Do you have generalized goals such as those discussed in Chapter 1, toward which you direct your work with children in science?
9. Do you have specific behavioral objectives for some of the science activities that you undertake?
10. Do you make a systematic attempt to ascertain the extent to which the children achieve the behavioral objectives?
11. Do you keep some kind of a record of each child's achievement and growth in science?
12. Are some of the activities that are developed in science a result of questions that children have raised?
13. Are children sometimes asked to use what they have learned in science to try to "think through" what may happen when they try an experiment?
14. Are children sometimes led to consider the methods and processes that they have used to deal with a question or problem?
15. Are children helped to learn how to locate and evaluate sources of information?
16. Do you systematically review some of the new science materials for children that are becoming available?
17. Do you read articles and books on science, view science programs on television, and take advantage of other opportunities to become better informed in science?

Selected References

ENGELHART, MAX D. *Improving Classroom Testing*. Washington, D.C.: National Education Association, 1964.

HEDGES, WILLIAM D. *Testing and Evaluation for the Sciences*. Belmont, Calif.: Wadsworth Publishing Co., 1966.

NELSON, CLARENCE H. *Improving Objective Tests In Science*. Washington, D.C.: National Science Teachers Association, 1967.

PETTY, MARY C. *How To Record And Use Data In Elementary School Science*. Washington, D.C.: National Science Teachers Association, 1965.

TANNENBAUM, HAROLD E., AND STILLMAN, NATHAN. *Evaluation in Elementary School Science*. Washington, D.C.: U.S. Government Printing Office, 1964

THORNDIKE, ROBERT L., AND HAGEN, ELIZABETH. *Measurement and Evaluation in Psychology and Education*. New York: John Wiley & Sons, Inc., 1961.

TYLER, RALPH W., GAGNE, ROBERT M., AND SCRIVEN, MICHAEL. *Perspectives of Curriculum Evaluation*. Chicago, Illinois: Rand McNally & Co., 1967.

Appendix

SCIENCE DICTIONARIES AND ENCYCLOPEDIAS

ABERCROMBIE, M., HICKMAN, C. J., AND JOHNSON, M. L. *A Dictionary of Biology*. Baltimore, Md.: Penguin Books, 1954.

ASIMOV, ISAAC. *Biographical Encyclopedia of Science and Technology*. Garden City, New York: Doubleday & Co., 1964.

Compton's Dictionary of the Natural Sciences, Chicago, Ill.: F. E. Compton Co., 1966. (2 Vol.)

Compton's Illustrated Science Dictionary, Indianapolis, Ind.: David-Stewart Publishing Company, 1963.

The Harper Encyclopedia of Science, New York: Harper & Row, 1963. (4 Vol.)

ROTHENBERG, ROBERT E. (Ed.). *The New Illustrated Medical Encyclopedia*, New York: Abradale Press, 1963. (4 Vol.)

Science Year. The World Book Science Annual. Chicago, Ill.: Field Enterprises Educational Corporation. (Issued annually.)

The Way Things Work. An Illustrated Encyclopedia of Technology. New York: Simon and Schuster, 1967.

UVAROV, E. B., AND CHAPMAN, D. R. *A Dictionary of Science*. Baltimore, Md.: Penguin Books, 1951.

Van Nostrand's Scientific Encyclopedia. New York: Van Nostrand Reinhold Co., 1968.

Index

A

Acid, 481–482
Activity center, 530
Adaptations, 64, 218–221, 244–248
  animals in oceans, 218–221
  food-getting, 248
  land environment, 244–245, 247
  mimicry, 247
  protective coloration, 247
  reproduction, 248
  study of, 248–255
Adrenal gland, 427
Air, 170–177
  heating and cooling, 175–176
  pollution of, 469, 490–491
  pressure, 172–175
  and space, 170
  water in, 176–177
    evaporation of, 177
    sublimation of, 177
Air mass theory, 187–191
  air masses, 187–192
  anticyclones, 191
  cyclones, 191
  polar front theory, 191
  symbols, 187–188
Air pollution, 491
  control of, 492–493
  effects of, 491–492
Airplane, 408
American Association for the Advancement of Science (AAAS), 17, 522
Amino acids, 241, 424, 450–451
Ampere, 33
Andromeda Galaxy, 107–108
Anecdotal records, 551
Anemometer, 197
Animal kingdom, 233–277
Antibodies, 465–466
Anticyclones, 191
Anti-matter, 124
Antitoxins, 466
Aorta, 425
Aquarium, 269–271
Archimede's Principle, 50, 55
Arteries, 425
Artificial respiration, 20, 117
Artificial stocking, 140

N